# Elementary-School Mathematics

## A MODERN APPROACH FOR TEACHERS

J. Houston Banks

*George Peabody College for Teachers*

# ELEMENTARY-SCHOOL MATHEMATICS

## *A MODERN APPROACH for TEACHERS*

Allyn and Bacon, Inc. Boston

Library of Congress Catalog Card Number 66-10508

Printed in the United States of America

# Preface

THE PLACE OF MATHEMATICS IN THE ELEMENTARY SCHOOL HAS RECENTLY undergone such significant changes that the term *arithmetic* is no longer an adequate description. The mathematical competence now required of the teacher is such as to imply the need for special courses specifically designed to meet the needs of the teacher in the elementary school.

It is necessary, but not sufficient, for the teacher to be conversant with the terminology of sets and mathematical structure. But the objectives of the modern elementary school mathematics program require more of the teacher than mere superficial acquaintance with the new terminology and topics.

The purpose of this text, then, is to provide mathematical experiences that will develop a mature grasp of the background necessary to place the modern elementary school mathematics program in proper perspective. The teacher must have mathematical training sufficient to enable him to see the significance of the mathematics he teaches. This implies a deeper grasp of concepts and a broader range of mathematical knowledge than is expected of the pupil.

The recommendations of the Committee on the Undergraduate Program in Mathematics of the Mathematical Association of America concerning the mathematical training of elementary school teachers have been used as guidelines in the selection and organization of the materials of the text. The recommendations for the two-course sequence on the structure of the real number system and the course devoted to basic concepts of algebra have been more than satisfied.

The organization of the text provides for reinforcement of concepts through a cyclic development. Topics developed in the first seven chapters are reintroduced and developed to greater depth in the chapters on algebra.

Finally, it is hoped that the text will help the student develop, along with greater knowledge and competence, a feel for the *spirit* of modern mathematics. This is an essential ingredient of adequate mathematical training.

J. H. B.

# Contents

# Elementary-School Mathematics

## A MODERN APPROACH FOR TEACHERS

# 1 Sets, Symbols, and Relations

IN THIS CHAPTER WE WISH TO DEVELOP SOME IDEAS WHICH ARE COMMON to much of human experience. They are basic to the logical development of much of mathematics. The idea of a set, or of a symbol, or of a relationship, is certainly nothing new. In this chapter it is our purpose to bring into sharper focus the meaning of these ideas as a mathematician uses them.

## 1.1 Sets

In any logical, deductive system some things must remain undefined. We have a choice as to what things are to be undefined. For example, it is possible but not essential to take the natural numbers $\{1, 2, 3, \ldots\}$ as undefined when developing the system of real numbers. Here, we choose to let *set* be undefined. We might have chosen to define *set* in a variety of ways. For example: "A set is a collection." "A set is an aggregate." "A set is a group." But this would merely be swapping synonyms.

To let *set* be undefined does not imply that we are not concerned with what it means. In fact, we hope it comes to have the same meaning for everyone. We are quite familiar with the idea, both where set is used and when more suggestive synomyms are used. *Set* of dishes, *flock* of geese, *school* of fish, *set* of false teeth, *herd* of cattle are a few examples. Notice that each italicized word is a noun. A set has an identity of its own; it is a thing. But in each of the illustrations we also see a qualifying expression: "of dishes," "of geese," "of fish," and so on. A set is a thing, but it has things as members. They are called the *elements* of the set.

We should make a clear distinction between a set and the elements of the set. They are different in kind, even when the set has exactly one element. Algebra I meets at 8:30. The class is a set. The pupils who are members of the class are elements of the set. Suppose Bill Jones is the only pupil who can take Algebra I at 8:30. Here we have a set that has exactly one element, Bill Jones. Bill Jones is not the class, he is the one member of the class. If the principal decides to kill the class does this mean Bill had better run for his life? No, Bill and the class of which he is the only member have different identities.

What are the elements of the set of all rich men in the United States? It is quite likely that this question would elicit a variety of responses. How rich is rich? Rich in what—money, power, talent, or friends? If a set is to be of much value in the study of mathematics we must know without doubt or ambiguity what its elements are. Such sets are called *well-defined sets.*

> A set is well defined if and only if there is a way to determine whether any object is or is not an element of the set.

There are two ways to make a set well defined: by *roster* and by *rule.* By the roster method, each element is simply listed. Consider the breakfast menu of coffee, toast, and eggs. If we wish to symbolize the set whose elements are coffee, toast, and eggs, we write,

$$\{\text{coffee, toast, eggs}\}$$

The braces are used to indicate a set, and the things enclosed in the braces are its elements. This illustrates the roster method for specifying a well-defined set. The expression,

$$N = \{1, 2, 3, 4, 5, 6, 7, 8, 9\}$$

describes the set $N$, whose elements are 1, 2, 3, 4, 5, 6, 7, 8, 9. We can also describe this set by the *rule* method:

$$N = \{\text{positive one-digit integers}\}$$

The rule removes any doubt as to whether any object is or is not an element. "Coffee" is not an element of $N$ because coffee is not a positive one-digit integer. Neither are 0, 16, or $5\frac{1}{2}$ elements, for 0 is not positive, 16 is not a one-digit number, and $5\frac{1}{2}$ is not an integer.

There are many other ways that $N$ can be described by rule. For example,

$$N = \{n \text{ such that } n \text{ is a positive integer less than } 10\}$$

Here $n$ is used as a *variable.*

> A *variable* is a symbol used to represent any member of a set called its *replacement* set.

In this example, the variable $n$ is used to represent any element of the set of positive integers. Suppose we designate the set of positive integers as $P$. We can indicate that $n$ is an element of $P$ by

$$n \in P\text{: “}n\text{ is an element of the set }P\text{”}$$

If $n$ is not an element of a set $X$, we write

$$n \notin X\text{: “}n\text{ is not an element of the set }X\text{”}$$

The last description of $N$ can be written

$$N < \{n \mid n \in P, n < 10\}$$

Here, we have introduced two new symbols other than $\in$. The vertical bar, when used in this context, is read “such that.” The sign $<$ is the familiar “less than” symbol.

We shall have much more to say about the symbols “$<$” and “$>$” shortly. They are symbols for a relation. For the present, we may rely on intuition. We know 9 is less than 10 and greater than 8. These facts can be written $9 < 10$; $9 > 8$. The same facts could be written $8 < 9 < 10$, which means “8 is less than 9 which is less than 10.” We are making two assertions here, 8 is less than 9 *and* 9 is less than 10.

We have already used the symbol for another relation which we shall examine in detail. This is the familiar $=$, or equal sign. We know $5 + 3 = 8$, but just what does this really mean? When we say

$$N = \{n \mid n \in P, n < 10\}$$

the $=$ sign is used to indicate a definition. We are saying “$N$ *is* the set of all $n$ such that $n$ is an element of $P$ and $n$ is less than 10.” What does it mean to assert that two sets are equal, $A = B$?

Two sets are equal, $A = B$, if and only if they have identical elements.

If $A = \{1, 3, 5, 7, 9\}$ and $B = \{5, 9, 3, 7, 1\}$ then $A = B$. They have exactly the same elements. *The order in which the elements are listed is of no consequence.*

If $C = \{1, 2, 3, 4, 5\}$ and $D = \{a, b, c, d, e\}$ are $C$ and $D$ equal? Certainly not; far from having the same elements, they have no elements in common. Yet there is a similarity between the two sets. Each has five elements. $C$ and $D$ are called *equivalent* sets because they have the same *number of elements*. We indicate the number of elements of set $A$ as $n(A)$. Thus, $n(C) = n(D) = 5$.

Two sets $A$ and $B$ are equivalent if and only if they have the same number of elements, $n(A) = n(B)$.

## EXERCISES

**1.** Use the roster method to describe each of the following sets:
(a) The set of states of the United States touching the Pacific Ocean.
(b) The set of odd positive integers less than 12.
(c) The set of even integers greater than 10 and less than 20.
(d) The set of fractions whose numerator is 1 and denominator is a one-digit positive odd integer.

**2.** Use the rule method to describe the following sets. There may be more than one correct answer.
(a) {Florida, Alabama, Mississippi, Louisiana, Texas}.
(b) $\{5, 10, 15, 20, 25\}$.
(c) $\{2, 4, 6, 8\}$.
(d) $\{\frac{1}{2}, \frac{1}{4}, \frac{1}{6}, \frac{1}{8}\}$.

**3.** Which of the following sets is well defined? Tell why you omitted any that you did omit.
(a) The set of all redheaded women.
(b) The set of all good Broadway plays.
(c) The set of smart children in a specific third-grade room.
(d) The set of all men 100 ft tall.

**4.** Let $N$ be the set of counting numbers, $N = \{1, 2, 3, 4, \ldots\}$. (The three dots ... mean that the sequence continues; the set includes all counting numbers.) List the elements in each of the following sets:

(a) $X = \{x \mid x \in N, 10 < x < 15\}$
(b) $Y = \{y \mid y \in N, y \text{ is an even number } < 8\}$
(c) $Z = \{z \mid z \in N, 3 < z < 5\}$

**5.** If two sets are equal are they necessarily equivalent? If they are equivalent are they necessarily equal? Discuss.

**6.** List all sets in Exercises 1 through 4 that are equal. List all sets in Exercises 1 through 4 that are equivalent.

## 1.2 Subsets

On page 3 we find

$$N = \{n \mid n \in P, n < 10\}$$

Two sets are involved in this statement, $N$ and $P$. The variable $n$ is a symbol which represents any element of $N$. But $n \in P$ requires that every replacement for $n$ be an element of $P$. Thus, every element of $N$ is an element of $P$. When two sets have this relationship we say $N$ is a *subset* of $P$. This is indicated symbolically as

$$N \subseteq P$$

Set $A$ is a subset of set $B$,

$$A \subseteq B$$

if and only if every element of $A$ is an element of $B$.

If $B = \{a, b, c\}$ then $\{a\}$, $\{b\}$, $\{c\}$, $\{a, b\}$, $\{a, c\}$, $\{b, c\}$, $\{a, b, c\}$ are all subsets of $B$. Notice that the definition requires every set to be a subset of itself.

In considering subsets it is frequently desirable to exclude the set itself. These are called *proper subsets*.

$A$ is a proper subset of $B$

$$A \subset B$$

if and only if $A \subseteq B$ and there is at least one element of $B$ that is not an element of $A$.

The set $E$ of positive even integers, $E = \{2, 4, 6, \ldots, 2n, \ldots\}$, is a proper subset of the set $P$ of positive integers, $P = \{1, 2, 3, \ldots, n, \ldots\}$, because every element of $E$ is an element of $P$, and there are elements of $P$ that are not elements of $E$. Notice the symbolism used in describing $E$ and $P$. $P = \{1, 2, 3, \ldots, n, \ldots\}$ means "the set $P$ of elements 1, 2, 3 continued to any integer $n$ (the first three dots) and continued indefinitely beyond $n$ (the last three dots)." That is, $P$ contains all positive integers. In describing $E$ we employ the same symbols except that the general term is $2n$, meaning 2 times any integer $n$.

It is possible for two sets to have elements in common even though neither is a proper subset of the other. The Jones family is a set of persons, $J = \{$Mr. Jones, Mrs. Jones, Tom Jones, Jim Jones, Mary Jones$\}$. The Jones boys play on a basketball team, another set of persons, $T = \{$Bill Smith, Tom Jones, John Brown, Jim Jones, Sidney Throgmorton$\}$. The two sets $J$ and $T$ have two elements in common: Tom Jones and Jim Jones. But $\{$Tom Jones, Jim Jones$\}$ is also a set. It is called the *intersection* of $T$ and $J$.

The intersection of two sets $A$ and $B$ is the set whose elements are those elements that are common to sets $A$ and $B$. This is written $A \cap B$, it is read "$A$ intersection $B$" or "$A$ cap $B$."

Another set which can be determined from two given sets is the set consisting of those elements which are members of either of the two original sets. This is called the *union* of two sets. The union of sets $A$ and $B$ is written $A \cup B$, and read "$A$ union $B$" or "$A$ cup $B$."

$T \cup J = \{$Bill Smith, Mr. Jones, Mrs. Jones, John Brown, Jim Jones, Tom Jones, Sidney Throgmorton, Mary Jones$\}$

It is not at all necessary that two sets have any elements in common. No positive integer can be both even and odd. The set of even positive integers $E = \{2, 4, 6, \ldots, 2n, \ldots\}$ and the set of odd positive integers $O = \{1, 3, 5, \ldots, 2n - 1, \ldots\}$ have no elements in common. Must we say the intersection $E \cap O$ does not exist? The concept of a set that has no elements has proven to be useful. Such a set is called the *empty set* or the *null set*; the symbol for the null set is $\varnothing$. In set symbols we have $\varnothing = \{\ \}$. Two sets that have no elements in common are called *disjoint sets*. Their intersection is the null set. $E \cap O = \varnothing$.

*Venn diagrams* are frequently helpful in visualizing relationships between sets. If we let the points within a circle represent the elements of a set, the points lying in either or both of two circles represent the union of the corresponding sets. The overlap, the points common to the two circles, represents their intersection.

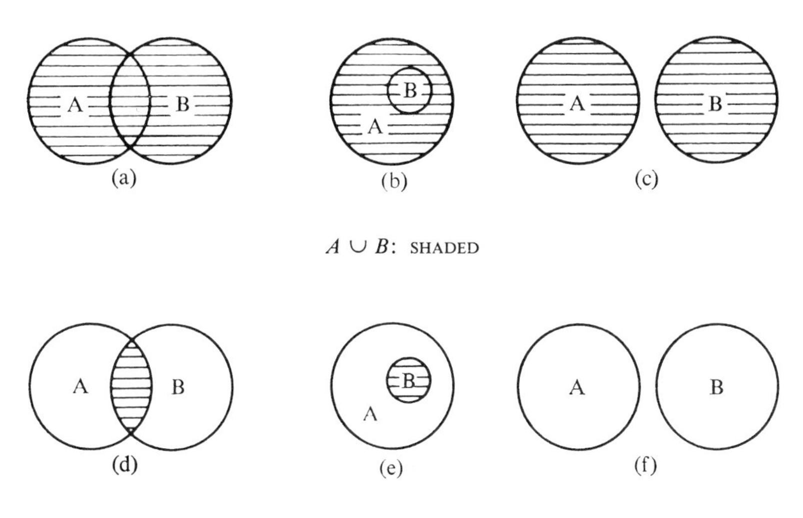


$A \cup B$: SHADED

$A \cap B$: SHADED

In figures (b) and (e) $B \subset A$. In (c) and (f) $A$ and $B$ are disjoint, and in (f) we have $A \cap B = \varnothing$.

The notion of the null set may seem a bit strange—the little man that wasn't there. To agree that it is possible to have a set without elements is, of course, a matter of definition. But as we proceed it will become evident why it is a useful idea. We use the term *the* null set. Does this mean there is only one null set? What about an empty orange crate and an empty egg carton? They are not the same. But an empty orange crate is not an example of the null set. The *set of oranges* in the empty orange crate is the null set. Then is the set of oranges in an empty orange crate the same set as the set of eggs in an empty egg carton? Yes, they are equal sets because they have identically the same elements—namely, none.

Of what set is the null set a subset? If $A$ has no elements then each of its elements certainly is an element of any set one cares to consider. Then the null set is a subset of all sets, even a subset of itself.

Of what set is the null set a proper subset? One might be tempted to respond, the null set isn't a part of any set. But a proper subset of $B$ was not defined as a set consisting of some but not all of the elements of $B$. Since $\varnothing$ is a subset of any set, and any set other than $\varnothing$ has at least one element which is not an element of $\varnothing$, we must conclude that the null set $\varnothing$ is a proper subset of any set except itself. This works out nicely, for we can say without exception a set is not a proper subset of itself.

Another useful concept is the idea of a *universal set*. The universal set $U$ is the set of all elements we wish to consider in a given discussion. For example, we might have under consideration all of the counting numbers. In this case the universal set is

$$U = \{1, 2, 3, \ldots, n, \ldots\}$$

In some other context we might prefer to restrict the consideration to the counting numbers less than 100. In this case the universal set would be

$$U = \{1, 2, 3, \ldots, 99\}$$

The universal set can be any set we want to consider, but in a given situation there is only one universal set.

> The universal set, $U$, is the set of all elements which are to be considered in a given situation.

It follows from the definition that all sets pertinent to a given situation are subsets of the universal set. Do you see why this is true? Suppose there exists an element $a \in A$, but $a \notin U$. Then $A$ is not a subset of $U$, $A \not\subset U$, and either $U$ is not the universal set of the discussion or $A$ has no place in the discussion.

To illustrate this idea suppose we designate the universal set

$$U = \{1, 2, 3, \ldots, n, \ldots\}$$

Now consider

$$A = \{1, \tfrac{1}{2}, \tfrac{1}{3}, \ldots, 1/n, \ldots\}$$

When we select $U$ we are, in effect, asserting that we want to talk about the set of counting numbers. If we insist on introducing set $A$ we simply are not talking about the universe of elements we said we were going to talk about.

One advantage to be derived from the idea of a universal set is immediate. Consider the universal set

$$U = \{1, 2, 3, 4, 5, 6, 7, 8, 9, 10\}$$

and the set

$$A = \{1, 3, 5, 7, 9\}$$

Now any element of $U$ either is or is not an element of $A$. All elements of $U$ that are not elements of $A$ constitute another set $A'$ called the complement of $A$. In this instance,

$$A' = \{2, 4, 6, 8, 10\}$$

Corresponding to any set $A$ there is a set $A'$, its complement, consisting of those elements of $U$ that are not elements of $A$. That is, $A' = \{u \mid u \in U, u \notin A\}$.

Venn diagrams can be used to picture complementary sets.

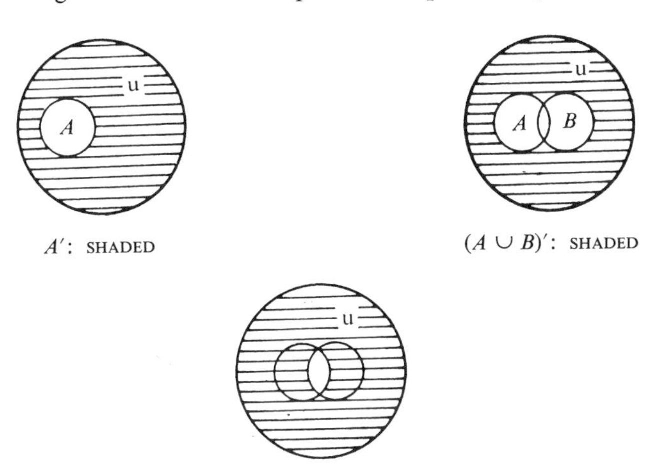


$A'$: SHADED

$(A \cup B)'$: SHADED

$(A \cap B)'$: SHADED

## EXERCISES

1. If $A = \{1, 2, 3, 4, 5, 6, 7, 8, 9, 10\}$ and
   $B = \{2, 4, 6, 8, 10, 12, 14\}$, find:
   (a) $A \cup B$ (b) $A \cap B$ (c) $B \cup A$ (d) $B \cap A$
2. Find all subsets of $C = \{1, 2, 3\}$. (There are eight.)
3. Find all subsets of $P = \{\text{cat, dog, bird, rabbit}\}$. How many did you find?
4. Find all subsets of $R = \{a, b\}$.
5. On the basis of Exercises 2, 3, and 4, how many subsets would you expect a set consisting of five elements to have?
6. Given $U = \{1, 2, 3, \ldots, 10\}$, $A = \{2, 4, 6, 8\}$
   $B = \{1, 3, 8, 9, 10\}$. Find the following:
   (a) $A'$ (b) $A \cap B$ (c) $(A \cup B)'$ (d) $A' \cap B'$
   (e) $A' \cup B$
7. If $U =$ the universal set, $\varnothing$ the null set, and $A =$ any set, find the following:
   (a) $A \cup A'$ (b) $A \cap A'$ (c) $U'$ (d) $\varnothing'$
   (e) $A \cup \varnothing$ (f) $A \cap \varnothing$ (g) $A \cup U$ (h) $A \cap U$

## SUBSETS

**8.** Draw a Venn diagram to show $(A \cup B)'$.

**9.** Draw a Venn diagram to show $A' \cap B'$. Compare with Exercise 8.

**10.** Draw a Venn diagram to show $(A \cap B)'$.

**11.** Draw a Venn diagram to show $A' \cup B'$. Compare with Exercise 10.

**12.** Prove: If $A \subseteq B$ and $B \subseteq A$ then $A = B$.

## 1.3 Properties of Sets

In Exercises 7–11 of the preceding exercises the elements of the sets involved are not specified. The results apply to any sets. In this section we wish to examine some general set properties, that is, properties of any sets.

The commutative properties,

$$A \cup B = B \cup A$$

and

$$A \cap B = B \cap A$$

are evident from the definitions of union and intersection. Since $A \cup B$ is the set of all elements in either $A$ or $B$, it is also the set of all elements in $B$ or $A$, that is, $B \cup A$. Similarly, $A \cap B$ being the set of all elements in both $A$ and $B$, it is also the set of all elements in both $B$ and $A$, that is, $B \cap A$.

Union and intersection are also associative.

$$(A \cup B) \cup C = A \cup (B \cup C)$$

and

$$(A \cap B) \cap C = A \cap (B \cap C)$$

$(A \cup B)$ being the set of all elements in either $A$ or $B$ or both, $(A \cup B) \cup C$ is the set of all elements in any one or more of the set $A$, $B$, and $C$. We reach the same conclusion relative to $A \cup (B \cup C)$.

*Example:* If $A = \{a, b, c\}$, $B = \{a, b, x\}$, $C = \{1, a, x\}$, show

$$(A \cup B) \cup C = A \cup (B \cup C).$$

*Solution:*

$$A \cup B = \{a, b, c, x\}$$
$$(A \cup B) \cup C = \{a, b, c, x, 1\}$$
$$B \cup C = \{a, b, x, 1\}$$
$$A \cup (B \cup C) = \{a, b, c, x, 1\}$$

# 11

This result can be shown by means of Venn diagrams.

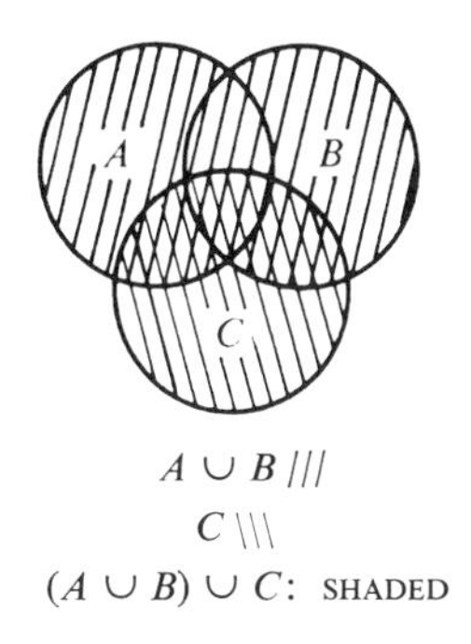


$A \cup B$ |||
$C$ \\\
$(A \cup B) \cup C$: SHADED

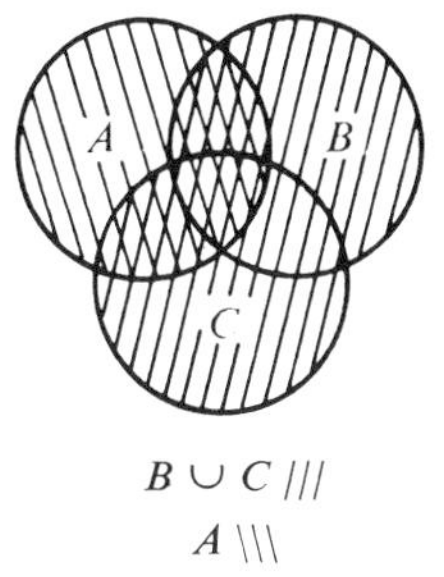


$B \cup C$ |||
$A$ \\\
$A \cup (B \cup C)$: SHADED

Since $(A \cap B)$ is the set of all elements in both $A$ and $B$, $(A \cap B) \cap C$ is the set of elements common to all three of the sets $A$, $B$, and $C$. Similarly, of $A \cap (B \cap C)$.

*Example:* If $A = \{a, b, c\}$, $B = \{a, b, x\}$, and $C = \{1, a, x\}$, show $(A \cap B) \cap C = A \cap (B \cap C)$.

*Solution:*

$$A \cap B = \{a, b\}$$
$$(A \cap B) \cap C = \{a\}$$
$$B \cap C = \{a, x\}$$
$$A \cap (B \cap C) = \{a\}$$

To picture this relationship by Venn diagrams we have

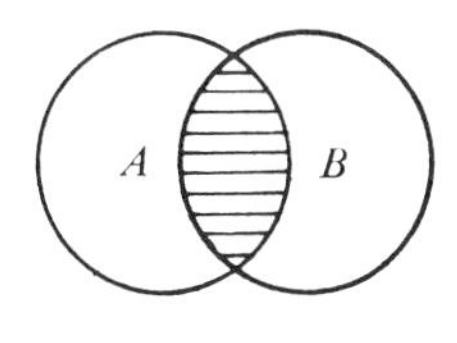


$A \cap B$: SHADED

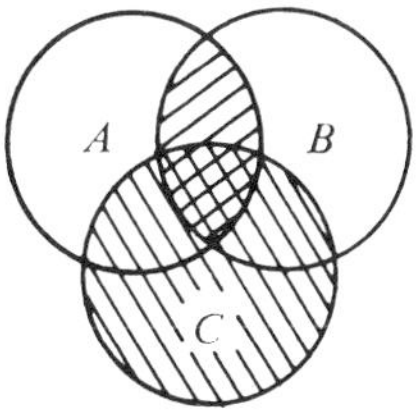

$(A \cap B) \cap C$: CROSSHATCHED

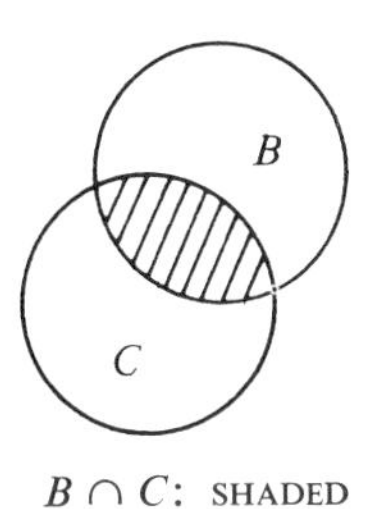


$B \cap C$: SHADED

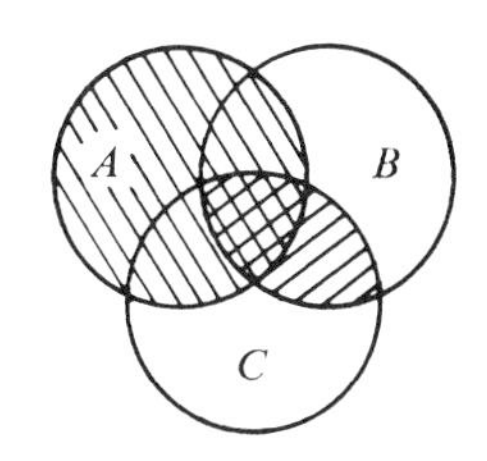


$A \cap (B \cap C)$: CROSSHATCHED

## PROPERTIES OF SETS

Sets obey two distributive rules:

$$A \cup (B \cap C) = (A \cup B) \cap (A \cup C)$$

and

$$A \cap (B \cup C) = (A \cap B) \cup (A \cap C)$$

$A \cup (B \cap C)$ is the set of all elements in $A$ as well as those common to $B$ and $C$. $A \cup B$ is the set of elements in either or both of sets $A$ and $B$. $A \cup C$ is the set of elements in either or both of $A$ and $C$. $(A \cup B) \cap (A \cup C)$ is the set of elements common to $(A \cup B)$ and $(A \cup C)$. But all elements of $A$ are in $(A \cup B)$ and in $(A \cup C)$ also. Hence all elements of $A$ are in $(A \cup B) \cap (A \cup C)$. Hence $(A \cup B) \cap (A \cup C)$ contains all elements of $A$ as well as those elements common to $B$ and $C$.

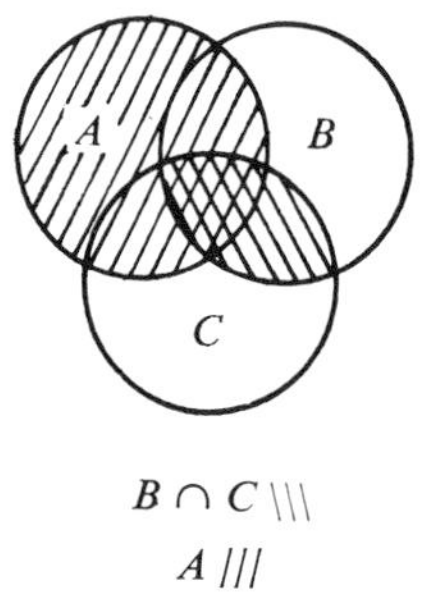


$B \cap C$ \\\

$A$ ///

$A \cup (B \cap C)$: SHADED

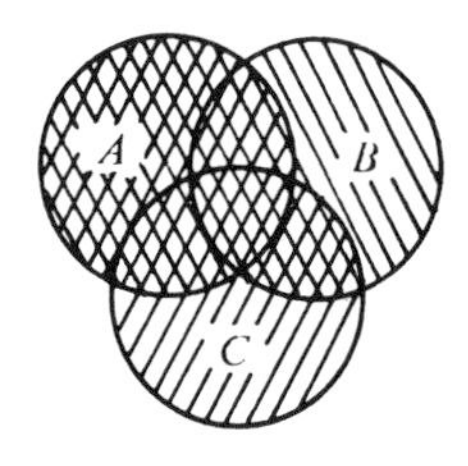


$A \cup B$ \\\

$A \cup C$ ///

$(A \cup B) \cap (A \cup C)$: CROSSHATCHED

*Example:* If $A = \{a, b, c\}$, $B = \{x, y, z\}$, and $C = \{a, x, y\}$, show

$$A \cup (B \cap C) = (A \cup B) \cap (A \cup C).$$

*Solution:*

$$B \cap C = \{x, y\}$$

$$A \cup (B \cap C) = \{a, b, c, x, y\}$$

$$A \cup B = \{a, b, c, x, y, z\}$$

$$A \cup C = \{a, b, c, x, y\}$$

$$(A \cup B) \cap (A \cup C) = \{a, b, c, x, y\}$$

$A \cap (B \cup C)$ is the set of all elements both in $A$ and in either $B$ or $C$. $A \cap B$ is the set of all elements common to both $A$ and $B$, $A \cap C$ is the set of all elements common to both $A$ and $C$. $(A \cap B) \cup (A \cap C)$ is the set of all elements in either or both of $A \cap B$ and $A \cap C$, hence it is the set of elements in both $A$ and either $B$ or $C$.

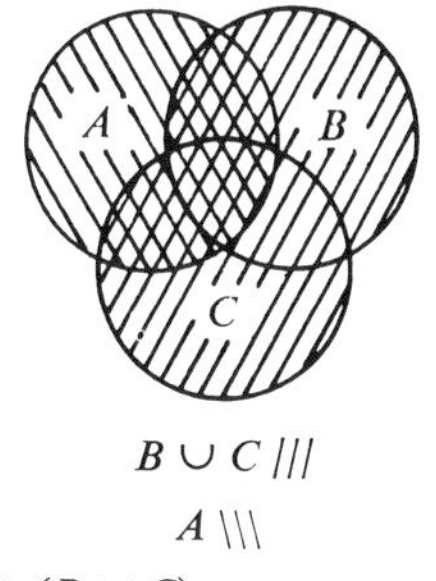


$B \cup C$ ///

$A$ \\\

$A \cap (B \cup C)$: CROSSHATCHED

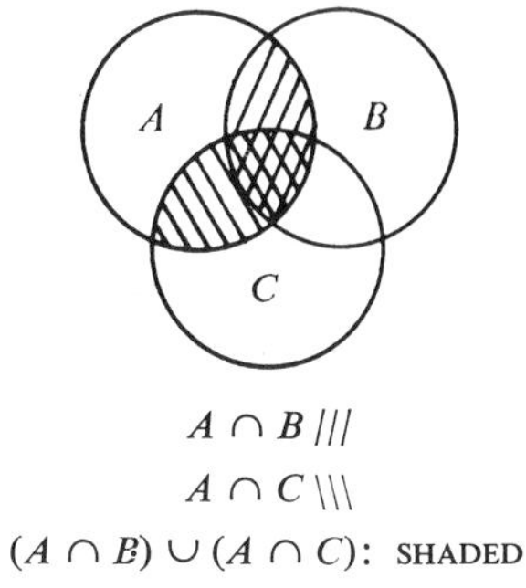


$A \cap B$ ///

$A \cap C$ \\\

$(A \cap B) \cup (A \cap C)$: SHADED

The two properties

$$(A \cup B)' = A' \cap B'$$
$$(A \cap B)' = A' \cup B'$$

are known as the De Morgan laws.

$(A \cup B)'$ is the set of all elements of the universal set which are not elements of either $A$ or $B$, $A'$ is the set of all elements of the universal set which are not elements of $A$, and $B'$ is the set of all elements of the universal set that are not elements of $B$. Hence $A' \cap B'$ is the set of elements of the universal set which are not elements of $A$ and are not elements of $B$.

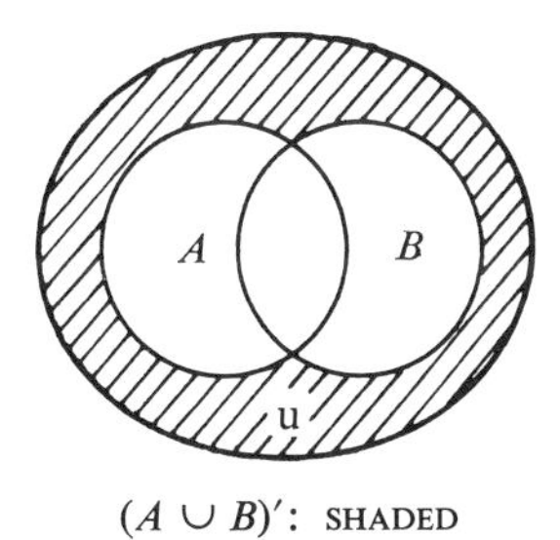


$(A \cup B)'$: SHADED

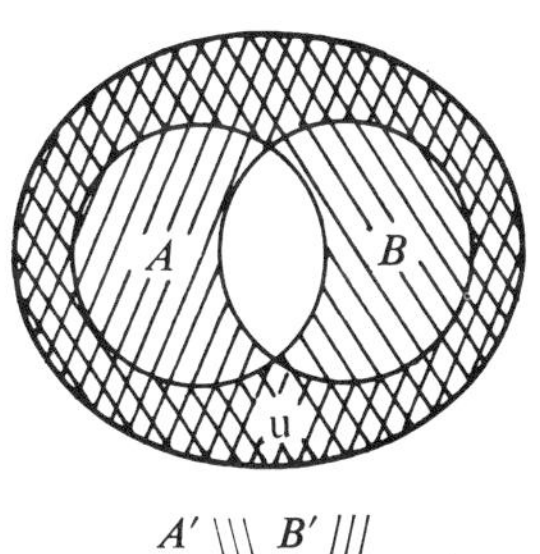


$A'$ \\\ $B'$ ///

$A' \cap B'$: CROSSHATCHED

*Example:* Let $U = \{1, 2, 3, \ldots, 10\}$,
$A = \{1, 2, 3, 4, 5\}$ $B = \{1, 3, 5, 7, 9\}$.
Show that $(A \cup B)' = A' \cap B'$.

*Solution:*

$$A \cup B = \{1, 2, 3, 4, 5, 7, 9\}$$
$$(A \cup B)' = \{6, 8, 10\}$$
$$A' = \{6, 7, 8, 9, 10\}$$
$$B' = \{2, 4, 6, 8, 10\}$$
$$A' \cap B' = \{6, 8, 10\}$$

## PROPERTIES OF SETS

$(A \cap B)'$ is the set of all elements of the universal set that are not elements of both $A$ and $B$. $A'$ is the set of all elements of the universal set that are not elements of $A$. $B'$ is the set of all elements of the universal set that are not elements of $B$. Hence $A' \cup B'$ is the set of all elements of the universal set that are not elements of $A$ or are not elements of $B$.

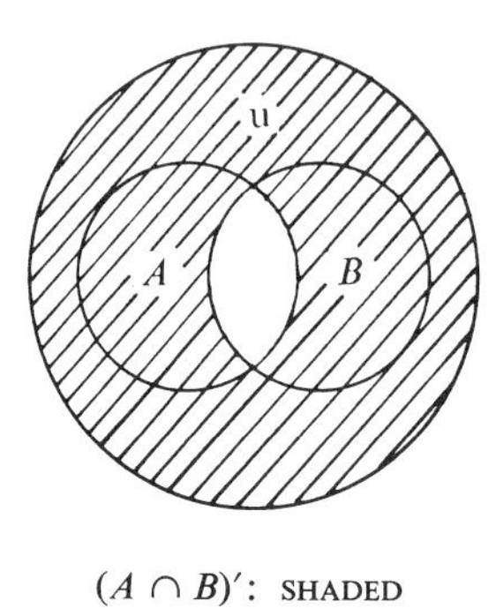


$(A \cap B)'$: SHADED

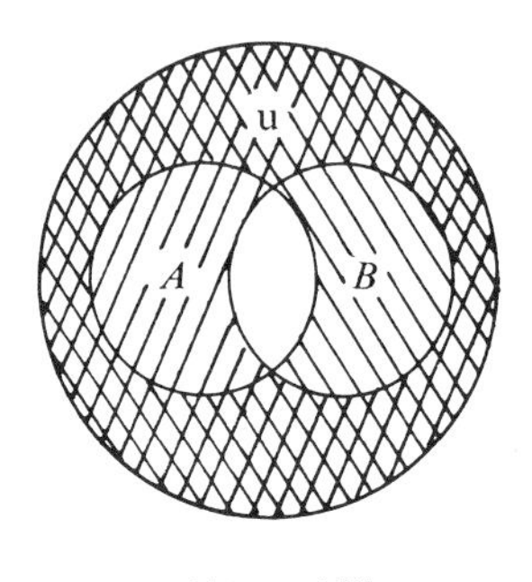


$A'$ \\\ $B'$ ///
$A' \cup B'$: SHADED

*Example:* If $U = \{1, 2, 3, \ldots, 10\}$, $A = \{1, 2, 3, 4, 5\}$, and $B = \{1, 3, 5, 7, 9\}$, show that $(A \cap B)' = A' \cup B'$.

*Solution:*

$$(A \cap B) = \{1, 3, 5\}$$
$$(A \cap B)' = \{2, 4, 6, 7, 8, 9, 10\}$$
$$A' = \{6, 7, 8, 9, 10\}$$
$$B' = \{2, 4, 6, 8, 10\}$$
$$A' \cup B' = \{2, 4, 6, 7, 8, 9, 10\}$$

The null set and the universal set have special properties.

$$A \cup \varnothing = A \cap U = A$$
$$A \cap \varnothing = \varnothing$$
$$A \cup U = U$$

Since $\varnothing$ has no elements, $A \cup \varnothing$ having as elements all elements of $A$ or $\varnothing$ or both, has as its elements the elements of $A$. Thus $A \cup \varnothing = A$.

Since $A \cap U$ has as elements those elements common to $A$ and $U$, and all elements of $A$ are elements of $U$, $A \cap U = A$.

Since $A \cap \varnothing$ has as its elements those elements common to $A$ and $\varnothing$, and $\varnothing$ has no elements, $A \cap \varnothing$ has no elements. Hence, $A \cap \varnothing = \varnothing$.

Since $A \cup U$ has as its elements those elements of $A$ or $U$ or both, and $U$ is the universal set, $A \cup U$ is the universal set, $A \cup U = U$.

Summarizing, the following are basic set properties:

I. $A \cup B = B \cup A$
II. $A \cap B = B \cap A$
III. $(A \cup B) \cup C = A \cup (B \cup C)$
IV. $(A \cap B) \cap C = A \cap (B \cap C)$
V. $A \cup (B \cap C) = (A \cup B) \cap (A \cup C)$
VI. $A \cap (B \cup C) = (A \cap B) \cup (A \cap C)$
VII. $(A \cup B)' = A' \cap B'$
VIII. $(A \cap B)' = A' \cup B'$
IX. $A \cup \varnothing = A$
X. $A \cap U = A$
XI. $A \cap \varnothing = \varnothing$
XII. $A \cup U = U$

These properties can be employed to establish many others.

*Example:* Show that $A \cap A = A$.

*Solution:* Although this is evidently a true statement when one considers the definition of intersection of sets, we wish to show that it follows from the ten properties listed above.

$$A \cap U = A \qquad \text{(by X)}$$
$$A \cup A' = U \qquad \text{(by definition of } A')$$

Now if in the first statement we replace $U$ with its equal $A \cup A'$ we have

$$A \cap (A \cup A') = A$$

Now apply VI to the left side of the equality, and we have

$$(A \cap A) \cup (A \cap A') = A$$

As an immediate consequence of the definition of $A'$ we have $A \cap A' = \varnothing$. Making this replacement, we have

$$(A \cap A) \cup \varnothing = A$$

Now if we apply IX we get the desired result.

$$(A \cap A) = A$$

*Example:* In a similar fashion we can show $A \cup A = A$.

*Solution:*

$A \cup \varnothing = A$ (by IX)

$A \cap A' = \varnothing$ (from the definition of $A'$)

Substituting this value of $\varnothing$ in the first statement, we have

$$A \cup (A \cap A') = A$$

Now apply V to the left side of the equality, and we have

$$(A \cup A) \cap (A \cup A') = A$$

But since $A \cup A' = U$ as a consequence of the definition of $A'$, we can replace $A \cup A'$ by $U$ and have

$$(A \cup A) \cap U = A$$

And applying X on the left, we have

$$(A \cup A) = A$$

These two examples illustrate a very significant aspect of set properties. If $\cap$ and $\cup$ are interchanged and $\varnothing$ and $U$ are interchanged in any one of the 12 set properties the result will be another one of the 12 properties. For example, consider the first of De Morgan's laws

$$(A \cup B)' = A' \cap B'$$

Interchanging $\cup$ and $\cap$ we get

$$(A \cap B)' = A' \cup B'$$

the second of De Morgan's laws.

This is known as the *Principle of Duality.* Union and intersection are dual operations and the null set and universal set are dual elements. The importance of duality stems from the fact that, corresponding to any new statement we can derive from the basic properties, there is another equally correct statement, the dual of the first. We merely have to interchange $\cup$ and $\cap$ and $\varnothing$ and $U$ in the first statement to obtain the second. We know the second statement is correct, for it can be derived by dualizing the derivation of the first one.

The statements established in the two exercises are dual statements:

$A \cap A = A$ and $A \cup A = A$. The derivation of the second statement is the dual of the derivation of the first. Notice further that two statements, consequences of the definition of $A'$, were used. $A \cup A' = U$ and $A \cap A' = \varnothing$ are themselves dual statements.

We shall close this discussion with the derivation of a new statement, the truth of which is not so readily apparent as was the case with the two above ones.

*Example:* Show that $A = (A \cap B) \cup (A \cap B')$

*Solution:* Apply property VI on the right and we have

$$A = A \cap (B \cup B')$$

But since $B \cup B' = U$, we have

$$A = A \cap U$$

and by X

$$A = A$$

## EXERCISES

1. Given $U = \{1, 2, 3, \ldots, 10\}$, $A = \{1, 3, 5, 7\}$,
   $B = \{4, 6, 8, 10\}$
   Find $A \cup (A' \cap B)$
2. Find $A \cup B$ and compare with Exercise 1.
3. By Venn diagrams show that $A \cup (A' \cap B) = A \cup B$.
4. Prove, using the twelve set principles, that $A \cup (A' \cap B) = A \cup B$.
5. If $A$ is the set of all positive odd integers and $A'$ is the set of all positive even integers, find the following:
   (a) $U$ (b) $A \cap A'$ (c) $A \cup (A' \cap A)$
6. Find the dual of $A \cup (A' \cap B) = A \cup B$.
7. Draw Venn diagrams to show the truth of the statement which is the answer to Exercise 6.
8. Given $U = \{1, 2, 3, \ldots, 10\}$, $A = \{1, 2, 3, 4\}$, $B = \{7, 8, 9\}$. Find $(A \cap B)'$. Find $A' \cup B'$ and compare with $(A \cap B)'$.
9. Using the sets defined in Exercise 8, find $(A \cap B) \cup (A' \cap B) \cup (A \cap B')$ and compare with $A \cup B$.
10. Dualize Exercise 9 and simplify the result.

## 1.4 Relations

We have said that two sets are equivalent if they have the same number of elements. However, two sets are called equal sets if they have exactly the same elements. The sets $A = \{2, 1, 3\}$ and $B = \{$ball, bat, glove$\}$ are equivalent. But set $C = \{$all one-digit positive integers$\}$ and $D = \{1, 2, 3, 4, 5, 6, 7, 8, 9\}$ are equal sets.

Sets $A$ and $B$ above are equal in the sense that they have an equal number of elements. Evidently, we use "equal" in a variety of ways. How is it used when we say set $A = \{2, 1, 3\}$? We would express the same idea if we said set $A$ *is* $\{2, 1, 3\}$.

The assertion that two things are equal is an assertion that a particular kind of relationship exists between them. Two things may be related in many different ways. Tom and Jim may have the "brother of" relation, the "father of" relation, or the "cousin of" relation. There are other relations beside that of blood kinship, such as "prettier than," "next to," "a part of," "in love with," ad infinitum. Some of the relations which may exist between mathematical objects are "is equal to," "is greater than," "implies," "is similar to." We use signs to indicate each kind of relation. For instance, if $a$ and $b$ are two mathematical elements (not necessarily numbers) the above relations between the two are indicated respectively $a = b$, $a > b$, $a \rightarrow b$, $a \sim b$. In general, if we wish to show a relation existing between $a$ and $b$ without specifying what the relation is we write $aRb$.

If a relation has the following properties it is called an equivalence relation:

Reflexive, or $aRa$.
Symmetric, or if $aRb$, then $bRa$.
Transitive, or if $aRb$ and $bRc$, then $aRc$.

A relation is reflexive if an element bears the relationship to itself. For example, the relation "knows the name of," applied to most people, is reflexive. This merely means that most people know their own names.

A symmetric relation is one such that if one element is related to a second then the second is related to the first in the same way. The "knows the name of" relation is not symmetric. Tom may know Jim's name without Jim knowing Tom's. But "kin to" is symmetric. If Tom is kin to Jim, then Jim is kin to Tom.

A transitive relation is one such that, if the first element is related to a second, and the second bears the same relation to a third, then the first bears this relation to the third. "Kin to" is not transitive. Tom may be

Joe's cousin because their fathers are brothers and Joe may be Jim's cousin because their mothers are sisters. But this does not make Tom kin to Jim. "Taller than" is transitive. If Tom is taller than Joe and Joe is taller than Jim, then Tom is taller than Jim.

Consider the relation among people "in love with." This is reflexive, or at least the Bible assumes so in stating the Golden Rule. Many a heart-broken swain knows it is not symmetric for all people. Nor is it transitive, although some people of the "love me, love my dog" persuasion seem to think so.

Relative to the set of male persons, "brother of" is symmetric and transitive but not reflexive. It is transitive because if Tom is Bill's brother and Bill is Jim's brother then Tom is Jim's brother. Here we must assume three distinct persons. Otherwise, we could have: Tom is Bill's brother, Bill is Tom's brother; hence, Tom is Tom's brother. It is symmetric because if Tom is Bill's brother, then Bill is Tom's brother. It is not reflexive; Tom is not Tom's brother, even though he is Tom's brother's brother.

The mathematical relation "greater than" applied to integers is transitive but not symmetric or reflexive. $10 > 8$ and $8 > 3$, therefore $10 > 3$. But 10 is not greater than 10, nor does $10 > 7$ imply that $7 > 10$. "Is an integral factor of" is reflexive (any number is a factor of itself) and transitive (3 a factor of 12 and 12 a factor of 36 implies 3 a factor of 36). But it is not symmetric (5 a factor of 15 does not imply that 15 is a factor of 5).

The relation "implies" applied to propositions is reflexive. The expression $a \rightarrow a$ simply means that the truth of proposition $a$ implies the truth of proposition $a$. But it is not symmetric. If $a \rightarrow b$ it does not necessarily follow that $b \rightarrow a$.

*Example:* Consider the two statements
$a$—The number ends in five.
$b$—The number is a multiple of five.

$a \rightarrow b$ If a number ends in 5 it has to be a multiple of 5.
$b \not\rightarrow a$ ($\not\rightarrow$ means does not imply) Thirty is a multiple of 5 but it ends in zero, not 5.

The fact that "implies" is transitive is a basic principle of logic. If the truth of proposition $a$ implies the truth of $b$, and the truth of $b$ implies the truth of $c$, we accept without hesitation that the truth of $a$ implies the truth of $c$. If we wish to indicate that a symmetric relation does exist between two particular propositions $a$, $b$ we indicate this by $a \leftrightarrow b$. In this case the two propositions are logically equivalent.

"Equal to" applied to the set of cardinal numbers is in equivalence relation.

It is reflexive: any number is equal to itself.

It is symmetric: if $3 + 2 = 5$ then $5 = 3 + 2$.

We express this by saying the equality sign can be read in either direction.

It is transitive: if $4 + 3 = 7$ and $7 = 5 + 2$ then $4 + 3 = 5 + 2$.

We might take the position that a relation which is reflexive, symmetric, and transitive is by definition the relation "equal." But there are other equivalence relations. Similarity of geometric figures is reflexive, symmetric, and transitive. We could think of similarity as a kind of equality—"equal" shape. Congruency used in the geometric sense (the word is also used in other mathematical contexts) is also an equivalence relation. As its sign $\cong$ indicates, we have "equal" shape and area. Equivalence is the more general term which includes equal as equivalence in the numerical

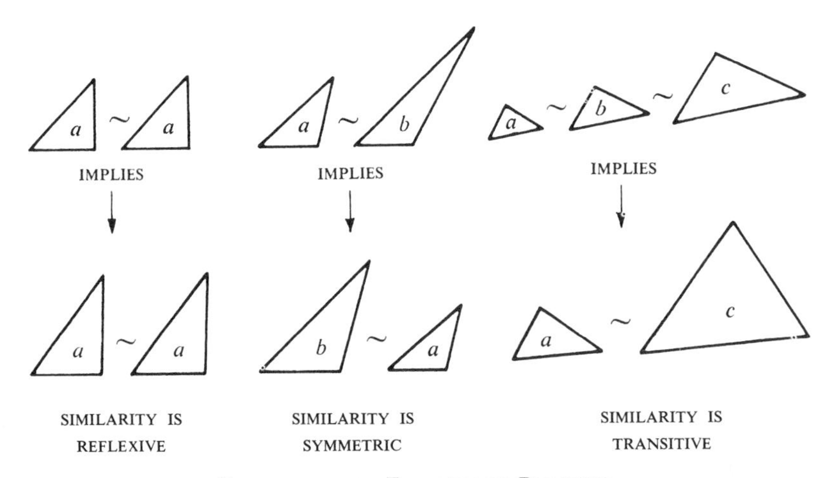


SIMILARITY IS AN EQUIVALENCE RELATION.

sense. Two numerical expressions are equal if they are two ways of saying the same thing. $2 + 3$, $5$, $6 - 1$ are three ways of representing the same numerical quantity.

Equivalence of sets if reflexive—a set has the same number of elements that it has.

Equivalence of sets if symmetric—if set $A$ has the same number of elements as set $B$ then set $B$ also has the same number of elements as set $A$.

Equivalence of sets is also transitive.

## SETS, SYMBOLS, AND RELATIONS

If $A$ is equivalent to $B$, $A$ and $B$ have the same number of elements. If $B$ is equivalent to $C$, $B$ and $C$ have the same number of elements. Hence $A$ and $C$ have the same number of elements, and are therefore equivalent. Hence equivalence of sets is an equivalence relation.

Equality of sets is also an equivalence relation. Here equality is used to mean *identically the same.* Surely set $A$ = set $A$ because $A$ has identically the same elements that it has. This is the reflexive property. Also if $A = B$ then $B = A$, if the elements of $A$ are identically the same as the elements of $B$ then the elements of $B$ are identically the same as the elements of $A$. This is the symmetric property. Finally, if $A = B$ and $B = C$ then $A = C$. If the elements of $A$ and $B$ are identically the same, and the elements of $B$ and $C$ are identically the same, surely the elements of $A$ and $C$ are identically the same. This is the transitive property.

## EXERCISES

**1.** State which of the properties, *reflexive*, *symmetric*, and *transitive*, the following relations possess:

(a) "Is the father of" applied to people.
(b) "Is the brother of" applied to people.
(c) "Is the brother of" applied to male people.
(d) "Is the cousin of" applied to people.
(e) "Is the stronger than" (on the basis of scores) applied to football teams.
(f) "Is acquainted with" applied to people.
(g) "Is north of" applied to locations on the earth.
(h) "Is east of" applied to locations on the earth, North and South Poles excluded.
(i) "Is one half of" applied to line segments.
(j) "Is perpendicular to" applied to lines in space.
(k) "Lives in the house with" applied to people.
(l) "Is the ancestor of" applied to people.
(m) "Is less than" applied to integers.
(n) "Is not equal to" applied to integers.

**2.** (a) Is $\subseteq$ an equivalence relation? Justify your answer.
(b) Is $\subset$ an equivalence relation? If not, which properties does it have?

**3.** Give an example of a relation which has the reflexive, but not the symmetric or transitive properties.

**4.** Give an example of a relation which has the reflexive and transitive, but not the symmetric properties.

**5.** Give an example of a transitive, but not symmetric or reflexive relation.

6. What property or properties do each of the following illustrate?
   (a) If $8 + 4 = 12$ then $12 = 8 + 4$.
   (b) If $6 > 3$ and $3 > 1$ then $6 > 1$.
   (c) "A rose is a rose is a rose . . . ."
   (d) $x + y = x + y$.
   (e) Jim is taller than Betty, Betty is prettier than Bob, so Jim is smarter than Bob. (Answer: none.)
   (f) Jim and Bob are brothers because Jim is Tom's brother and Tom is Bob's brother.
   (g) If $2 + 3 = 5$ and $105 - 100 = 5$, then $2 + 3 = 105 - 100$.
   (h) Jim is the brother of Bob and Bob is the brother of Mary, therefore Mary is the brother of Jim. (What is wrong here—what property is present and what property is not?)

## CHAPTER SUMMARY

The term *set* is used in mathematics as an undefined term. The mathematical use of the term is not inconsistent with its ordinary use. A set of things is simply a collection of things.

The things that make up a set are its *elements*. Although we make no attempt to define the word "set," in mathematics we insist that the sets that are considered must be *well-defined* sets. A set is well defined when there is a criterion whereby it can be determined whether any object is or is not an element of the set. Sets can be defined by *roster*, a listing of all elements, or *rule*, an adequate description of the elements.

When the rule method is employed to define a set, *variables* are frequently used. A variable is a symbol that represents any element of a set, called the *replacement set* of the variable. Capital letters are usually used to name sets and the corresponding small letter is the variable to represent the elements.

$$N = \{n \mid n \in P,\ n < 100\}$$

means "the set $N$ of elements $n$ such that $n$ is an element of the set $P$, of positive integers, and $n$ is less than 100."

*Equal sets* are sets that have exactly the same elements. *Equivalent sets* are sets that have the same number of elements.

Set $A$ is a *subset* of $B$, $A \subseteq B$, if and only if every element of $A$ is an element of $B$. $A$ is a *proper subset* of $B$ ($A \subset B$) if $A \subseteq B$ and $B$ has at least one element that is not an element of $A$.

There are two basic set operations: intersection and union. The intersection of $A$ and $B$, $A \cap B$, is the set of elements common to $A$ and $B$. The union of $A$ and $B$, $A \cup B$, is the set of elements that are elements of $A$, or $B$, or both $A$ and $B$.

If two sets have no elements in common they are called *disjoint* sets. Their intersection is called the *null set*, $\varnothing$. The null set is the set that has no elements. The set of all elements germane to a discussion is called the *universal set*, $U$. The complement $A'$ of set $A$ is the set of all elements of $U$ that are not elements of $A$.

Sets, under the operations of union and intersection, obey certain basis properties. These are:

The commutative properties:

$$A \cup B = B \cup A$$
$$A \cap B = B \cap A$$

The associative properties:

$$(A \cup B) \cup C = A \cup (B \cup C)$$
$$(A \cap B) \cap C = A \cap (B \cap C)$$

The distributive properties:

$$A \cup (B \cap C) = (A \cup B) \cap (A \cup C)$$
$$A \cap (B \cup C) = (A \cap B) \cup (A \cap C)$$

De Morgan's properties:

$$(A \cup B)' = A' \cap B'$$
$$(A \cap B)' = A' \cup B'$$

Properties of the null set and universal set:

$$A \cup \varnothing = A$$
$$A \cap U = A$$
$$A \cap \varnothing = \varnothing$$
$$A \cup U = U$$

This set of properties is a *dual* set. If $\cap$ and $\cup$ are interchanged, and $\varnothing$ and $U$ interchanged in any one of the properties, the resulting statement is another one of the properties.

**CHAPTER SUMMARY**

Mathematical relations may have one or more of the three properties.

Reflexive: $aRa$.
Symmetric: if $aRb$ then $bRa$.
Transitive: if $aRb$ and $bRc$ then $aRc$.

Any relation that has all three properties is an *equivalence relation.*

Both equality of sets and equivalence of sets are equivalence relations. The relation "is a subset of," $\subseteq$, is reflexive and transitive but not symmetric. It is not an equivalence relation. The relation "is a proper subset of," $\subset$, is neither reflexive nor symmetric but it is transitive.

# 2 Counting, Adding, Subtracting

HOW MANY COUNTING NUMBERS ARE THERE? WHY DOES $4 + 3 = 3 + 4$? If we count these marks //// and continue the count through these marks /// we get the same total as if we started with the set of three first and continued the count through the set of four. This can be verified by actually carrying out the count. Is this true of any two counting numbers $a$ and $b$? Just what is a counting number anyway?

These are some of the questions we shall investigate in this chapter. We shall give a formal description of the behavior of the counting numbers when they are combined by addition and the related operation subtraction. The system of numbers will be enlarged so that subtraction will always be possible.

## 2.1 One-to-One Correspondence

Consider the two sets of objects $A = \{\text{bee, wagon, car, ship, plane}\}$ and $B = \{\text{apple, banana, pear, peach, polecat}\}$. In set $A$ each element of the set is a transportation vehicle, except the bee. Set $B$ might be thought of as a set of fruit, but for the polecat. The elements of a set may have many properties in common which might characterize the set. For example, $C = \{\text{ball, moon, ring, coin, marble}\}$ could be characterized as a set of round objects. Or $D = \{\text{fire, pepper, steam, coffee, stove}\}$ might be considered a set of hot objects. But we would hardly claim that $C$ is a round set or $D$ a hot set. In Chapter I the point was made that there is a difference in kind between the objects of a set and the set itself. The members of a basketball team are Tom, John, Bill, Cliff, and Algernon. The team is a set $T = \{\text{Tom, John, Bill, Cliff, Algernon}\}$, but Tom is not a basketball team. Perhaps you have known a player who thought he was the whole team. Even in the case where a set has only one element, the element and the set are not the same. Quite often the elements of a set are themselves sets. The National League is a set of baseball teams. Each team is a set of players. Suppose the teams in an independent league withdraw until only one team remains a member. The league and the one member team in the league are not the same. The league can vote itself out of existence without affecting the team. There is the story of the man who organized an exclusive club for the sole purpose of blackballing his enemies. He was the only member of the club. The club met weekly to vote on prospective members. When all of his enemies had been blackballed he killed the club, but he did not commit suicide.

All of the sets $A$, $B$, $C$, and $T$ have a property in common which is independent of the nature of the individual elements. Any two of them can be placed in one-to-one correspondence.

> A one-to-one correspondence exists between two sets if it is possible to associate one and only one element of each set with one and only one element of the other.

In other words, a one-to-one correspondence exists between two sets if the elements of each can be paired off, no element of either unused, and no element used more than once.

The matching

| bee | wagon | plane | car | ship |
|---|---|---|---|---|
| $\updownarrow$ | $\updownarrow$ | $\updownarrow$ | $\updownarrow$ | $\updownarrow$ |
| polecat | pear | peach | apple | banana |

establishes the correspondence between set $A$ and set $B$. There are, of course, other pairings that could have been used. All that is necessary is a matching which corresponds each element of each set with exactly one element of the other.

One-to-one correspondence is basic to the counting process. This is not to say that they are synonymous. The notion of one-to-one correspondence is a more primitive concept; it is in no way dependent on the notion of counting.

If upon boarding a bus I find exactly one vacant seat and no one but me standing, I know there are the same number of persons on the bus as there are seats. As passengers are picked up and discharged it is possible to determine at any time whether the number of passengers is less than, equal to, or greater than the number of seats merely by observing whether there are empty seats, all seats taken and no one standing, or all seats taken and passengers standing. The set of seats serves as a reference set. The set of passengers can be compared to it without benefit of counting or even the existence of number names.

If two sets of things can be placed into one-to-one correspondence the sets are said to have the same *cardinal number*; they are *equal in number*. The correspondence does not have to be done in a physical sense, nor do the members of either necessarily have to have a physical existence. One set might be the adjectives (not the words but the ideas which they symbolize) {*round*, *rough*, *black*, *loud*} while the other could be the nonsense syllables (*dru*, *aug*, *tol*, *sner*}. The essential element of one-to-one correspondence is the *existence* of exactly one member of each set to pair with each member of the other. The actual pairing may be done mentally.

In case the one-to-one correspondence cannot be established, the cardinal number of that set which has members unmatched in the other set is said to be greater than the cardinal number of the other.

The sets $A$, $B$, $C$, and $T$ each *have* the same cardinal number, the cardinal number five, $n(A) = n(B) = n(C) = n(T) = 5$. But what *is* the cardinal number five? It is the set of *all* sets that can be placed in one-to-one correspondence with set $A$, or $B$, or any other set equivalent to them. More particularly, it is the set of all sets that can be placed in one-to-one correspondence with the set {one, two, three, four, five}. Hence, it is a set of equivalent sets. It may seem a bit surprising to define the cardinal number five in this way. But we must keep in mind the fact that there is a difference in kind between the elements of a set and the set itself. Thus, sets $A$, $B$, $C$, and $T$ are elements of the cardinal number five, which is itself a set of equivalent sets. Any other set that can be placed in one-to-one correspondence with the set {one, two, three, four, five} is an element of the set five. Any set which cannot be so placed in this correspondence is not an element of the set five; it does not have five as its cardinal number.

## EXERCISES

**1.** How can one use a six-foot rope to devise a one-to-one correspondence with ten sheep without cutting the rope?

**2.** Without resorting to any form of counting, determine which has the more letters, *California* or *Colorado*.

**3.** Which of the following pairs of sets has a one-to-one correspondence relationship?

(a) Husbands–wives

(b) Mothers–daughters

(c) States of the United States–United States Senators
(d) One-digit integers–two-digit integers
(e) Even integers–odd integers
(f) Months of the year–days of the week
(g) Brothers–sisters

**4.** In how many ways can the sets $A = \{\text{chair, desk, table, lamp}\}$ and $B = \{\text{shoe, tie, shirt, hat}\}$ be placed in one-to-one correspondence?

**5.** In Exercise 3(c) we see an example of two sets that can be placed in a one-to-two correspondence. Name another pair of sets which has this property.

## 2.2 Counting the Infinite

The first set of numbers a child encounters is

$$\{1, 2, 3, \ldots, n, \ldots\}$$

We have referred to this as the set of *counting numbers*. They are the numbers with which we count the objects of a collection. This set is also called the set of *natural numbers*. This usage is not universally accepted in mathematical circles. Some writers call

$$\{0, 1, 2, 3, \ldots, n, \ldots\}$$

the set of counting numbers, or the set of natural numbers. Although we have already made reference to the set of positive integers, this is really not cricket because the set of integers has not been introduced.

There is a growing tendency in arithmetic circles to call the set

$$\{0, 1, 2, 3, \ldots, n, \ldots\}$$

the set of *whole numbers*. If we use the term, this is the set to which we shall refer unless there is a qualifying adjective such as "even" to indicate a subset of the set of whole numbers.

One may properly raise the question: No matter what you call them, what are the elements of such a set? We propose to answer this question by defining the set of *finite cardinal numbers*

$$\{0, 1, 2, 3, \ldots, n, \ldots\}$$

We may use interchangeably the terms natural numbers and zero, counting numbers (including zero), positive integers and zero, non-negative integers, and finite cardinal numbers.

The great Greek mathematician Archimedes, using the Greek's cumbersome number system, succeeded in writing a number greater than the number of grains of sand which would be required to fill the universe. He was a piker; his number is puny compared to the number expressed by means of four 9's: $9^{9^{9^9}}$. The immensity of this number defies the imagination, but there are larger numbers. No matter how large a number we consider, there is always a larger one. Every counting number has a successor. This cannot be proved. The fact that we can add one to any specified number is not sufficient, for this assertion is justified only on the assumption that there is an endless succession of numbers. The fact that we cannot reach an end to counting proves nothing. Maybe we just cannot count long enough, or live long enough to get to the end. The endlessness of the counting numbers is an *assumption* which is basic to the entire number system and to all of arithmetic. We express the idea by saying the set of positive integers is *infinite.*

The set of positive even integers is also an infinite set. Any even integer, being an integer, must have a successor, but its successor also has a successor that is an even integer. Thus any even integer has an even integer successor.

Since only every other whole number is an even number, can we say the infinite set of positive even integers is only half as large as the infinite set of positive integers ? We have agreed that two sets have the same cardinal number if they can be placed into one-to-one correspondence. Consider the array

$$\begin{array}{cccccccc} 1 & 2 & 3 & 4 & 5 & \dots & n & \dots \\ \updownarrow & \updownarrow & \updownarrow & \updownarrow & \updownarrow & & \updownarrow & \\ 2 & 4 & 6 & 8 & 10 & \dots & 2n & \dots \end{array}$$

The top line consists of all positive integers and the bottom line all positive even integers. We say all because the three dots following the 5 mean "and so on" out to any number $n$, and the three dots following the $n$ mean "and so on" endlessly. The double-pointed arrows indicate the means of pairing the elements of the two sets. Corresponding to any positive integer $n$ of the set of positive integers we pair the even integer $2n$ of the set of even integers. Remember, we do not have to write down all the pairs. The essential thing is to show how we can match each element of each set with exactly one element of the other. Each member of the set of positive integers is paired with the even integer that is twice as large, and each positive even integer is paired with the integer half as large. But how can this be, since all of the positive even integers are found among the positive integers ? Can half of the positive integers be just as numerous as all the positive integers? This seeming paradox stems from the fact that we are dealing with infinite sets rather than finite. This is precisely what we need to make the distinction between finite and infinite sets. An infinite set is one which can be placed in one-to-one correspondence with a proper subset of itself. Not just any proper subset; we could hardly set up the correspondence between the first ten integers and all the integers. But if there exists a proper subset such that the correspondence can be set up, we have an infinite set. The set of positive even integers is a proper subset of the set of positive integers.

> An infinite set is a set that can be placed in one-to-one correspondence with some proper subset of itself.

Just as all finite sets that can be placed in one-to-one correspondence have the same cardinal number, so also do all infinite sets. All sets that can be placed in one-to-one correspondence with the counting numbers have the same cardinal number. Obviously, such numbers are not finite; they are called *transfinite* numbers.

## 2.3 Denumerable Infinity

Any infinite set which can be placed in one-to-one correspondence with the set of positive integers is said to be *denumerably* or *countably* infinite. Such sets have the transfinite cardinal number $\aleph_0$ (Aleph Null).

> If $P$ is the set of positive integers $n(P) = \aleph_0$

We can easily show the set of positive odd integers has the same cardinal number as the set of positive integers. Since the positive integers consist of the even positive integers plus the odd positive integers we must conclude

$$\aleph_0 + \aleph_0 = \aleph_0$$

The set of unit fractions, that is, fractions whose numerator is one and denominator a positive integer, is countably infinite.

$$\begin{array}{ccccccccc} 1 & 2 & 3 & 4 & 5 & \ldots & n & \ldots \\ \updownarrow & \updownarrow & \updownarrow & \updownarrow & \updownarrow & & \updownarrow & \\ \frac{1}{1} & \frac{1}{2} & \frac{1}{3} & \frac{1}{4} & \frac{1}{5} & \ldots & \frac{1}{n} & \ldots \end{array}$$

Even if these were all the fractions between zero and one (for instance, if there were no fractions between $\frac{1}{2}$ and $\frac{1}{3}$), we would have shown there are as many fractions between the consecutive integers zero and one as there are integers. There are, however, a countably infinite number of such intervals created by the integers. Then the fractions consist of a countably infinite number of countably infinite sets. Surely there are more fractions than integers! The arithmetic of the infinite behaves rather strangely. We can show there are just as many positive integers as there are positive fractions. Consider the array:

$$
\begin{array}{ccccccccc}
\frac{1}{1} & \rightarrow & \frac{1}{2} & & \frac{1}{3} & \rightarrow & \frac{1}{4} & \frac{1}{5} & \cdots & \frac{1}{n} & \cdots \\
& \swarrow & & \nearrow & & \swarrow & & & & & \\
\frac{2}{1} & & \frac{2}{2} & & \frac{2}{3} & & \frac{2}{4} & \frac{2}{5} & \cdots & \frac{2}{n} & \cdots \\
\downarrow & \nearrow & & \swarrow & & & & & & & \\
\frac{3}{1} & & \frac{3}{2} & & \frac{3}{3} & & \frac{3}{4} & \frac{3}{5} & \cdots & \frac{3}{n} & \cdots \\
\cdot & & \cdot & & \cdot & & \cdot & \cdot & \cdots & \cdot & \cdots \\
\cdot & & \cdot & & \cdot & & \cdot & \cdot & \cdots & \cdot & \cdots \\
\cdot & & \cdot & & \cdot & & \cdot & \cdot & \cdots & \cdot & \cdots \\
\frac{n}{1} & & \frac{n}{2} & & \frac{n}{3} & & \frac{n}{4} & \frac{n}{5} & \cdots & \frac{n}{n} & \cdots \\
\cdot & & \cdot & & \cdot & & \cdot & \cdot & \cdots & \cdot & \cdots \\
\cdot & & \cdot & & \cdot & & \cdot & \cdot & \cdots & \cdot & \cdots
\end{array}
$$

The first row contains all unit fractions, the second all possible fractions with numerator 2, and so on. In each row we use every possible denominator and in each column we use every possible numerator. If we follow the arrows we see the scheme for counting the array—for placing its elements in one-to-one correspondence with the positive integers. As we move along the arrows we drop out any fraction previously appearing as $\frac{2}{2}$, $\frac{4}{2}$, $\frac{3}{3}$, $\frac{2}{4}$. The pairing begins

$$
\begin{array}{ccccccccccc}
1 & 2 & 3 & 4 & 5 & 6 & 7 & 8 & 9 & 10 & 11 \\
\updownarrow & \updownarrow & \updownarrow & \updownarrow & \updownarrow & \updownarrow & \updownarrow & \updownarrow & \updownarrow & \updownarrow & \updownarrow \\
\frac{1}{1} & \frac{1}{2} & \frac{2}{1} & \frac{3}{1} & \frac{1}{3} & \frac{1}{4} & \frac{2}{3} & \frac{3}{2} & \frac{4}{1} & \frac{5}{1} & \frac{1}{5}
\end{array}
$$

Note that the fractions do not have to be counted in order of magnitude. This would be impossible because we can show that between any two fractions there is a countable infinity of others. We merely have to display a scheme for setting up the pairs such that each member of each set is paired with one and only one member of the other.

The set of elements in each row is countably infinite, the denominators being the set of counting numbers. The set of rows is countably infinite, each counting number being used as the numerator throughout a row. Hence we must conclude that

$$\aleph_0 \cdot \aleph_0 = \aleph_0$$

Perhaps the thought has presented itself that all infinite sets have the same cardinal number. This is not the case. As we shall see, there are more real numbers between zero and one than all of the rational numbers.

## EXERCISES

1. Show a one-to-one correspondence between the set of positive odd integers and the set of positive integers.
2. If there is a one-to-one correspondence between set $A$ and set $C$, and a one-to-one correspondence between set $B$ and set $C$, show that there must be a one-to-one correspondence between set $A$ and set $B$.
3. Prove that there are as many multiples of five as there are unit fractions.
4. Show, by means of one-to-one correspondence, which of the two sets has the greatest number of elements: $A = \{1, 2, 3, 4, 5, 6, 7, 8, 9, 10\}$; $B = \{\frac{1}{1}, \frac{1}{3}, \frac{1}{5}, \frac{1}{7}, \frac{1}{11}, \frac{1}{13}, \frac{1}{17}, \frac{1}{19}\}$.
5. How can one show that two infinite sets do not have the same transfinite cardinal number?
6. Show that $\aleph_0 - 10 = \aleph_0$.
   Show that $\aleph_0 + 100 = \aleph_0$.
7. What does $10\,\aleph_0$ equal?
8. Can one say what $\aleph_0 - \aleph_0$ is equal? Why?
9. Complete the following one-to-one correspondence:

$$\begin{array}{cccccccc} 1 & \frac{1}{2} & \frac{1}{3} & \frac{1}{4} & \cdots & & \frac{1}{n} & \cdots\cdot \\ \updownarrow & \updownarrow & \updownarrow & \updownarrow & & & \updownarrow & \\ 10 & 20 & 30 & 40 & \cdots & & & \cdots\cdot \end{array}$$

   This shows which two infinite sets have the same cardinal number?
10. Show that one-to-one correspondence is an equivalence relation.

## COUNTING, ADDING, SUBTRACTING

## 2.4 Cardinal Numbers

The child's first contacts with addition consist of combining sets of concrete objects into a single set. He combines sets of pennies, sets of marbles, sets of children. This putting together of sets into a single set is a kind of abridged counting. He learns that a set of five chairs put with a set of three chairs forms a new set of eight chairs. This result

could be obtained by counting the first set and continuing to count uninterrupted through the second.

The next step is the realization that a set of five of anything combined with a set of three of the same thing yields a set of eight of the same thing. Finally, he adds numbers, $3 + 5 = 8$, without the necessity of relating the numbers to any particular object or set of objects.

One of the most hard to achieve, yet indispensable, attributes of a skillful teacher is the ability to see the learning situation from the learner's point of view. In elementary instruction we frequently take for granted many difficult concepts underlying elementary arithmetic. When the child is made to memorize "three plus five equals eight" it is small wonder that he is merely parroting sound patterns. What does "plus" mean? What does "equals" mean? For that matter what do three, five, and eight mean?

There is the story of little Bobby, who could not learn to add problems involving "carrying." The teacher left Bobby and Bill to their own devices in a corner by themselves. In short order Bobby was all smiles—he had caught on. The teacher in amazement asked Bill what he did. Bill's reply: "Well, you know where you told us to carry, I just told him to tote it." There is a valuable lesson in this feeble joke. We should never assume that as a matter of course our words convey the intended adult meaning to the child. We are prone to think the words "numerator" and "denominator" could hardly be more descriptive of their correct mathematical interpretation. Quite true, from the adult standpoint. But what about the child? "Numeration" and "denomination" may not be in his vocabulary, and if they are their meanings are probably quite hazy.

It is well that we inquire into some of the most obvious, and therefore most obscure, concepts which the child is expected to develop in arithmetic. We shall attack them from an adult, abstract point of view, not that the approach is recommended for children, but so that you, the teacher, may have a fuller grasp and deeper appreciation of what is involved.

In Section 2.1 we saw that the cardinal number five is the set of all sets equivalent to the set $\{1, 2, 3, 4, 5\}$. A set such as this is called an *equivalence class.*

> If any two elements of a set are equivalent, and any element equivalent to an element of the set is also an element of the set, the set is an equivalence class.

> A cardinal number is an equivalence class of sets.

Thus, the cardinal number 1 is the set of all *unit sets*, that is, sets that have one element.

$$1 = \{\{a\}, \{b\}, \{1\}, \{\text{apple}\}, \ldots\}$$

Each element of the set 1 has 1 as its cardinal number.

The cardinal number 2 is the set of *all* sets equivalent to $\{1, 2\}$.

$$2 = \{\{1, 2\}, \{a, b\}, \{\text{apple, peach}\}, \ldots\}$$

Each element of set 2 has 2 as its cardinal number.

We have said that every set, finite or infinite, *has* a cardinal number, and each cardinal number *is* an equivalence class. What about the null set $\varnothing$? We did not include zero in the set of natural numbers, but it is a cardinal number. It is the cardinal number of the null set. Here we must be careful to observe the distinction between a set with one element $\{a\}$ and that one element $a$. The cardinal number 0 is the set of sets equivalent to the null set. But there is just one null set. The set of women presidents of the United States is the same set as the set of men twenty feet tall, that is, the null set. The set $\varnothing$ is zero. In this one case we define the cardinal number of the set as the set itself, $0 = \varnothing$. The set whose single element is the set $\varnothing$ has the cardinal number 1. But the cardinal 1 *is* the set of equivalent sets of which $\{0\}$ may be considered a representative element. That is, $\{0\}$ is not the null set, $\{0\}$ is a set with one element. This one element happens to be the cardinal number 0.

Since $\{1, 2, 3\}$ is an element of the set of equivalent sets which is the cardinal number 3, are we guilty of circular defining? Is the cardinal number 3 an element of an element of itself? Here again it is imperative that we keep before us the distinction between a set and its elements. It is true that 1, 2, and 3 are cardinal numbers; but $\{1, 2, 3\}$ is a *set of* cardinal numbers, a different kind of object.

It is possible to select, as representative element of a set of equivalent sets, a set constructed from $\varnothing$ as follows:

$0 = \varnothing$; zero is by definition the null set.
$1 = \{\varnothing\} = \{0\}$; a set with one element.
$2 = \{\varnothing, \{\varnothing\}\} = \{0, 1\}$; a set with two elements.
$3 = \{\varnothing, \{\varnothing\}\{\varnothing, \{\varnothing\}\}\} = \{0, 1, 2\}$; a set with three elements.
$4 = \{\varnothing, \{\varnothing\}, \{\varnothing, \{\varnothing\}\}, \{\varnothing, \{\varnothing\}, \{\varnothing, \{\varnothing\}\}\}\} = \{0, 1, 2, 3\}$; a set with four elements.

Evidently this process may be continued indefinitely, each representative set having one more element than its predecessor, that element being the predecessor. Thus, it is possible to represent each cardinal number after zero as the *set* of cardinal numbers preceding it.

## EXERCISES

**1.** If $A = \{1, 2, 3, 4, 5, 6, 7, 8, 9, 10\}$ and $B = \{2, 4, 6, 8, 10, 12, 14\}$ find $A \cap B$ and $A \cup B$.

**2.** If $C = \{\text{cat, dog, bird, rabbit}\}$ list as many proper subsets of $C$ as you can. (There are 15 proper subsets.)

**3.** Is the null set a proper subset of any other set? Is it a proper subset of itself?

**4.** Name three elements of the cardinal number three.

**5.** Is the cardinal number 1 an element of itself? Explain.

**6.** Distinguish between: $A = \{1, 2, 3, 4, 5\}$ and $B = \{\{1, 2, 3\}, \{4, 5\}\}$.

**7.** Distinguish between $C = \{1, 2, 3, 4\}$ and $D = \{\frac{1}{2}, \frac{3}{4}\}$.

**8.** If $A = \{\text{apple, orange, egg}\}$ and $B = \{\text{fire, skillet, egg}\}$ what is $n(A)$? $n(B)$? $n(A \cap B)$? $n(A \cup B)$?

**9.** If $A = \{1, 2, 3, 4, 5\}$ and $B = \{1, 2, 3, 4\}$ what is $n(A)$? $n(B)$? $n(A \cap B)$? $n(A \cup B)$?

**10.** If $A = \{\text{Tom, Dick, Harry}\}$ and $B = \{\text{Bill, George, Sam, Mike}\}$ what is $n(A)$? $n(B)$? $n(A \cap B)$? $n(A \cup B)$?

**11.** If $A = \{13, 2, 7, 11\}$ and $B = \{5, 3, 17\}$ what is $n(A \cup B)$? $n(B \cap A)$?

**12.** If $A = \{16, 5, 19, 23\}$ and $B = \{22, 16, 8, 5\}$ what is $n(A \cup B)$? $n(B \cup A)$?

## 2.5 Addition of Cardinal Numbers

We are now able to state formally what the addition of two cardinal numbers means. Consider two disjoint sets $A$, with cardinal number $a$, and $B$, with cardinal number $b$. By $a + b$ we mean the cardinal number of the set $A \cup B$.

> Definition of addition of cardinal numbers: If $a = n(A)$, $b = n(B)$ and $A \cap B = \varnothing$ then $a + b = n(A \cup B)$.

Notice carefully the requirement that $A$ and $B$ are disjoint. If $P = \{\text{Smith, Jones, Brown}\}$ and $R = \{\text{Johnson, Jones, Jensen}\}$, then $P \cup R = \{\text{Smith, Jones, Brown, Johnson, Jensen}\}$. $P$ and $R$ are not disjoint since $P \cap R = \{\text{Jones}\}$. The cardinal number of $P$ is 3, the cardinal number of $R$ is 3. But the cardinal number of $P \cup R$ is 5, not $3 + 3$.

It seems the child who holds up three fingers on one hand and four on the other, then counts the fingers to find $3 + 4$, knows more about addition than does the teacher who censures him!

We have observed that the order in which the elements of a set are named is of no consequence, $\{2, 4, 6\} = \{6, 2, 4\}$. Evidently $A \cup B = B \cup A$, since in either case the identity of the elements is our only concern. If $A = \{3, 5, 7, 8\}$ and $B = \{9, 6, 12\}$ then $A \cup B = \{3, 5, 7, 8, 9, 6, 12\}$ and $B \cup A = \{9, 6, 12, 3, 5, 7, 8\}$ but in either case the elements are 3, 5, 6, 7, 8, 9, and 12, and the order in which they are arranged is immaterial. Since $A \cup B = B \cup A$ the cardinal number of $A \cup B$ must be the same as the cardinal number $B \cup A$. We conclude that for any two cardinal numbers $a$ and $b$

$$a + b = b + a$$

This is known as the *commutative property*. The cardinal numbers are commutative with respect to addition. Under the usual interpretation of addition, $a + b$ and $b + a$ are not identical, $12 + 7$ means that we start with 12 and add 7 to it, but $7 + 12$ means we start with 7 and add 12 to it. In 50 years a one-year-old child will be 51, but in one year a 50-year-old man will be 51. Hardly the same situation. When we say that addition is a commutative operation we merely mean that the numerical result is the same whether we add $b$ to $a$ on the one hand or $a$ to $b$ on the other.

Union is a binary operation, that is, an operation involving two sets. However, we can find the union of more than two sets, $A \cup B \cup C$, by finding the union of $A$ and $B$, then finding the union of this result with $C$, $(A \cup B) \cup C$. Since $A \cup B$ is the set of all elements in $A$ or $B$ or both, the union of $A \cup B$ with $C$ is the set of all elements in any one or more of the sets $A$, $B$, and $C$. We reach the same conclusion relative to $A \cup (B \cup C)$.

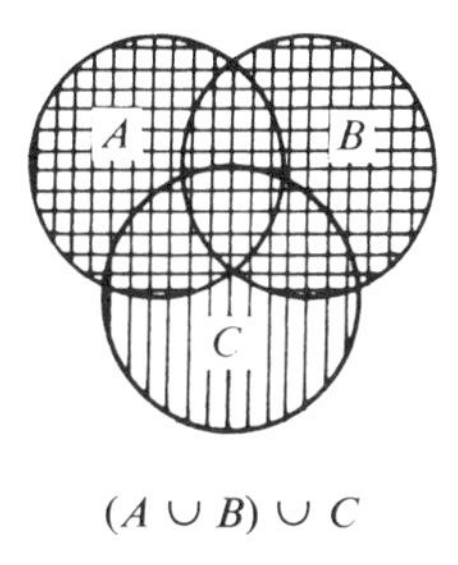

$(A \cup B) \cup C$

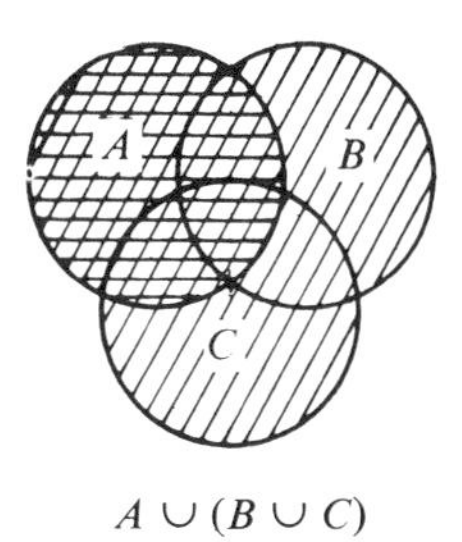

$A \cup (B \cup C)$

Since $(A \cup B) \cup C = A \cup (B \cup C)$ we know the two sets have the same cardinal number. If $A$, $B$, $C$ are disjoint, that is, no element is common to any two of them, and $n(A) = a$, $n(B) = b$, and $n(C) = c$, we have

$$(a + b) + c = a + (b + c)$$

This is the *associative property*

$$(3 + 6) + 8 = 3 + (6 + 8)$$

On the left we are required to find $3 + 6 = 9$ then $9 + 8 = 17$. On the right we must find $6 + 8 = 14$ then $3 + 14 = 17$. By the associative property, for any three (not necessarily different) cardinal numbers, the end result is unaltered whether we add the first and second, and to this sum add the third, or, on the other hand, add the sum of the second and third to the first. Since the null set $\varnothing$ has no elements, it has no elements in common with any set. Hence $\varnothing$ and any set $A$ are disjoint. Since the cardinal number of $\varnothing$ is 0, if the cardinal number of $A$ is $a$, we have

$$a + 0 = a$$

for any cardinal number $a$. Zero is the *addition identity element*. Adding 0 to any number $a$ leaves $a$ unchanged.

Is there any assurance that the sum of two counting numbers $a$ and $b$ is always a counting number? The assumption, stated on page 29, that every counting number has a successor establishes the existence of $a + 1$, the successor of $a$. But $a + 1$ has the successor $a + 1 + 1$. Since $b$ is finite, if we apply the successor principle $b$ times, we have the counting number $a + b$. This is equivalent to the proposition that if $A$ and $B$ are finite sets, $A \cup B$ is a finite set. This seems reasonable. If, to the contrary, $A \cup B$ is an infinite set it has an infinite proper subset $C$. But $C$ includes at most a proper subset of at least one of the sets $A$ and $B$. Now $C$, being infinite, has an infinite subset $D$. $D$ includes at most a proper subset of at least one of the two disjoint subsets of $C$ obtained from $A$ and from $B$. If this process is continued, since both sets $A$ and $B$ are finite, one of them will ultimately be exhausted. We will then be in the awkward position of claiming an infinite set is a proper subset of some finite set.

The fact that, if $a$ and $b$ are counting numbers, $a + b$ is a counting number is the *closure* property. The counting numbers are closed with respect to addition. A set is closed with respect to an operation if and only if the operation on elements of the set always produces an element of the set. The set of odd numbers is not closed with respect to addition because the sum of two odd numbers is not an odd number, $3 + 5 = 8$, an even number. However, the set of odd numbers is closed with respect to multiplication; the product of two odd numbers is invariably an odd number. For example, $3 \times 7 = 21$; 3 and 7 are odd numbers and so is the product 21.

To summarize—the cardinal numbers (natural numbers and zero) are governed by the following principles:

1. *Closure:* if $a$ and $b$ are cardinal numbers, $a + b$ is a cardinal number.
2. *Commutativity:* $a + b = b + a$
3. *Associativity:* $(a + b) + c = a + (b + c)$
4. *Identity:* $a + 0 = a$

## EXERCISES

**1.** In which of the following is the set closed with respect to the operation? If not closed illustrate.
   (a) The set of counting numbers with respect to division.
   (b) The set of odd counting numbers with respect to subtraction.
   (c) The set of counting numbers with respect to subtraction.
   (d) The set of one-digit counting numbers with respect to addition.
   (e) The set of English words with respect to rearrangement of letters.

**2.** Which of the following is commutative?
   (a) 12, 4—operation division.
   (b) Read the morning paper, eat breakfast—operation "and then."
   (c) 3, 5—operation multiplication.
   (d) Put on shirt, put on shoes—operation "and then."
   (e) 8, 6—operation subtraction.
   (f) Put on coat, put on shirt—operation "and then."

3. Which of the following pairs of expressions are equal?
   (a) $(12 - 5) - 1$ and $12 - (5 - 1)$
   (b) $(5 + 3) - 2$ and $5 + (3 - 2)$
   (c) $(3 \times 4) \times 5$ and $3 \times (4 \times 5)$
   (d) $(12 \div 4) \div 2$ and $12 \div (4 \div 2)$
   (e) $(9 - 6) + 3$ and $9 - (6 + 3)$

4. (a) If $A$ is any non-empty set what is $A \cap A$? $A \cup A$?
   (b) If $A$ is any non-empty set and $\varnothing$ is the empty set what is $A \cap \varnothing$? $A \cup \varnothing$?
   (c) Show that $\varnothing \cap \varnothing = \varnothing \cup \varnothing = \varnothing$.
   (d) Justify the assertion that $\varnothing \cup \varnothing$ is the union of disjoint sets.
   (e) Use $c$ and $d$ above to justify the equation $0 + 0 = 0$.
5. Does multiplication have an identity element? If so, what is it?

## 2.6 Inverse Operations

The concept of *inverse* is an extremely important one in mathematics. Two operations are inverse if either one "undoes" the other.

"What goes up must come down." Sometimes things like prices take quite a while. But something that has "gone down the drain" seldom comes back up. There is nothing inherent in the nature of things that requires the universal existence of an inverse. If operation $A$ is the inverse of operation $B$, then $B$ is also the inverse of $A$. This implies that either one may occur first and that the application of the other counteracts it.

The acts of starting and stopping an automobile are inverses. If the automobile is running, stopping it, then starting it, leaves it in the original state—running. If the motor is not running, starting it, then stopping it, leaves it in its original state. On the other hand, in spite of the fact that it won't stay cut, cutting the grass does not have an inverse; one cannot "uncut" the grass. Going to sleep and waking up are inverse except that it would hardly be correct to assert that the person's condition is unchanged after a good night's sleep.

A really good analogy to inverse mathematical operations would involve two elements, that is, a binary operation. If we could unscramble our breakfast eggs, this and scrambling the eggs would illustrate inverse operations nicely. Getting married illustrates the idea. The two "elements," single people, are "combined" into one married couple. As an aside we note that we do not have closure here; the resulting couple is not an element of the set of single people. The inverse, divorce, returns us to the original state at least to the extent that we then have two single people again. Yes, either operation may occur first. Married couples have been known to get divorced and then remarry. Even so, this is still not a perfect analogy to mathematical inverses. Two single persons do not have the choice of getting divorced, then getting married. Nor can we say that *any* two elements of the set of single people may be "combined" in marriage. If we go along with the numerologists this would be equivalent to combining an odd (male) number with an even (female) number. If marriage means plus the result is always odd (male), but if it means times the result is even (female). Let us let the numerologists worry about it!

We have said in a vague sort of way that two operations are inverse if either "undoes" the other. By definition, subtraction is the inverse of addition. This means that if we add a number, then subtract the same number, the result is the original number:

$$12 + 3 = 15; \ 15 - 3 = 12$$

We define subtraction by means of the pair of equations

$$a - b = x \qquad \text{if and only if} \qquad x + b = a$$

Hence $15 - 3 = 12$ because $12 + 3 = 15$. In words we are saying the difference, $a - b$, is whatever we must add to $b$ to get $a$. If we substitute the value of $x$ from the first equation, that is, $a - b$, in the second we get

$$a - b + b = a \tag{1}$$

If we subtract $b$ from $a$, then add $b$ to the result, we obtain the original $a$.

Suppose we add $b$ first, then subtract

$$a + b - b = x$$

According to the definition of subtraction $x$ is that number that we must add to $b$ to obtain the sum $a + b$. But since $b + a = a + b$ the required number is surely $a$.

$$a + b - b = a \tag{2}$$

Thus, whether we add $b$ then subtract it, Equation (2), or subtract $b$ and then add it, Equation (1), the end result is the original $a$.

In addition the two numbers added are called *addends* and the result the *sum*. When we subtract we are in a sense starting with a sum and taking away one of the addends. We call the original sum the *minuend*, the addend which we take away the *subtrahend*, and the remaining addend the *remainder* or the *difference*. Thus, in $a - b = x$ the minuend is $a$, the subtrahend is $b$, and the remainder is $x$.

## 2.7 Negative Numbers

We have defined subtraction *in terms of* addition. Regardless of how we define addition the definition of subtraction stands: it is the inverse of whatever addition means.

We have shown that it makes no difference which operation is performed first if we are to perform both addition and subtraction with the same element. However, it does not follow that we can combine any two elements by either or both operations. Suppose we are working with the set of finite cardinal numbers. We grant that we can always add any two of them. Having done so, we can subtract either addend from the sum. In this sense the inverse is always possible. We can undo what we have done. However, we know that we cannot always perform the undoing operation with any two elements. We have said that $a - b = x$ if and only if $x + b = a$. Now there may not be any number $x$ which we can add to $b$ and get $a$. We know from experience with finite cardinal numbers that there can be an $x$ only if $b$ is less than $a$. There is no finite cardinal number which we can add to 5 and get the sum 3. Hence $3 - 5$ is meaningless in the set of finite cardinal numbers.

We wish to enlarge the set of numbers so that subtraction will always be possible. To this end, we create the set of negative integers. Recall (Section 2.2) that another name for the set of non-zero finite cardinal numbers is the set of positive integers.

> *Definition:* If $a$ is any positive integer, $-a$ is a negative integer such that
>
> $$a + -a = 0$$

The set of integers is composed of the positive integers, zero, and the negative integers. By definition, $-5$ is an integer which can be added to 5 to get the sum 0, the addition identity. Any two numbers whose sum is the addition identity are *additive inverse* numbers. Every integer has an additive inverse. The inverse of 3 is $-3$ because $3 + -3 = 0$. If addition of integers is to be commutative the inverse of $-7$ is 7 because $-7 + 7 = 7 + -7 = 0$. The inverse of 0 is 0 because $0 + 0 = 0$. In the above definition we used $a$ to indicate a positive integer. If we let $a$ be any integer, the additive inverse is $-a$. If $a = -5$ then $-a = -(-5)$. But the inverse of $-5$ is 5, hence $-(-5) = 5$.

The motive for creating negative numbers was to make subtraction always possible. This is accomplished because subtracting a number can be shown equivalent to adding its additive inverse. We wish to show

$$a - b = a + -b$$

If we add $b$ to each side of the equation we have

$$a - b + b = a + -b + b$$
$$a = a + 0$$
$$a = a$$

The left side is equal to $a$ because we have both added and subtracted $b$, inverse operations. The right side is $a + 0$ because $-b + b = 0$, inverse elements.

This is all very well, but how much is $3 - 5$? If we add the inverse of 5 rather than subtract 5 we have $3 + -5$. Evidently, in order for this to be any help, we must find out how to add integers when negative numbers are involved.

Since we have agreed that addition of positive integers means finding the cardinal number of the union of disjoint sets we can define the addition of negative numbers by stating what it means in terms of addition or subtraction (if subtraction is possible) of positive integers.

There are three cases to consider. If $a$ and $b$ are positive integers then we have $a + (-b)$, $(-a) + b$, and $(-a) + (-b)$ as the three possibilities involving addition of negative numbers. When we select our definitions we must be sure the result satisfies the properties of the cardinal numbers listed on page 38. We can adopt a slightly different point of view. *We shall assume that the set of integers has these properties and prove that addition and multiplication of negative numbers mean what they do as a consequence.*

In either event, the definitions must be such that $a + (-b) = (-b) + a$ since the second of the three cases might just as well have been written $(-b) + a$ and since the commutative property must hold.

Consider the first case:

$$a + (-b) = x$$

If we add $b$ to both sides we get

$$a + (-b) + b = x + b,$$

but since

$$(-b) + b = 0$$

then

$$a = x + b$$

This last equation is the condition on $x$ which makes it equal to $a - b$. Then if $a - b$ exists $a + (-b) = a - b$. And $a - b$ does exist if $a$ is greater than $b$. Hence, Rule I.

(I) $a + (-b) = (-b) + a = a - b$ if $a$ is greater than $b$.

*Example:* $5 + -2 = 5 - 2 = 3$

$10 + -8 = 10 - 8 = 2$

Notice that this is merely what we have already shown; subtraction is equivalent to addition of the additive inverse.

Suppose $a$ is less than $b$. Then to

$$a + -b = x \qquad \text{we add} \qquad -a + b$$

$$a + -b + -a + b = x + -a + b$$

and since addition is commutative

$$a + -a + b + -b = x + -a + b$$

$$0 = x + -a + b$$

Thus, $x$ is the additive inverse or *negative* of $b + (-a)$. But by Rule I if $b$ is greater than $a$, $b + (-a) = b - a$. Hence $x$ is the negative of $(b - a)$, or $-(b - a)$ and we have Rule II.

(II) $a + (-b) = (-b) + a = -(b - a)$ if $b$ is greater than $a$.

*Example:* $2 - 5 = -(5 - 2) = -3$

$9 - 10 = -(10 - 9) = -1$

$6 - 100 = -(100 - 6) = -94$

Now the third case $(-a) + (-b)$. If to

$$(-a) + (-b) = x \qquad \text{we add} \qquad a + b$$

then $$(-a) + (-b) + a + b = x + a + b,$$

and since addition is commutative,

$$a + (-a) + b + (-b) = x + a + b,$$
$$0 = x + a + b$$

Here $x$ is the additive inverse or *negative* of $(a + b)$; it is $-(a + b)$. Hence Rule III.

$$\text{(III)}\ (-a) + (-b) = -(a + b)$$

*Example:* $(-5) + (-6) = -(5 + 6) = -11$
$(-8) + (-3) = -(8 + 3) = -11$

Now let us consider the question: does this extension of the integers make it possible to subtract any two positive integers? Let $a$, $b$, be any two positive integers such that $b$ is greater than $a$. (We know we can subtract if $a$ is greater than or equal to $b$.)

$$a - b = x \qquad \text{if and only if} \qquad b + x = a$$

Add $(-b)$ to both sides and we get

$$b + (-b) + x = a + (-b)$$
$$x = a + (-b)$$

But by Rule II, $a + (-b) = -(b - a)$. Substituting this in the original equation we get

$$a - b = -(b - a)$$

This shows that we can now subtract any two positive integers. But can we subtract any two integers? If the two integers are equal their difference is zero. We know that $a - a = 0$ because $a + 0 = a$. We may show that $(-a) - (-a) = 0$ as follows. Let

$$(-a) - (-a) = x$$

Then if we apply the definition of subtraction $(-a) + x = -a$ and adding $a$ to both sides,

$$a + (-a) + x = a + (-a)$$
$$0 + x = 0$$
$$x = 0$$

Then we have the following cases to consider, $a$ and $b$ integers;

$a - b = a + (-b)$ because, by the definition of subtraction, we must have

$$b + [a + (-b)] = a,$$

But

$$\begin{aligned} b + [a + (-b)] &= (b + a) + (-b) \\ &= [a + (-b)] + b \\ &= a + [(-b) + b] \\ &= a + 0 \\ &= a \end{aligned}$$

$a - (-b) = a + b$ because by the definition of subtraction we must have

$$-b + (a + b) = a.$$

But

$$\begin{aligned} -b + (a + b) &= (-b + a) + b \\ &= [a + (-b)] + b \\ &= a + [(-b) + b] \\ &= a + 0 \\ &= a \end{aligned}$$

$(-a) - b = (-a) + (-b)$ because by the definition of subtraction we must have

$$b + [(-a) + (-b)] = (-a).$$

But,

$$\begin{aligned} b + [(-a) + (-b)] &= [b + (-a)] + -b \\ &= [-a + b] + (-b) \\ &= -a + [b + (-b)] \\ &= -a + 0 \\ &= -a \end{aligned}$$

$(-a) - (-b) = (-a) + b$ because by the definition of subtraction we must have

$$(-b) + [(-a) + b] = -a.$$

But,

$$\begin{aligned} -b + [-a + b] &= [(-b) + (-a)] + b \\ &= [-a + (-b)] + b \\ &= -a + [(-b) + b] \\ &= -a + 0 \\ &= -a \end{aligned}$$

We have applied the definition of subtraction and shown that we can always subtract any two integers because we can always add any two integers. We have not only shown that we can always subtract, we have also shown that *we never have to.* Two integers $a$ and $-a$ are *inverse elements* under both *addition* and *subtraction.* The four equations above show us that we can add the inverse rather than subtract. We can also of course subtract the inverse rather than add. In other words, we can replace either operation, addition or subtraction, by the other if we also replace the number (to be added or subtracted) by its inverse.

We illustrate the addition and subtraction of negative numbers with the following examples:

Add $12 + (-7)$. Since 12 is greater than 7 we apply Rule I. $12 + (-7) = 12 - 7 = 5$.

Add $15 + (-23)$. Since 23 is greater than 15 we apply Rule II. $15 + (-23) = -(23 - 15) = -8$.

(We note that in each case the sum is obtained by adding or subtracting two positive integers and making the result positive or negative.)

Subtract $7 - (-12)$. Using the inverse operation and inverse element this becomes $7 + 12 = 19$.

Subtract $(-7) - 12$. This is equivalent to $-7 + (-12) = -(7 + 12) = -19$.

(Since $a + (-b) = a - (+b)$ the minus sign may be interpreted as either the sign of the operation subtraction or the sign of a negative number.)

Subtract $(7 - 12)$. We may think of this as either $7 - (+12)$ or $7 + (-12) = -5$.

## EXERCISES

**1.** Evaluate each of the following expressions, giving the rule used for each:

(a) $(-9) + 13$ (b) $(-16) + (-29)$
(c) $(-27) + 19$ (d) $(-15) + 37$
(e) $(-8) + (-26)$ (f) $17 + (-63)$
(g) $63 + (-17)$ (h) $(-23) + (-42)$

**2.** Verify each of the following by evaluating each side of the equality independently:

(a) $(-7) + 9 + [(-9) + (-15)] = (-7) + [9 + (-9)] + (-15)$
(b) $[(-8) + (-6)] + (-9) = (-8) + [(-6) + (-9)]$
(c) $[15 + 9] + (-23) = 15 + [9 + (-23)]$
(d) $[16 + (-23)] + (-19) = 16 + [(-23) + (-19)]$

**3.** Evaluate each of the following:

(a) $15 - (-7) - 6 - (-5)$ (b) $15 - [(-7) + 6 + (-5)]$

(c) $15 + 7 - (6 - 5)$
(d) $23 - 19 - 6 - 12$
(e) $23 - (19 + 6 + 12)$
(f) $76 - 8 - 17 - 40$
(g) $76 - (8 + 17 + 40)$

## 2.8 Properties of Subtraction

The integers are closed with respect to both addition and subtraction; each integer has an additive inverse. Zero is the addition identity. We could also call it the subtraction identity in that $a - 0 = a$ just as $a + 0 = a$. Addition obeys the commutative and associative laws. Since subtraction is the inverse of addition one might assume that it too obeys these laws, particularly since we can avoid subtraction by adding the inverse element.

That subtraction is not commutative it is sufficient to note that $10 - 7$ does not equal $7 - 10$. Although the latter expression is meaningless in the set of natural numbers, both expressions have meaning in the set of integers. But $10 - 7 = 3$, which is not equal to $7 - 10 = -3$.

Does $a - b$ ever equal $b - a$? If $a - b = b - a$, apply the definition of subtraction to the left side of the equation, $a - b$, and we have $b + (b - a) = a$, or

$$(b + b) - a + a = a + a$$
$$2b = 2a$$
$$b = a$$

We conclude that subtraction will obey the commutative law only when a number is subtracted from itself.

If we replace $b$ with its additive inverse $-b$ and add, the commutative property does hold:

$$a + (-b) = (-b) + a$$

since both expressions are defined as $(a - b)$ if $a$ is greater $b$ and as $-(b - a)$ if $b$ is greater than $a$ (Rules I and II).

Although it is not a commutative operation, *the order of successive applications of subtraction can be changed.* For example,

$$10 - 6 - 2 = 10 - 2 - 6$$

The things that have been commuted, reversed, are the operations, subtracting six and subtracting two, not minuend and subtrahend. The six and the two both remain subtrahends. We may justify the above property by replacing subtraction by addition of additive inverse. We must show that $a - b - c = a - c - b$, and to establish this we note that $a - b - c = a + (-b) + (-c)$. But since addition is both associative and commutative:

$$[a + (-b)] + (-c) = a + [(-b) + (-c)] = a + [(-c) + (-b)]$$
$$= [a + (-c)] + (-b) = a + (-c) + (-b) = a - c - b$$

Two facts should be noted. First, the corresponding statement applied to addition cannot be justified by commutativity alone. Consider the expression $10 + 5 + 2$. This does not mean $10 + (5 + 2)$. However, the two expressions are equivalent because *addition is associative*. We may say $10 + 5 + 2 = 10 + 2 + 5$ only because we first regroup by the associative property

$$(10 + 5) + 2 = 10 + (5 + 2)$$

then commute the last two addends

$$10 + (5 + 2) = 10 + (2 + 5)$$

and apply the associative property again

$$10 + (2 + 5) = (10 + 2) + 5$$

We further note that the above property has only limited application if we restrict ourselves to positive numbers. In the expression $a - b - c$ we may be able to subtract neither $b$ nor $c$ from $a$, as $10 - 15 - 20$. We may be able to subtract either $b$ or $c$ but not both, as $10 - 8 - 7$. And we may be able to subtract one but not the other, as $10 - 8 - 12$.

If subtraction were associative this would mean $(a - b) - c = a - (b - c)$. To show that this is not correct consider

$$(10 - 5) - 3 = 5 - 3 = 2$$

but

$$10 - (5 - 3) = 10 - 2 = 8$$

However, if we express the above in terms of addition we can apply the associative property and get

$$[10 + (-5)] + (-3) = 10 + [(-5) + (-3)]$$

Applying Rule III to the bracket on the right, we get

$$10 + [(-5) + (-3)] = 10 + [-(5 + 3)]$$

Here we are adding the negative number $-(5 + 3)$ to 10, which is equivalent to subtracting the positive number $(5 + 3)$. We conclude that we can add the subtrahends 5 and 3 and subtract the sum rather than subtract them individually:

$$10 - 5 - 3 = 10 - (5 + 3)$$

The principle applies to any number of successive subtrahends. In general, $a - b - c - d -, \ldots, = a - (b + c + d + \ldots)$. *Successive subtractions may be performed by subtracting the sum of the subtrahends.*

Another property of subtraction is utilized in one of the subtraction algorithms. *The result is unaffected by adding the same amount to the minuend and subtrahend:*

$$5 - 3 = (5 + 4) - (3 + 4) = 9 - 7 = 2$$
$$a - b = (a + c) - (b + c)$$

If we apply the definition of subtraction to the right side of the equation, $(a + c) - (b + c)$, we have

$$(b + c) + (a - b) = (a + c)$$
$$(b + c) + a + (-b) = (a + c)$$
$$(b + c + a) + (-b) = (a + c)$$
$$(a + c + b) + (-b) = (a + c)$$
$$(a + c) + b + (-b) = (a + c)$$
$$(a + c) + 0 = (a + c)$$
$$(a + c) = (a + c)$$

A justification for this lies in the fact essentially that we have added (add to the minuend $a$) and subtracted (add to subtrahend $b$) the same quantity, which means we have added zero. Or, since subtraction is the inverse of addition, we may think of the minuend as a sum, the subtrahend as one of the addends, and the remainder as the other addend. If we increase one of the addends, $b$, the sum, $a$, will be increased by the same amount:

| | *Addition:* | | *Subtraction:* |
|---|---|---|---|
| If | $a + b = c$ | If | $c - b = a$ |
| then | $a + (10 + b) = (10 + c)$ | then | $(10 + c) - (10 + b) = a$ |

Another property of subtraction stems from the fact that addition is commutative. If $a + b = c$, then $b + a = c$. But $a + b = c$ implies that $c - b = a$, and $b + a = c$ implies that $c - a = b$. *The minuend minus the remainder equals the subtrahend:*

$$12 - 5 = 7 \qquad \text{and} \qquad 12 - 7 = 5$$

A generalization of this is extremely useful to the child in learning the subtraction facts. Each subtraction fact implies another, obtained by interchanging subtrahend and remainder.

Summarizing: In subtracting integers the following rules hold. (They also hold with natural numbers and zero except for the fact that sometimes subtraction in this set is not possible.)

1. In continued subtraction, the order of subtrahends can be changed.

$$a - b - c = a - c - b$$

2. Continued subtraction may be performed by subtracting the sum of the subtrahends.

$$a - b - c = a - (b + c)$$

3. Increasing (or decreasing) both minuend and subtrahend by the same amount leaves the remainder unchanged.

$$a - b = (a + n) - (b + n) = (a - n) - (b - n)$$

4. Increasing (or decreasing) the minuend produces the same change in the remainder.

If $a - b = c$ then $(a + n) - b = c + n$
and $(a - n) - b = c - n$

5. Any subtraction fact implies another obtained by interchanging subtrahend and remainder.

If $a - b = c$ then $a - c = b$ also

## EXERCISES

**1.** Verify each of the following by evaluating each side of the equation separately:

(a) $17 - 9 - 6 = 17 - 6 - 9$
(b) $23 - (-50) - 70 = 23 - 70 - (-50)$
(c) $12 - 19 - 26 - 5 = 12 - 26 - 5 - 19$
(d) $37 - (-42) - 23 - 19 = 37 - 23 - 19 - (-42)$

**2.** Evaluate each of the following:

(a) $72 - (-13) - 15 - (-6)$
(b) $72 - [(-13) + 15 + (-6)]$
(c) $8 - 19 - 33 - 14$
(d) $8 - (19 + 33 + 14)$

3. Verify each of the following:
   (a) $37 - 75 = (37 + 12) - (75 + 12)$
   (b) $86 - 53 = (86 - 42) - (53 - 42)$
   (c) $43 - 37 = (43 + 3) - (37 + 3)$

4. Evaluate each of the following:
   (a) $17 - (-73)$ (b) $17 - 90$
   (c) $(-23) - (-69)$ (d) $(-23) - 46$
   (e) $(-19) - (-25)$ (f) $(-19) - 6$

5. Verify and state the principle upon which each of the following is based:
   (a) $25 - 5 - 6 - 11 = 25 - 11 - 6 - 5$
   (b) $100 - 9 - 3 - 27 - 15 = 100 - (9 + 3 + 27 + 15)$
   (c) $50 - 17 = (12 + 50) - (12 + 17)$

6. If $a - b = 10$, what does $a - 10$ equal?

## 2.9 Interpretation of Negative Numbers

We cannot give negative integers the same interpretation that we gave positive integers. We cannot say that $-5$ is the cardinal number of any set. If zero is the cardinal number of an empty set we need no cardinal numbers less than that; a set cannot have fewer than no elements in it.

One interpretation which we have given addition is that of counting on a number line. We visualize $3 + 2$ as starting at zero

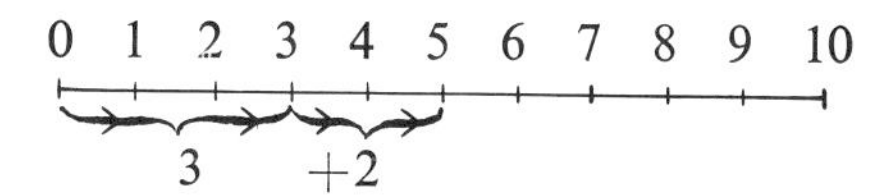


and counting to 3, then counting on 2 more places. Here the number line is numbered from the left to right. Then addition means "move to the right." The inverse, subtraction, should mean "move to the left." Then $3 - 2$ should mean: start at zero and move 3 places to the right, then move 2 places to the left. This

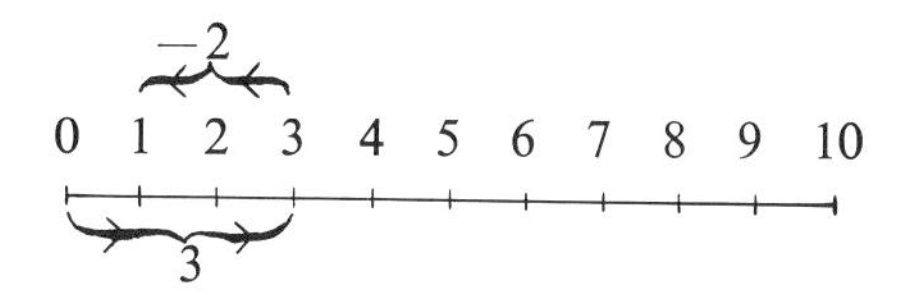


same interpretation should serve to illustrate the meaning of $3 + (-2)$, since we can use the inverse operation with the inverse element.

But suppose our problem is $3 - 4 = 3 + (-4)$. If we move 4 places to the left of 3 we run off the line. We have associated with each positive number $a$ a distance to the right of the starting point. If we now extend the number line to the left we can associate the same distance to the left with the number $-a$. If we do this we won't run off the line when we move 4 places

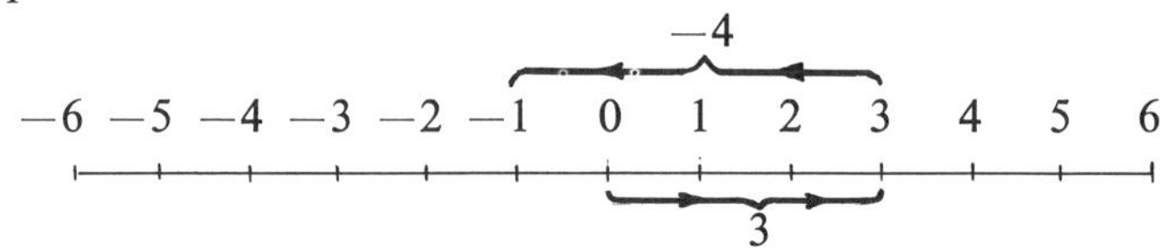


to the left of 3. In fact, we can then move any number of places to the right or left regardless of where we start. This is the heart of the matter involving negative numbers. The natural numbers merely designate magnitude, size. Positive and negative numbers designate a magnitude *and a direction.* We think of 5 as the cardinal number of the set ▨. But $+5$ is a directed number, 5 units in a direction, and $-5$ is a directed number, 5 units in the direction opposite that of $+5$.

All of the rules for addition of integers can be verified on the number line. For example, to find $-5 + (-3)$ on the line, we can change this to

−10 −9 −8 −7 −6 −5 −4 −3 −2 −1 0 1 2 3 4 5 6 7 8 9 10

−3 −5

$-5 - 3$. We start at 0 and move to the point $-5$ then move to the left 3 more places. We are then at $-8$; $-5 + (-3) = -(5 + 3)$ according to Rule III.

We may also interpret subtraction on the number line as finding the missing addend. To find $8 - 15$, letting subtraction mean "move to the left," we start at 8 and move to the left 15 places,

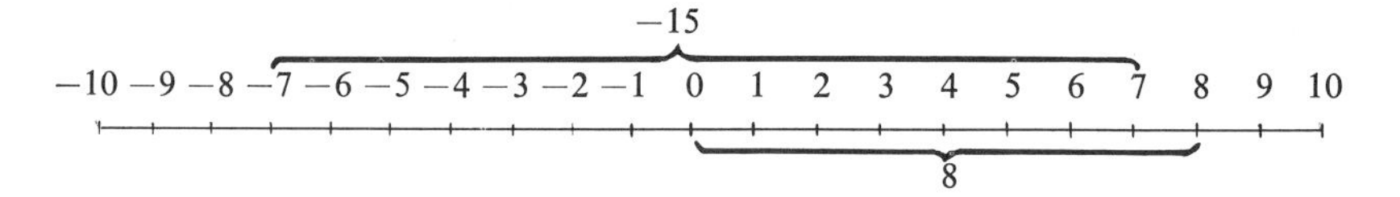


ending at $-7$. By the missing addend method the problem is to find what to "add" to 15 in order that we stop at 8. Since we must move 7 steps to the *left* the answer is $-7$.

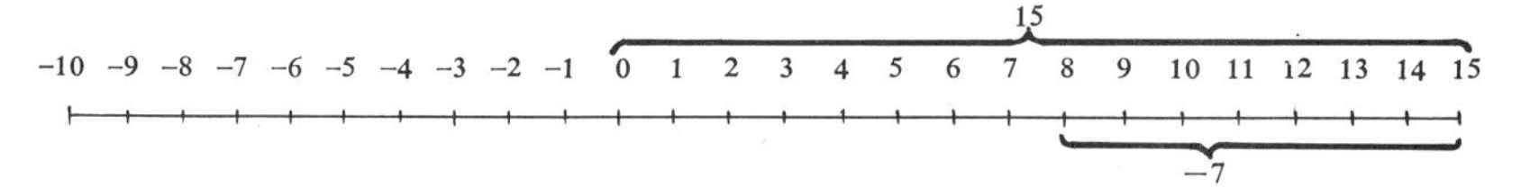

### EXERCISES

**1.** If a positive number indicates each of the following, what does a negative number indicate?
(a) a profit.
(b) a distance north.
(c) population growth since the last census.
(d) a distance south.
(e) an acceleration.
(f) feet above sea level.
(g) a date A.D.

**2.** If the temperature is 12° below zero what will it be after it:
(a) drops 20°?
(b) rises 12°?
(c) rises 15° then drops 6°?
(d) drops 2° then rises 16°?

**3.** From Rules I and II, page 43, formulate a statement telling how to add integers with unlike signs.

**4.** Justify on the number line the statement obtained in Exercise 3 when
(a) we have $a + (-b)$ with $a > b$
(b) we have $a + (-b)$ with $a < b$
(c) we have $(-a) + b$ with $a > b$
(d) we have $(-a) + b$ with $a < b$

**5.** From Rule III, page 44, and the addition of two positive integers formulate a statement for the addition of two integers with like signs.

**6.** Justify on the number line the statement obtained in Exercise 5.

**7.** Draw on the number line the illustration of each of the following:
(a) $3 + (-2) + (-6)$
(b) $16 - (-4)$
(c) $-7 + (-6) - 4$
(d) $12 - 15 + (-3)$

## 2.10 Addition on a Circle

We began our study of the integers by considering the positive integers as cardinal numbers of sets of objects. Addition, related as it is to the union of disjoint sets, means the putting together of two sets and finding the count of the new set thus created. Subtraction, although defined as the inverse of addition, can be interpreted as removing a subset of objects from a set and finding the count of the remaining subset.

With the creation of the complete set of integers we find that we need a new interpretation of number. Negative numbers cannot be interpreted as the cardinal numbers of sets. With the introduction of negative integers, an integer is interpreted as indicating a magnitude in one of two opposite directions.

Interpretation of the integers on the number line suggests another possibility, involving only a finite number of elements. A line can be considered a circle with an infinite radius. Let us construct a number circle. From an arbitrarily chosen point on the circle designated as 0 we indicate positive numbers to the right (clockwise) and negative numbers to the left (counterclockwise). In the figure we have used $\frac{1}{7}$ of the circumference as the unit distance. For convenience, the negative numbers

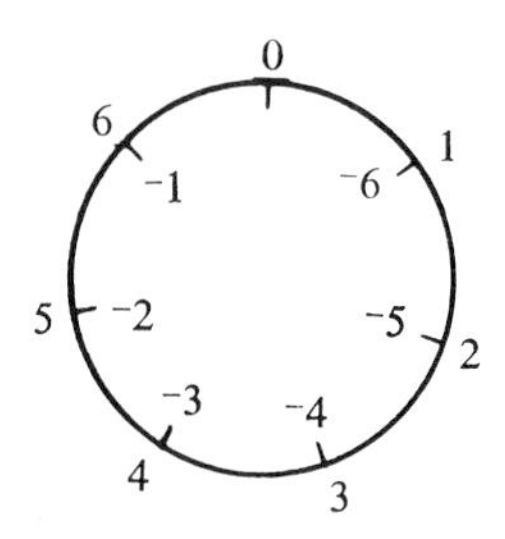


are placed inside the circle. We designate addition precisely as we did on the line. To find $a + b$ start at 0, move clockwise to $a$, then move clockwise $b$ more steps. To find $a - b$, move to $a$, then move counterclockwise $b$ steps. $2 + 3$ is found by moving to 2 then moving clockwise 3 steps. We stop at 5; hence $2 + 3 = 5$.

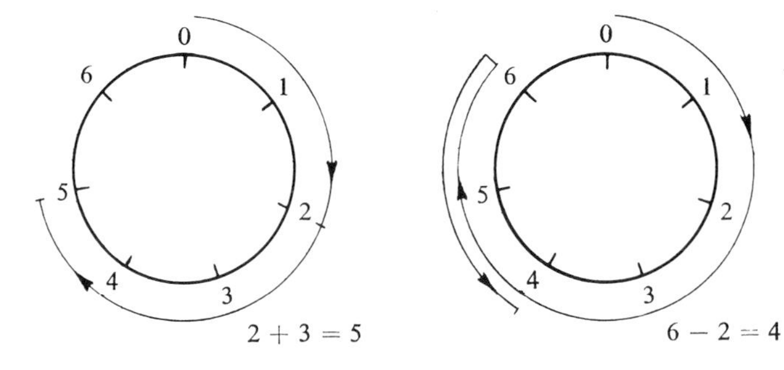


$6 - 2$ is found by starting at 0, moving to 6, and moving counterclockwise 2 steps, $6 - 2 = 4$.

We must be prepared for some unusual results. Let us find $5 + 6$. If we move to 5 then move 6 steps clockwise we stop at 4; hence $5 + 6 = 4$.

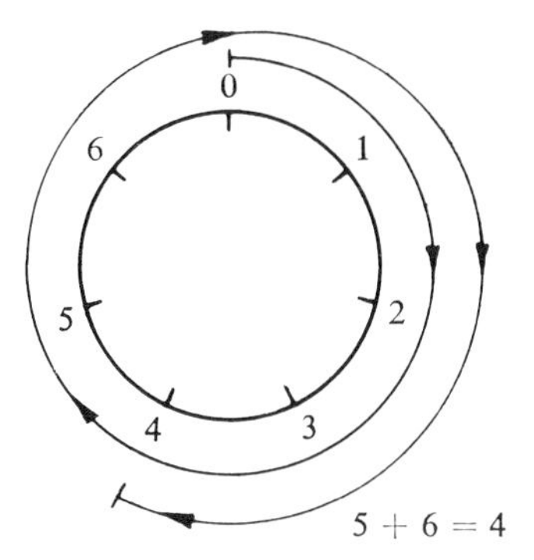


We certainly have closure with respect to addition. From any of the seven positions we can move clockwise from 0 to 6 steps and will stop on one of the seven positions. The correctness of the following addition table should be verified by actual addition on the circle.

| | 0 | 1 | 2 | 3 | 4 | 5 | 6 |
|---|---|---|---|---|---|---|---|
| 0 | 0 | 1 | 2 | 3 | 4 | 5 | 6 |
| 1 | 1 | 2 | 3 | 4 | 5 | 6 | 0 |
| 2 | 2 | 3 | 4 | 5 | 6 | 0 | 1 |
| 3 | 3 | 4 | 5 | 6 | 0 | 1 | 2 |
| 4 | 4 | 5 | 6 | 0 | 1 | (2) | 3 |
| 5 | 5 | 6 | 0 | 1 | 2 | 3 | 4 |
| 6 | 6 | 0 | 1 | 2 | 3 | 4 | 5 |

We agree to read the table as follows: to find $4 + 5$ we find 4 in the left margin and 5 in the top margin; the sum is in the row of the 4 and in the column of the 5. The sum, 2, is circled in the table. In general, to find $a + b$, locate $a$ in the left column and $b$ in the top row. The required sum is in the row with $a$ and the column with $b$. If we wish to find $b + a$ this merely means that we interchange columns and rows: $b$ is now found in the left column and $a$ is found in the top row. Examination of the table reveals that entries symmetrically placed relative to the upper left to the lower right diagonal are identical in every case. Hence, an interchange of rows and columns will in no way change the table. This shows that the commutative property is satisfied.

It is easy to identify 0 as the addition identity element. From the standpoint of the definition of addition on the circle, $a + 0$ means move to $a$ and take 0 steps clockwise, $0 + a$ means move to 0 and take $a$ steps clockwise. In both cases we terminate at $a$. From the table, it is seen that the top row is repeated in the row opposite 0 in the left column, and the left column is repeated in the column headed with 0 in the top row.

Each element has an inverse. From the table:

$0 + 0 = 0$, hence 0 is its own inverse
$1 + 6 = 0$, hence 1 and 6 are inverses
$2 + 5 = 0$, hence 2 and 5 are inverses
$3 + 4 = 0$, hence 3 and 4 are inverses

The negative numbers on the inside of the circle in the first diagram are superfluous. However, it is of interest to notice that 6 and $-1$ are at the same point on the circle; similarly for 5 and $-2$, and for 4 and $-3$, and so on. Hence we are justified in saying $6 = -1$, $5 = -2$, $4 = -3$, $3 = -4$, $2 = -5$, and $1 = -6$; then, as with ordinary integers, 1 and $-1$ are inverses as are 2 and $-2$, and so on. We can now indicate inverses in the usual way, $a$ and $-a$ are additive inverses.

The table can also be used as a subtraction table. Think of subtraction as the inverse of addition; $1 - 5$ equals whatever must be added to 5 to get the sum 1. If we look in the next to last row, the row with 5 in the left margin, we find a 1. Then the number at the head of the column in which the 1 is found, added to 5, will equal 1. Since this column is headed with 3 we know that $1 - 5 = 3$ because $5 + 3 = 1$. Since the system is commutative we could also have found a 1 in the column headed with a 5 and observed that it is in the row with 3 in the left margin.

Since all elements have additive inverses we can use the table in another way to find $1 - 5$. We can subtract by adding the additive inverse. From the table we know the inverse of 5 is 2 because opposite 5 and under 2 we find 0. We now add $1 + 2 = 3$; therefore, $1 - 5 = 3$.

Does this system obey the associative law? Does $(2 + 5) + 6 = 2 + (5 + 6)$? Using the table, we have $(2 + 5) + 6 = 0 + 6 = 6$, and $2 + (5 + 6) = 2 + 4 = 6$. This does not prove that the associative law holds. It merely shows that it holds in this one case. Since there is only a finite number of cases to consider, we could settle the question by examining them all. This would become boring; there are only 343 cases to consider.

Consider again the definition of addition on the circle. We are to show that $(a + b) + c = a + (b + c)$. We have already shown that addition is commutative; hence $a + (b + c) = (b + c) + a$. Then it will be sufficient to show $(a + b) + c = (b + c) + a$. On the right-hand side of the equation $(a + b) + c$ means move to $a$ and move $b$ steps clockwise then $c$ more steps clockwise. In other words, we start at 0 and move clockwise $a + b + c$ steps. Here the $a + b + c$ is to be interpreted as ordinary addition of integers. Adding on the circle, $(b + c) + a$ means move to $b$ and move clockwise $c$ steps then clockwise $a$ more steps. This amounts to starting at 0 and moving $b + c + a$ steps clockwise, with $b + c + a$ interpreted as ordinary addition. Hence, we end at the same point whether we find $(a + b) + c$ or $a + (b + c)$.

*Example:* $(5 + 6) + 4 = 5 + (6 + 4)$ because $(5 + 6) + 4$ means move from 0 clockwise 15 steps. But $5 + (6 + 4) = (6 + 4) + 5$ also means move from 0 clockwise 15 steps.

To summarize: We find the set of seven elements 0, 1, 2, 3, 4, 5, 6, with respect to addition on a circle of seven divisions has the properties:

1. *closure*
2. *commutativity*
3. *associativity*
4. *identity element*
5. *inverse elements*

These are precisely the properties which were derived for the infinite set of integers with respect to ordinary addition.

Aside from the fact that we have seen a finite set which is structurally identical with the set of integers with respect to addition, of what value is this, other than chasing oneself around a circle?

We chose seven as the number of equal divisions of the circle because there are seven days in a week. We could have used any number. The face of the clock uses 12. If the numeral 12 is replaced by 0 we have the same kind of system except for the number of divisions. On the face of the clock 8 plus 7 does not equal 15, it equals 3. Here, of course, we mean start at 8 o'clock and move clockwise 7 hours.

Ordinary clocks do not tell you the day of the month. In fact if the clock shows 10 o'clock, you need something other than the clock to know whether it is 10 A.M. or 10 P.M. The clock adds hours for us but it throws out multiples of 12. It merely keeps track of the number of hours in excess of some multiple of 12.

We can interpret the table, page 55, as a table for the addition of days of the week. Let 0 represent Sunday, 1 represent Monday, and so on to 6 for Saturday, and let $5 + 6$ stand for Friday plus 6 days, or six days after Friday. From the table $5 + 6 = 4$, but 4 stands for Thursday. Six days after Friday will be Thursday; $2 - 4$ means Tuesday minus 4 days, or 4 days before Tuesday. Using the table for subtraction we find $2 - 4 = 5$. Since 5 stands for Friday, we conclude that 4 days before Tuesday is Friday.

There is another interpretation which is much more significant mathematically. If any integer is divided by 7 the remainder will be one of the numbers 0 through 6. This statement includes the negative integers. If we divide $-15$ by 7 the quotient is $-2$ and the remainder is $-1$, but remember that in our system $-1 = 6$. It is possible then to classify each element of the infinite set of integers into one of the seven categories, the category being determined by the remainder when the integer is divided by 7. We find $-96$ and 9 in the same category because $-96$ has the remainder $-5 = 2$ and 9 has the remainder 2 when divided by 7. This relationship is stated "$-96$ is congruent to 9; modulo 7" and written

$$-96 \equiv 9, \bmod 7$$

Any two numbers are congruent, modulo 7, if they have the same remainder upon division by 7. The remainder is called the residue of the number.

Our table can be interpreted as an addition table for all integers, modulo 7. For example, $6 + 5 = 4$ now means any number whose residue is 6 added to any number whose residue is 5 will yield a number whose residue is 4.

76 has a residue 6

33 has a residue 5

$76 + 33 = 109$ has a residue $6 + 5 = 4$

## EXERCISES

**1.** Use the table, page 55, to find the following:

(a) $3 + 6 + 4 + 5$ (b) $3 - 1 - 3 - 2$
(c) $3 - (1 + 3 + 2)$ (d) $3 + 4 = 3 - ? = ?$
(e) $2 + 3 - ? = 4$ (f) $4 - 2 = 4 + ? = ?$
(g) $4 - 5 = ?$

**2.** Draw a circle with six divisions and construct a circle addition table for the elements 0, 1, 2, 3, 4, 5.

**3.** From the table, Exercise 2, find the inverse of each element.

**4.** Use the table, Exercise 2, to find the following:

(a) $4 + 3 + 5 + 2$ (b) $4 - 3 - 1 - 4$
(c) $4 - (3 + 5 + 2)$ (d) $3 + 4 = 3 - ? = ?$
(e) $2 + 3 = 2 - ? = ?$ (f) $4 - 2 = 4 + ? = ?$
(g) $4 - 5 = ?$

5. In the table, Exercise 2, does $2 + 3 = 2 - 3$? Does $1 + 4 = 1 - 4$? Does $4 + 3 = 4 - 3$? If $a + b = a - b$ what do we know about $b$?

6. We have shown that with ordinary integers $a - b = b - a$ if and only if $a = b$. Is this true of addition on a circle with seven divisions? Is it true of addition on a circle with six divisions? Can you explain the difference?

## CHAPTER SUMMARY

A *one-to-one correspondence* exists between two sets if corresponding to each element of one set there is exactly one element of the other. Two sets that have a one-to-one correspondence have the same *cardinal number*.

An *infinite set* is a set that can be placed in one-to-one correspondence with one of its proper subsets. Any infinite set that can be placed in one-to-one correspondence with the set of counting numbers has the *transfinite* cardinal number $\aleph_0$.

A cardinal number is an equivalence class of equivalent sets. For example, the cardinal number *five* is the set of all sets equivalent to $\{0, 1, 2, 3, 4\}$. Each element of the equivalence class has the number 5 as its cardinal number. If a set such as this is $A$ we indicate its cardinal number by $(n)A = 5$.

Addition of cardinal numbers $a$ and $b$ is defined:
If $a = n(A)$, $b = n(B)$ and $A \cap B = \varnothing$

then
$$a + b = n(A \cup B)$$

If $A$ and $B$ are finite sets, then $A \cup B$ is a finite set. Hence the sum of two finite cardinal numbers is a finite cardinal number. The cardinal numbers are closed under addition.

Addition of cardinal numbers is *commutative*.

Since $n(A \cup B) = n(B \cup A)$ it follows that $a + b = b + a$.

Addition of cardinal numbers is *associative*.

Since $n[(A \cup B) \cup C] = n[A \cup (B \cup C)]$ it follows that

$$(a + b) + c = a + (b + c).$$

Since $A \cap \varnothing = \varnothing$ and $A \cup \varnothing = A$ for any set $A$, 0 is the *addition identity*.

$$a + 0 = a \qquad \text{for any cardinal number} \qquad a$$

Subtraction is defined as the inverse of addition.

$$a - b = x \quad \text{if and only if} \quad x + b = a$$

The set of cardinal numbers is not closed under subtraction. Hence we create *negative integers.*

> If $a$ is a positive integer (cardinal number), $-a$ is a negative integer such that $a + -a = 0$.

The set of *integers* is the union of the set of positive integers, zero, and the set of negative integers.

Two integers whose sum is zero are *additive inverses.* Thus, if $a$ is any integer, $a$ and $-a$ are additive inverses.

We assume that the integers satisfy the properties of the cardinal numbers of closure, commutativity, associativity, and identity; and we derive the following rules for addition involving negative integers:

If $a$ and $b$ are positive integers and

(I) If $a > b$ then $a + (-b) = a - b$

(II) If $a < b$ then $a + (-b) = -(b - a)$

(III) $-a + -b = -(a + b)$

For any integer $a$, $a + 0 = a$. Subtraction of any integers, $a - b$ can be performed by adding the inverse of $b$

$$a - b = a + (-b)$$

Hence, subtraction of integers is a closed operation.

Although subtraction is neither commutative nor associative, subtraction does satisfy the following properties:

$$a - b - c = a - c - b$$

In continued subtraction the order of the subtrahends can be reversed.

$$a - b - c = a - (b + c)$$

Continued subtraction can be performed by subtracting the sum of the subtrahends

$$a - b = (a + n) - (b + n) = (a - n) - (b - n)$$

Increasing (or decreasing) both minuend and subtrahend by the same amount does not affect the remainder.
If

$$a - b = c \qquad \text{then} \qquad (a + n) - b = (c + n)$$

and

$$(a - n) - b = (c - n)$$

Increasing (or decreasing) the minuend produces the same change in the remainder.
If

$$a - b = c \qquad \text{then} \qquad a - c = b$$

Any subtraction fact implies another obtained by interchanging subtrahend and remainder.

A graphic interpretation of the integers can be obtained by plotting equally spaced points on a number line, to the right of an arbitrarily chosen zero point for positive integers, and to the left for negative integers.

If a similar interpretation is applied to a circle divided into $n$ equal segments, the result is a finite system of $n$ elements which satisfies the properties of the integers of closure, commutativity, associativity, identity, and inverses.

CHAPTER SUMMARY

# 3 Multiplication and Division

IN CHAPTER 2 WE SAW THAT CARDINAL NUMBERS, WHICH WE CAN CONSIDER synonymous with counting numbers, are definable in terms of sets. A cardinal number is a class of equivalent sets. We also defined addition of cardinal numbers in terms of the union of disjoint sets.

Addition can be described in terms of counting. Multiplication can be described as the addition of equal addends. $3 \times 4 = 4 + 4 + 4$. However, in this chapter we wish to consider multiplication in terms of set operations.

## 3.1 Cartesian Products

A bunch of the boys and girls got together for some dancing. The set of boys was $B =$ (Tom, Jim, Ed, Rocky); the set of girls was $G =$ {Alice, Sue, Martha}. They decided that each boy would dance one number with each girl. What was the set of dancing partners? We can keep the list straight by starting with Tom, listing him with each girl, then doing the same for each of the remaining boys. We get the set of couples {(Tom, Alice), (Tom, Sue), (Tom, Martha), (Jim, Alice), (Jim, Sue), (Jim, Martha), (Ed, Alice), (Ed, Sue), (Ed, Martha), (Rocky, Alice), (Rocky, Sue), (Rocky, Martha)}.

This new set, the set of couples, is called the *Cartesian Product* of the sets $B$ and $G$.

> If $A$ and $B$ are sets, the symbol $A \times B$ indicates their cartesian product, the set of ordered pairs obtained by pairing each element of $A$ as first member with each element of $B$ as second member.

*Example:* If $A = \{1, 3, 5\}$ and $B = \{2, 4, 6\}$

$$\text{then } A \times B = \{(1, 2), (1, 4), (1, 6), (3, 2), (3, 4), (3, 6), (5, 2), (5, 4), (5, 6)\}$$

We may upon occasion refer to a cartesian product as merely a product. The qualifying word "cartesian" is used because the intersection of two sets is referred to by some writers as a product of sets. Notice that the cartesian product is not a union nor an intersection of sets. The elements of the product are pairs of elements, one from each of the original sets. The two sets do not have to be disjoint in order to have a cartesian product.

$$\{1, 2, 3\} \times \{2, 3, 5\} = \{(1, 2), (1, 3), (1, 5), (2, 2), (2, 3), (2, 5), (3, 2), (3, 3), (3, 5)\}$$

The elements of any set are distinct, $\{1, 2, 2, 2, 3\} = \{1, 2, 3\}$. In the notation $\{1, 2, 2, 2, 3\}$ we are merely repeating ourselves, its only elements are 1, 2, and 3. Since the pairs of a cartesian product are ordered, its elements are unique even though the sets forming the product have common elements. In the product under consideration each set has 2 and 3 for elements, but (2, 3) and (3, 2) are not the same *ordered* pair.

In fact, it is possible to find the product of a set with itself.

$$\{1, 2, 3\} \times \{1, 2, 3\} = \{(1, 1), (1, 2), (1, 3), (2, 1), (2, 2), (2, 3), (3, 1), (3, 2), (3, 3)\}$$

## EXERCISES

**1.** Find the cartesian product $A \times B$ when $A$ and $B$ are each of the following:
(a) $A = \{a, b, c\}$; $B = \{1, 2\}$
(b) $A = \{1, a, x\}$; $B = \{a\}$
(c) $A = \{1, a, x\}$; $B = \{2, b, z\}$
(d) $A = \{1, 2\}$; $B = \{a, b, c\}$

**2.** In each part of Exercise 1 find $n(A)$, $n(B)$, and $n(A \times B)$.

**3.** How many subsets are there of the set $\{a, b, c\}$? (Do not forget to count the empty set.) How many elements are there in the set $\{a, b, c\} \times \{a, b, c\}$?

**4.** For any set $A$, how does $n(A)$ compare with $n(A \times A)$?

**5.** What is the product $A \times B$ if $A = \{1, 2, 3\}$ and $B =$ the empty set?

**6.** Find $A \times A$ when $A = \{a\}$.

## 3.2 Cartesian Products and Multiplication

Every set has a cardinal number. The cartesian product of two sets is a set, hence it has a cardinal number. We can now define the product of two cardinal numbers.

> Given set $A$ whose cardinal number is $a$ and set $B$ whose cardinal number is $b$. The product of the cardinal numbers $a$ and $b$, written $a \times b$, $a \cdot b$, or $ab$, is the cardinal number of the cartesian product $A \times B$ of the sets $A$ and $B$.
>
> If $n(A) = a$, $n(B) = b$, then $ab = n(A \times B)$

*Example:* Set $A = \{0, 1, 2\}$ has the cardinal number 3.
Set $B = \{0, 1, 2, 3\}$ has the cardinal number 4.
By definition of multiplication, $3 \times 4$ is equal to the cardinal number of $A \times B = \{(0, 0), (0, 1), (0, 2), (0, 3), (1, 0), (1, 1), (1, 2), (1, 3), (2, 0), (2, 1), (2, 2), (2, 3)\}$. But the cardinal number of this set is 12. Then by definition, $3 \times 4 = 12$.

Under the usual interpretation of multiplication of whole numbers $3 \times 4$ does not mean the same as $4 \times 3$, although both equal 12. Is this consistent with our definition of multiplication? Consider the two cartesian products $\{a, b, c\} \times \{d, e\}$ and $\{d, e\} \times \{a, b, c\}$:

$$X = \{a, b, c\} \times \{d, e\} = \{(a, d), (a, e), (b, d), (b, e), (c, d), (c, e)\}$$
$$Y = \{d, e\} \times \{a, b, c\} = \{(d, a), (d, b), (d, c), (e, a), (e, b), (e, c)\}$$

They certainly are not the same set. In fact, they are disjoint. They do have exactly the same set of pairs, but the order of the elements in each pair is reversed. For example, the ordered pair $(a, d)$ is an element of $X$, and the ordered pair $(d, a)$ is an element of $Y$. Thus, there is a one-to-one correspondence between the elements of $X$ and the elements of $Y$. Any element $(x, y)$ of $X$ is paired with $(y, x)$ of $Y$. This must be true of any two cartesian products $A \times B$ and $B \times A$. In each case the elements of the product consist of each element of $A$ paired with each element of $B$. We conclude that the number of elements of a cartesian product is unaffected by changing the order of the sets. Given set $A$ with cardinal number $a$, set $B$ with cardinal number $b$. The product $a \times b$ is the cardinal number of the cartesian product $B \times A$. The product $b \times a$ is the cardinal number of the cartesian product $B \times A$. Since $n(A \times B) = n(B \times A)$ it follows that $ab = ba$.

> The multiplication of cardinal numbers is *commutative:*
>
> $$ab = ba$$

In showing the commutativity of multiplication it was assumed that if sets $A$ and $B$ are finite then $A \times B$ is finite. We have shown, page 38, that the union of two finite sets is a finite set.

Let set $A$ be a finite set with $n(A) = a$: let $x$ represent any one of its $a$ elements. Let set $B$ be a finite set with $n(B) = b$; let $y$ represent any one of its $b$ elements. The set of $(x_1, y)$ ordered pairs is a finite set since it has $b$ elements. Call this set $C_1$. The symbol $(x_1, y)$ means that we select a particular one of the $a$ elements of $A$ and pair it with each of the $b$ elements of $B$. Similarly, the set of $(x_2, y)$ ordered pairs is a finite set. Call it $C_2$. Continuing in this way there are $a$ such sets of $(x_i, y)$ ordered pairs. The union of these sets of ordered pairs is the cartesian product $A \times B$.

$$C_1 \cup C_2 \cup C_3 \ldots \cup C_i = A \times B$$

Now, since the union of two finite sets is a finite set, $(C_1 \cup C_2) \cup C_3$ is a finite set; and $((C_1 \cup C_2) \cup C_3) \cup C_4$ is a finite set, and so on.

Since there is a finite number of sets $C_i$ this establishes the fact that multiplication of finite cardinal numbers is closed. That is, the product of two finite cardinal numbers is a finite cardinal number.

We know from experience with numbers that $3 \times (4 \times 5) = (3 \times 4) \times 5$. On the left we multiply $4 \times 5 = 20$ and then $3 \times 20 = 60$. On the right we multiply $3 \times 4 = 12$ and $12 \times 5 = 60$. This is called the *associative property* for multiplication. Can this be proved from our definition of multiplication?

We wish to show that for $a$, $b$, $c$, the number of elements of sets $A$, $B$, $C$, respectively,

$$(a \times b) \times c = a \times (b \times c)$$

It is sufficient to show a one-to-one correspondence of the elements of the cartesian products $(A \times B) \times C$ and $A \times (B \times C)$. Let $x$ represent any element of set $A$, $y$ any element of set $B$, and $z$ any element of set $C$.

$A \times B$ is the set of all $(x, y)$ pairs. $(A \times B) \times C$ is the set of all pairs whose first member is an $(x, y)$ pair and second member is a $z$; that is, $(A \times B) \times C$ is the set of all pairs $((x, y), z)$.

$B \times C$ is the set of all $(y, z)$ pairs. $A \times (B \times C)$ is the set of all pairs whose first element is an $x$ and whose second element is a $(y, z)$ pair; that is, $A \times (B \times C)$ is the set of all pairs $(x, (y, z))$.

Hence a one-to-one correspondence exists between the elements of $(A \times B) \times C$ and those of $A \times (B \times C)$. Corresponding to each $((x, y), z)$ in $(A \times B) \times C$ there is $(x, (y, z))$ in $A \times (B \times C)$ where $x$, $y$, and $z$ have the same replacement value.

*Example:* Let $A = \{a, b\}$, $B = \{c, d\}$, $C = \{e, f\}$
Then $A \times B = \{(a, c), (a, d), (b, c), (b, d)\}$
and $(A \times B) \times C = \{((a, c), e), ((a, c), f), ((a, d), e), ((a, d), f), ((b, c), e), ((b, c), f), ((b, d), e), ((b, d), f)\}$
But $(B \times C) = \{(c, e), (c, f), (d, e), (d, f)\}$
and $A \times (B \times C) = \{(a, (c, e)), (a, (c, f))), (a, (d, e)), (a, (d, f)), (b, (c, e)), (b, (c, f)), (b, (d, e), b, (d, f))\}$
We have the correspondence $((a, c), e) \leftrightarrow (a, (c, e))$, and so on.

Since the one-to-one correspondence exists we know the two sets $(A \times B) \times C$ and $A \times (B \times C)$ have the same cardinal number. Since the cardinal number of $(A \times B) \times C$ is $(ab)c$ and the cardinal number of $A \times (B \times C)$ is $a(bc)$ it follows that $(ab)c = a(bc)$.

> The multiplication of cardinal numbers is *associative:*
>
> $$a(bc) = (ab)c$$

We know from experience with numbers that multiplication of whole numbers is equivalent to addition of equal addends. The product $3 \times 5$ means $5 + 5 + 5$. Is this result consistent with addition and multiplication as we have defined them in terms of sets? This relationship can be proved with the aid of the *distributive property*. The distributive property is illustrated by

$$3 \times (4 + 5) = 3 \times 4 + 3 \times 5$$

We can justify this specific case by evaluating each side of the equality independently.

$$3 \times (4 + 5) = 3 \times 9 = 27$$

and

$$3 \times 4 + 3 \times 5 = 12 + 15 = 27$$

The principle requires that for any integers $a$, $b$, and $c$

$$a(b + c) = ab + ac$$

It can be generalized to any number of addends.

$$a(b + c + d + e + \dots) = ab + ac + ad + ae + \dots$$

With this principle we can prove $3 \times 5 = 5 + 5 + 5$

$5 + 5 + 5 = 5(1 + 1 + 1)$ by the distributive principle
$5(1 + 1 + 1) = 5 \times 3$ definition of addition
$5 \times 3 = 3 \times 5$ multiplication is commutative
$3 \times 5 = 5 + 5 + 5$ substitution of equals for equals

This brings us to the question: can the distributive principle be proved from the definition of addition and multiplication?

Let $A$, $B$, $C$ be sets with cardinal numbers $a$, $b$, and $c$ respectively. Further, let $B$ and $C$ be disjoint sets. Then $n(B \cup C) = b + c$ by definition of addition. The number $n(A \times (B \cup C)) = a(b + c)$ by the definition multiplication. Also by the definition of multiplication $n(A \times B) = ab$ and $n(A \times C) = ac$. Furthermore, since $B$ and $C$ are disjoint, $A \times B$ and $A \times C$ are disjoint. This is because the second components of the elements of $A \times B$ must all differ from any of the second components of the elements of $A \times C$. Then by definition of addition, $n[(A \times B) \cup (A \times C)] = ab + ac$. The distributive property is established, $a(b + c) = ab + ac$, provided $n[A \times (B \cup C)] = n[(A \times B) \cup (A \times C)]$. But this is surely true. The two sets are equal, they have exactly the same elements. In both cases the elements consist of the set of ordered pairs whose first components are the elements of $A$ and whose second components are the elements of $B$ and the elements of $C$.

> Multiplication of cardinal numbers is distributive over addition of cardinal numbers.
>
> $$a(b + c) = ab + ac$$

*Example:* To illustrate the fact that $A \times (B \cup C) = (A \times B) \cup (A \times C)$ if $B$ and $C$ are disjoint, consider:
$A = \{a, b\}$, $B = \{c, d\}$, and $C = \{e, f\}$
$B \cup C = \{c, d, e, f\}$

$A \times (B \cup C) = \{(a, c), (a, d), (a, e), (a, f), (b, c), (b, d), (b, e), (b, f)\}$
$A \times B = \{(a, c), (a, d), (b, c), (b, d)\}$
$A \times C = \{(a, e), (a, f), (b, e), (b, f)\}$
$(A \times B) \cup (A \times C) = \{(a, c), (a, d), (b, c), (b, d), (a, e), (a, f), (b, e), (b, f)\}$

But this is exactly the same set of elements as the elements of $A \times (B \cup C)$. (Remember that the order of listing of the elements of a set is of no significance.)

We are familiar with the fact that any number multiplied by zero has the product zero. $a \times 0 = 0 \times a = 0$. Is this consistent with the definition of multiplication developed here?

Consider the set $A = \{a, b, c\}$ and $B = \{\ \}$, that is, the empty set. The cardinal number of $A$ is 3, the cardinal number of $B$ is 0. Hence $3 \times 0 = 0 \times 3$ is equal to the cardinal number of the set $A \times B$. The elements of $A \times B$ are ordered pairs. Each pair has for first component $a$, or $b$, or $c$. The second component of each pair is an element of $B$. But $B$ has no elements; hence there are no second components, there are no pairs. We must conclude that $A \times B$ is the empty set, whose cardinal number is 0. Hence $3 \times 0 = 0 \times 3 = 0$. One can readily see that if $A$ is replaced by a set with any other cardinal number the result will be the same.

*The product of any cardinal number and zero is zero.*

$$a \times 0 = 0 \times a = 0$$

Suppose that rather than being the empty set $B = \{0\}$. We now have

$$A \times B = \{(a, 0), (b, 0), (c, 0)\}$$

But the cardinal number of $B$ is now 1, not 0. If $B$ were any other set containing one element the number of elements in $A \times B$ would be unaffected. Let $B = \{x\}$, then

$$A \times B = \{(a, x), (b, x), (c, x)\}$$

If the set $B$ of the cartesian product $A \times B$ has one element its cardinal number is 1. Since that one element is the only second component available for the pairs of the cartesian product there must be the same number of elements in the cartesian product as in set $A$. (Is this true if $A$ is the empty set?) We conclude:

> *Any number times 1 equals that number.*
>
> $$a \times 1 = 1 \times a = a$$

*Summary:* Combining the results on page 38 with those of this section, we can now list the properties of the cardinal numbers.

*Addition*

1. Closure: The sum of two cardinal numbers is a cardinal number.
2. Cummutativity: The order of the addends does not affect the sum:
$$a + b = b + a$$
3. Associativity: The grouping of 3 addends does not affect the sum:
$$(a + b) + c = a + (b + c)$$
4. Identity: The sum of any number $a$ and 0 is $a$:
$$a + 0 = a$$

*Multiplication*

1. Closure: The product of two cardinal numbers is a cardinal number.
2. Commutativity: The order of the factors does not affect the product:
$$ab = ba$$
3. Associativity: The grouping of 3 factors does not affect the product:
$$(ab)c = a(bc)$$
4. Identity: The product of any number $a$ and 1 is $a$:
$$a \times 1 = a$$

5. Distributivity: One factor can be distributed over the addends of another factor.
$$a(b + c) = ab + ac$$

We see that addition and multiplication are abstractly quite similar. They have properties 1 through 4 in common. The fifth, the distributive property, is the only one that links the two operations.

Another property of fundamental importance is the property of zero as a factor.

6. If $a$ is any cardinal number:
$$a \times 0 = 0$$

## EXERCISES

Given $A = \{1, a, x\}$ $B = \{0, y\}$ $C = \{x, y\}$ find the following:

**1.** $A \times B$

**2.** $B \times A$

**3.** $A \times C$

**4.** $A \times (B \cup C)$

**5.** Why is the cardinal number of $A \times B$ plus the cardinal number of $A \times C$ not equal to the cardinal number of $A \times (B \cup C)$?

**6.** Are $\{x, y\}$ and $\{y, x\}$ equal sets?
Are $\{x, y\}$ and $\{(x, y)\}$ equal sets?
Are $\{(x, y)\}$ and $\{(y, x)\}$ equal sets?
Explain your answers.

**7.** State the principle by which we may say that each of the following is an equality:
(a) $2 \times (3 + 7) = 2 \times 3 + 2 \times 7$
(b) $2 \times (3 + 7) = (3 + 7) \times 2$
(c) $12 \times (3 - 3) = 0$
(d) $(3 + 5) + 9 = 3 + (5 + 9)$
(e) $(3 + 5) + 9 = (3 + 9) + 5$

**8.** In view of Exercises 7 (a) and (b) what additional step is required to reach the conclusion $(3 + 7) \times 2 = 3 \times 2 + 7 \times 2$?

## 3.3 Exponents and Powers

In our system of notation 10, $10 \times 10$, $10 \times 10 \times 10$, and so forth, play an important role. These specific products, consisting of a single number called the *base* used as a factor one or more times, may be written in a most convenient form. A superscript to the right of the base number is used to indicate the number of times the base is used as a factor. The superscript is called an *exponent*. The indicated product is called a *power* of the base. Thus $10^4 = 10 \times 10 \times 10 \times 10 = 10{,}000$. Ten is the base, 4 is the exponent, and $10^4$ or 10,000 is the power of 10. When written in exponential form the exponent tells *what* power of the base we have. Since $1000 = 10 \times 10 \times 10 = 10^3$ we say 1000 or $10^3$ is the third power of 10.

Under the foregoing definition of an exponent any number in superscript position other than a positive integer is meaningless. One might argue that zero as an exponent means that we use the base as a factor no times at all. This interpretation might prove satisfactory except for the fact that it states something is not done, a situation which is in general unproductive. If we consider a negative integer as an exponent we could hardly use a factor fewer than no times. If we use anything other than positive integers as exponents we must define what the symbolism is to mean. So long as our only guide is the earlier definition of the positive integral exponents, we are free to define other numbers as exponents in any way we please, or to leave them undefined. However, as we shall see presently, zero and negative integers are quite as useful in connection with a study of notation systems as are the positive integers.

Observe that by definition

$$10^3 \times 10^4 = (10 \times 10 \times 10) \times (10 \times 10 \times 10 \times 10) = 10^7$$

or in general if $a$, $b$ are positive integers, for any number $c$:

$$c^a \times c^b = \underbrace{c \times c \times c}_{a \text{ factors}} \times \underbrace{c \times c \times c \times c}_{b \text{ factors}} = c^{a+b}$$

In other words, when we multiply two powers of the same base the product has for exponent the sum of the exponents of the factors.

Again, by definition

$$10^5 \div 10^3 = \frac{10 \times 10 \times 10 \times 10 \times 10}{10 \times 10 \times 10} = 10^{5-3} = 10^2$$

or in general if $a$, $b$ are integers and $a$ greater than $b$

$$c^a \div c^b = \frac{\overbrace{c \times c \times c}^{a \text{ factors}}}{\underbrace{c \times c \times c}_{b \text{ factors}}} = c^{a-b}$$

for any number $c \neq 0$.

We restricted the case to $a$ greater than $b$ in order that the difference be a positive integer. If we disregard the restriction and permit $a = b$ we get $10^5 \div 10^5 = 10^{5-5} = 10^0$ which is meaningless until defined. But we know that $10^5 \div 10^5 = 1$. Therefore we define $10^\circ$ as being 1. In fact, any number $c$, except $c = 0$, to the zero power is by definition 1.

$$c^\circ = 1, c \neq 0$$

## 3.4 The Inverse of Multiplication

Division is by definition the inverse of multiplication. This means that if we multiply by a number, then divide the result by the same number, the final result is the original number.

$$12 \times 3 = 36, \quad 36 \div 3 = 12$$

We state the definition of division by means of the equations

$$a \div b = x, \text{ if and only if } xb = a\,(b \neq 0)$$

Hence $36 \div 3 = 12$ because $12 \times 3 = 36$.

Here we are saying the quotient $a \div b$ is whatever $b$ must be multiplied by to get $a$. If we substitute the value of $x$, that is, $a \div b$, from the first equation in the second we get

$$a \div b \times b = a \tag{1}$$

If we divide $a$ by $b$, then multiply the result by $b$, we obtain the original $a$.

Suppose we multiply by $b$ first, then divide

$$a \times b \div b = x$$

According to the definition of division, $x$ is that number that we must multiply $b$ by to obtain the product $a \times b$. But since $b \times a = a \times b$ the required number is surely $a$.

$$a \times b \div b = a \tag{2}$$

Thus, whether we multiply by $b$, then divide by $b$, Equation (2), or divide by $b$ then multiply by $b$, Equation (1), the end result is the original $a$. We can always divide by $b$ if we have already multiplied by $b$ as in Equation (2). But in Equation (1) we have no assurance that we can divide by $b$ and get a cardinal number.

*Example:* We know that $13 \times 7 \div 7 = 13$, since $13 \times 7$ is a cardinal number. But in $13 \div 7 \times 7$ we have no assurance that $13 \div 7$ is a cardinal number. In fact it is not.

This same situation exists relative to subtraction of cardinal numbers. In order that subtraction will always be possible we created negative numbers. Does this extension of number make division always possible? Before this question can be answered we must decide how we can multiply with negative numbers. However, the definition of division precludes the possibility of division *always* being possible. In the definition the possibility of zero as a divisor was excluded. Why was this done?

What does $5 \div 0$ equal? According to the definition of division, it must equal some number which multiplied by zero will equal 5. Symbolically, we are saying

$$5 \div 0 = a \text{ if and only if } a \times 0 = 5$$

But we saw in the previous section that zero multiplied by any number will equal zero. Hence, we can find no value for $a$ which will satisfy the equation $a \div 0 = 5$. If 5 were replaced by any other number, except zero, the same situation would confront us. What if we do replace 5 with 0? We then have

$$0 \div 0 = a \text{ if and only if } a \times 0 = 0$$

In the equation $a \times 0 = 0$ any value whatever for $a$ will make the equation true. Hence division of any number by zero is undefined.

## EXERCISES

1. If $A = \{\ \}$, the empty set, and $A \times B$ has the cardinal number 4 we can write $A \times B$ in dummy form as $\{(a, b), (a, b), (a, b), (a, b)\}$ where $a$ represents an element of $A$ and $b$ represents an element of $B$. Why is the above situation impossible?
2. If $A = \{\ \}$ and $A \times B = \{\ \}$ show why $B$ can be any set one wishes to consider.
3. If neither $A$ nor $B$ is a unit set, that is, has one element, show why it is impossible for $A \times B$ to have the cardinal number 5.
4. Show with an example that it is impossible for $A \times B$ to have eight elements and $A$ to have three elements.
5. If $B = \{a, b, c\}$ and $A \times B = \{(x, a), (x, b), (x, c), (y, a), (y, b), (y, c)\}$ what is set $A$?
6. If $m \times p = n$, from the definition of division what division fact is implied?
7. Since multiplication is commutative, what other multiplication fact is implied in Exercise 6? What division fact is implied by this multiplication fact?

**8.** Since for any number $a$, $a \times 1 = a$ it follows that $a \div a = 1$ if $a \neq 0$. Why is this not true when $a = 0$?

## 3.5 Multiplication of Negative Numbers

We introduced negative numbers in order that we may always subtract. Rules for the addition of positive and negative numbers were shown to be a consequence of the properties established for cardinal numbers. We now wish to extend this procedure to multiplication. We shall assume that the integers—positive, negative, and zero—are consistent with the properties established for cardinal numbers, page 69, and derive the rules for multiplication of positive and negative numbers.

There are three cases involving negative numbers. If $a$ and $b$ are positive we have (I) $a \times (-b)$, (II) $(-a) \times b$, (III) $(-a) \times (-b)$. First consider $a \times [b + (-b)]$. Since $b + (-b) = 0$, we have

$$a \times [b + (-b)] = a \times 0 = 0$$

But if we apply the distributive property

$$a \times [b + (-b)] = a \times b + a \times (-b)$$

Then by substitution

$$a \times b + a \times (-b) = 0$$

That is, $a \times (-b)$ is the negative of $a \times b$. But the negative of $a \times b$ is $-(a \times b)$. Hence,

$$a \times (-b) = -(a \times b) \qquad \text{(I)}$$

If we apply the commutative property we have

$$a \times (-b) = (-b) \times a$$

Since both $a$ and $b$ represent any positive integer $(-b) \times a$ can just as well be written $(-a) \times b$. Hence for case (II) we have

$$(-a) \times b = -(a \times b) \qquad \text{(II)}$$

Consider the product $(-a) \times [b + (-b)]$
Since $b + (-b) = 0$ we have

$$-a \times [b + (-b)] = -a \times 0 = 0$$

But, applying the distributive property,

$$-a \times [b + (-b)] = -a \times b + (-a) \times (-b)$$

Hence, applying Equation II, and substituting on the left, we have

$$0 = -(a \times b) + (-a) \times (-b)$$

It follows that $(-a) \times (-b)$ is the negative of $-(a \times b)$. That is, for case (III) we have

$$(-a) \times (-b) = a \times b \qquad \text{(III)}$$

## 3.6 Multiplication on the Number Line

Multiplication can be illustrated on the number line when it is interpreted as successive addition of equal addends. For example, $3 \times 5 = 5 + 5 + 5$.

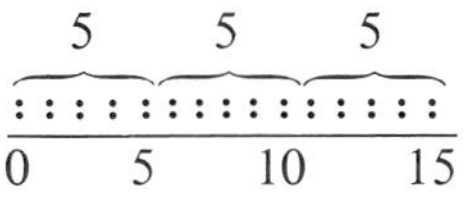

$3 \times 5$ ON THE NUMBER LINE.

With the proper conventions we can illustrate the laws of signs for multiplication on the number line.

Let $a \times b$ mean we move $a$ steps to the right, $b$ units per step. This is what we have done in the above illustration, showing $3 \times 5 = 15$. We agreed, page 51, that in adding a negative number (or subtracting a positive number) this should be interpreted as moving to the left. Hence, $3 \times (-5)$ we interpret as moving *to the left* five units at a time for 3 steps.

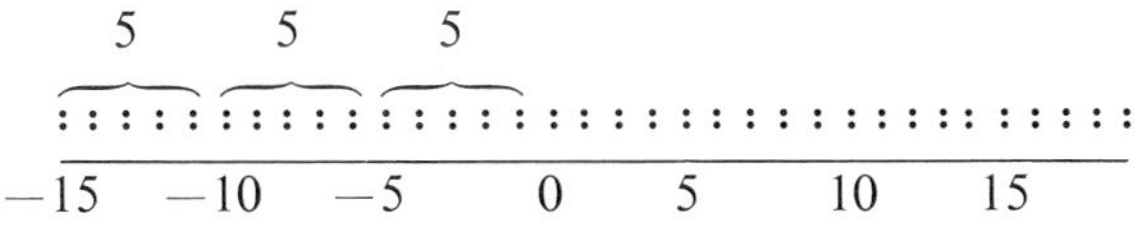

$3 \times (-5) = -15$

We make the further convention that in the event we are required to make a given move for a negative number of steps, this shall mean the corresponding move *in the opposite direction* that positive number of times. For example, $(-3) \times 5$ requires a move of 5 units to the right $-3$ times.

We agree that this means the steps of 5 units are to be taken to the left and there are 3 steps. Hence, on the number line $(-3) \times 5$ will appear precisely the same as $3 \times (-5)$.

Using the same interpretation, how will $(-3) \times (-5)$ appear on the number line? The $-5$ means move to the *left* in steps of 5 units. The $-3$ means take $-3$ such steps. We have agreed that since this cannot be done we shall take 3 such steps in the opposite direction, or to the right. Hence, on the number line $(-3) \times (-5)$ appears precisely the same as $3 \times 5$.

## EXERCISES

**1.** Evaluate each of the following:

(a) $-2 \times (3 + -4)$ (b) $-2 \times 3 + -2 \times -4$
(c) $-6 \times (-5 \times 9)$ (d) $(-6 \times -5) \times 9$
(e) $-4 \times (3 \times -12)$ (f) $3 \times -12 \times -4$

**2.** The interpretation of multiplication $a \times b = b + b + b + \ldots$ for $a$ terms is meaningless when $a$ is negative. If $-3 \times 4$ must equal either 12 or $-12$ let us assume it is 12. Since $3 \times 4 = 12$, and if $-3 \times 4 = 12$, we have $3 \times 4 = -3 \times 4$. Then if we divide both sides by 4 we have $3 = -3$. We conclude that $-3 \times 4 = -12$. Use an argument similar to this to show that $-3 \times -4 = 12$.

**3.** Evaluate $-a \times (b + -c)$ if $a$, $b$, and $c$ are each of the following:

(a) $a = -5, b = -4, c = -7$
(b) $a = 3, b = -5, c = 2$
(c) $a = -3, b = 12, c = -5$
(d) $a = 4, b = 5, c = 3$

**4.** Since division is the inverse of multiplication, find each of the following:

(a) $(-12) \div (-3)$
(b) $6 \div (-2)$
(c) $15 \div 5$
(d) $(-20) \div 4$

**5.** Determine the sign of each of the following if $a$ and $b$ are positive:

(a) $a \div b$
(b) $(-a) \div b$
(c) $a \div (-b)$
(d) $(-a) \div (-b)$

**6.** As a result of Exercise 5 formulate a rule for division of positive and negative numbers.

**7.** If "$a$ greater than $b$" ($a > b$) means that $a$ is further to the right on the number line than $b$, which is the greater?

(a) $-3 \times 5$ or $-2 \times -4$ (b) $6 \times -5$ or $1 \times -2$
(c) $-10$ or 2

**8.** What is the sign of $-a \times -b$ if $a$ is positive and $b$ is negative?

**9.** Use the number line to illustrate each of the following:
(a) $8 - 15 = -7$
(b) $3 - 8 = -5$
(c) $-5 + -3 = -8$
(d) $-5 - 3 = -8$
(e) $5 \times -2 = -10$
(f) $-3 \times -4 = 12$

**10.** Multiply $a$ by $-b$ when $a$ is 3 and $b$ is $-4$.

**11.** Supply the missing numbers
(a) $3 + -5 + 8 = ? + 8 + 3$
(b) $2 \times -10 \times -5 = -5 \times (? \times -2)$
(c) $? \times -2 \times 3 = -3 \times (4 \times -2)$

## 3.7 Multiplication on the Circle

In Section 3.5 we saw that multiplication of integers—that is, positive and negative whole numbers and zero—is always possible. Furthermore, the result is always an integer.

If the definition of division as the inverse of multiplication holds for integers is division, other than division by zero, always possible?

Equations I, II, and III of Section 3.4 merely indicate whether the product is positive or negative. Otherwise, multiplication is the same. For example, since $3 \times 4 = 12$, Equation I merely tells us whether $3 \times -4$ is 12 or $-12$.

We know that division of natural numbers is not always possible. There is no natural number $n$ such that $n \times 3 = 13$. Then neither is division of integers always possible, even with division by zero excluded. There can be no integer $n$ such that $n \times -3 = -13$. Hence, $-13 \div -3$ is not an integer.

Negative numbers were created in order that we have a system of numbers that is closed under subtraction. This merely means that subtraction is always possible in the system and the result is also in the system. In Chapter 6 we shall discuss the set of rational numbers, a system in which division other than by zero is always possible.

In Section 2.9 the idea of addition on a circle was introduced. We can extend the idea to multiplication. As on page 54, consider a circle with seven divisions, numbered 0, 1, 2, 3, 4, 5, 6.

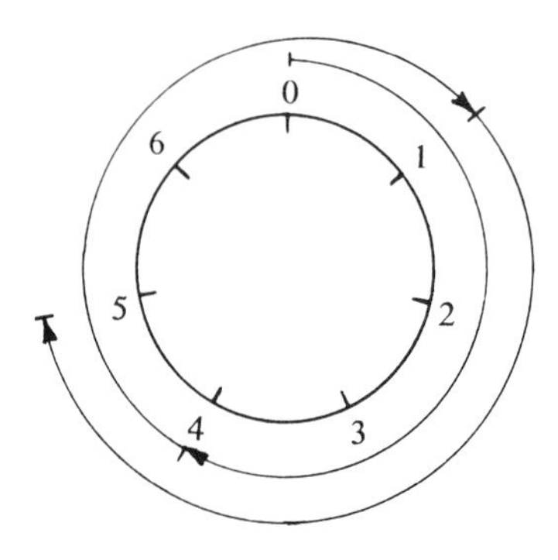


We interpret multiplication on the circle as we did on the number line; $a \times b$ means start at 0 and move clockwise $b$ units, then $b$ units more, and continue for $a$ such steps. For example, to find $3 \times 4$, we go clockwise from 0 to 4, 4 to 1, and 1 to 5. Hence $3 \times 4 = 5$. The correctness of the following multiplication table should be verified by actual multiplication on the circle.

| | 0 | 1 | 2 | 3 | 4 | 5 | 6 |
|---|---|---|---|---|---|---|---|
| 0 | 0 | 0 | 0 | 0 | 0 | 0 | 0 |
| 1 | 0 | 1 | 2 | 3 | 4 | 5 | 6 |
| 2 | 0 | 2 | 4 | 6 | 1 | 3 | 5 |
| 3 | 0 | 3 | 6 | 2 | 5 | 1 | 4 |
| 4 | 0 | 4 | 1 | 5 | 2 | 6 | 3 |
| 5 | 0 | 5 | 3 | 1 | 6 | 4 | 2 |
| 6 | 0 | 6 | 5 | 4 | 3 | 2 | 1 |

It can be verified from the table that all of the properties of multiplication listed on page 69 for cardinal numbers also apply here. Furthermore, division other than by zero is always possible. From the definition of division $3 \div 2$ is equal to whatever 2 must be multiplied by to produce 3. In row 2 we find 3 in column 5, hence $3 \div 2 = 5$ because $2 \times 5 = 3$. It becomes apparent that division by nonzero numbers is always possible when we observe that in each row, and in each column, other than the 0th column and row, each of the numbers 0–6 appears exactly one time. If this were not so, for example, if there were no 4 in row 3, it would be impossible to find $4 \div 3$ because there would be nothing by which to multiply 3 in order to produce 4. Note that in the table it is still true that 0 divided by anything other than 0 is equal to 0. Also, division by 0 is impossible. Why?

We can approach the question of division in another way. Recall, Section 2.7, that with the introduction of negative numbers we can always subtract; but we never have to—we can add the inverse of $a$ rather than subtract $a$.

When we extend numbers to the rational numbers all nonzero numbers will have multiplication inverses, 5 and $\frac{1}{5}$ are inverses because $5 \times \frac{1}{5} = 1$, and 1 is the multiplication identity. (See Section 3.2.) Also division by 5 and multiplication by its inverse $\frac{1}{5}$ produce the same result.

In multiplication on a circle of 7 divisions each nonzero number has its multiplicative inverse. If we take steps of 2 units from 0 on the circle, 4 steps will bring us to 1. Hence $4 \times 2 = 1$;

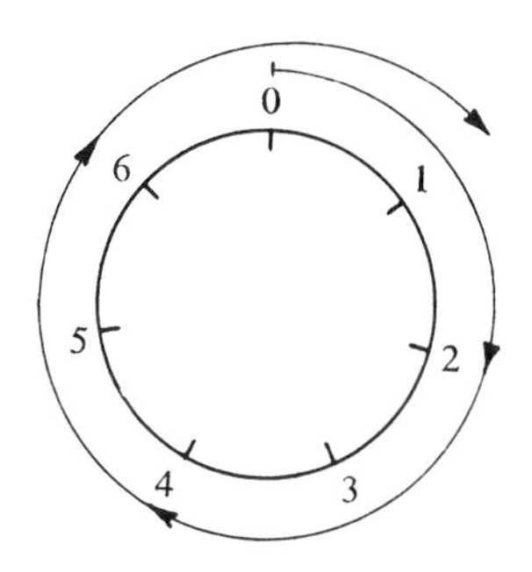


and it follows that 2 and 4 are multiplicative inverses. Examination of the multiplication table reveals that 1 appears in each nonzero row and column exactly one time. Therefore each nonzero number has a multiplicative inverse.

From the table we find that 4 is the inverse of 2. Also, from the table we find $3 \times 4 = 5$. But above we found $3 \div 2 = 5$. This is one example of the general principle that division by a number produces the same result as multiplication by its multiplicative inverse.

In Section 2.10 we saw that addition on a circle of seven divisions could be interpreted as the addition of residues, modulo 7 (see page 58). The same interpretation can be given multiplication on the circle. The result $3 \times 5 = 1$ means any number whose remainder is 3 when divided by 7, multiplied by any number whose remainder is 5 when divided by 7, yields a product that has a remainder 1 when divided by 7.

*Example:* $24 = 3 \times 7 + 3$; $24 \equiv 3$, mod 7
$47 = 6 \times 7 + 5$; $47 \equiv 5$, mod 7
$24 \times 47 = 1128 = 161 \times 7 + 1$; $24 \times 47 \equiv 1$, mod 7

The idea of number congruence need not be restricted to the modulus 7. Any integer greater than 1 can be used as modulus.

*Example:* $135 \equiv 21$, mod 6 because
$135 = 22 \times 6 + 3$ and
$21 = 3 \times 6 + 3$

Any two integers $a$, $b$ are congruent, modulo $c$ if they have the same remainder when divided by $c$.

$$\text{If } a = k_1c + r \text{ and } b = k_2c + r$$
$$\text{then} \quad a \equiv b, \text{ mod } c$$

Congruence is a reflexive, symmetric, and transitive relation. It may be characterized as a kind of equality—equality of remainders. All integers are congruent to some number 0 through 6, modulo 7, since 0 through 6 are the only possible remainders. As we move around the circle of 7 divisions we may think of each number as being its own remainder upon division by 7. For example, $5 \div 7 = 0$, with remainder 5. When we get back to 0 we have the remainder of $7 \div 7$. Continuing, 1 is the remainder of $8 \div 7$, 2 the remainder of $9 \div 7$, and so on.

We interpret the addition table, page 55, as follows: $4 + 5 \equiv 2$ means $4 + 5$ has the remainder 2 upon division by 7. $6 + 6 \equiv 5$ means $6 + 6$ has the remainder 5 when divided by 7. The multiplication table, page 78, is interpreted in the same way: $6 \times 6 \equiv 1$ means $6 \times 6$ has the remainder 1 when divided by 7. $4 \times 4 \equiv 2$ means $4 \times 4$ has the remainder 2 when divided by 7.

From the addition table we find $5 + 4 \equiv 2$. This means of course that $9 \div 7$ gives a remainder 2. But it means more; the 5 represents any integer congruent to 5 modulo 7, and the 4 any integer congruent to 4 modulo 7. Let $m$, $n$ be any two integers such that $m \equiv 5$ mod 7, and $n \equiv 4$ mod 7. This means that $m$ is some integral multiple of 7 plus 5 and $n$ is some integral multiple of 7 plus 4. Adding we get

$$m = 7k_1 + 5$$
$$n = 7k_2 + 4$$
$$m + n = 7(k_1 + k_2) + 9 = 7(k_1 + k_2 + 1) + 2$$

The sum $(m + n)$ is congruent to 2 just as the sum of their remainders is. The similar property holds true for multiplication.

$$\begin{aligned} m &= 7k_1 + 5 \\ n &= 7k_2 + 4 \\ \hline m \times n &= 49k_1k_2 + 35k_2 + 28k_1 + 20 \\ &= 49k_1k_2 + 35k_2 + 28k_1 + 14 + 6 \\ &= 7(7k_1k_2 + 5k_2 + 4k_1 + 2) + 6 \end{aligned}$$

Therefore $m \times n \equiv 6$, mod 7 and from the multiplication table $5 \times 4 \equiv 6$. We summarize these results by stating: If $a \equiv b$ and $c \equiv d$, then $a + c \equiv b + d$ and $a \times c \equiv b \times d$ (all modulo 7). As a matter of fact we can replace the 5, 4, and 6 in the illustrations with any arbitrary integers, and the summarizing statement applies to any modulus as well as 7.

We illustrate the two principles above with numerical examples. Consider two numbers, 96 and 60. We may express 96 as $7 \times 13 + 5$ and 60 as $7 \times 8 + 4$. Now we add the two:

$$\begin{aligned} 96 &= 7 \times 13 + 5 \\ 60 &= 7 \times 8 + 4 \\ \hline 156 &= 7 \times (13 + 8) + 5 + 4 = 7 \times 21 + 9 \end{aligned}$$

But if we divide 156 by 7 we get a remainder 2, and if we divide 9 by 7, we also get 2 for remainder. Thus the sum of the numbers, 156, and the sum of their residues, 9, are congruent modulo 7 since each is congruent to 2.

Similarly for multiplication:

$$\begin{aligned} 96 &= 7 \times 13 + 5 \\ 60 &= 7 \times 8 + 4 \\ \hline 5760 &= 7 \times 8 \times 7 \times 13 + 7 \times 8 \times 5 + 7 \times 13 \times 4 + 5 \times 4 \\ &= 7(8 \times 7 \times 13 + 8 \times 5 + 13 \times 4) + 5 \times 4 \end{aligned}$$

But if we divide 5760 by 7, we get 6 for remainder. We also get remainder 6 when we divide $5 \times 4 = 20$ by 7. Thus 5760, the product of the numbers, and 20, the product of their residues, are congruent, modulo 7 since each is congruent to 6.

If we choose a modulus other than 7 the result may or may not be a system closed to division. Let us construct addition and multiplication tables, modulo 4. To do this we merely divide the ordinary sums and products by 4. The remainders are the corresponding modulo 4 results. For example, $3 \times 3 = 9$, $9 \div 4 = 2$, remainder 1, therefore $3 \times 3 \equiv 1$.

ADDITION, MODULO FOUR

| | 0 | 1 | 2 | 3 |
|---|---|---|---|---|
| 0 | 0 | 1 | 2 | 3 |
| 1 | 1 | 2 | 3 | 0 |
| 2 | 2 | 3 | 0 | 1 |
| 3 | 3 | 0 | 1 | 2 |

MULTIPLICATION, MODULO FOUR

| | 0 | 1 | 2 | 3 |
|---|---|---|---|---|
| 0 | 0 | 0 | 0 | 0 |
| 1 | 0 | 1 | 2 | 3 |
| 2 | 0 | 2 | 0 | 2 |
| 3 | 0 | 3 | 2 | 1 |

Here $3 \div 2$ is meaningless. In row 2 we find no 3; hence there is no number $n$ such that $2 \times n = 3$. Furthermore, there is no 1 in either row 2 or column 2, so 2 does not have a multiplicative inverse.

## EXERCISES

**1.** Construct addition and multiplication tables for integers, modulo 2. Your only elements will be 0 and 1.

**2.** In the tables of Exercise 1, replace 0 with *even* and 1 with *odd*. Are the results consistent with the behavior of even and odd numbers under addition and multiplication?

**3.** A perfect square is an integer multiplied by itself. $5 \times 5 = 25$; 25 is a perfect square. Since any number is congruent to 0, 1, 2, or 3, modulo 4, prove that any odd perfect square is 1 more than a multiple of 4.

**4.** Use modulo 24 to determine the time of day 127 hours after 9 P.M.

**5.** In modulo 12 multiplication find $3 \times 8 \equiv ?$; $4 \times 6 \equiv ?$ Are the numbers 0, 1, 2, 3, 4, 5, 6, 7, 8, 9, 10, 11 under multiplication, modulo 12 closed under division?

**6.** Which of the numbers in modulo 12 multiplication have inverses? What is the inverse of each?

**7.** Use the multiplication table, page 78, to test the correctness of:

$$32 \times 73 \equiv 16 \times 41, \text{ mod } 7$$

**8.** Use the tables, pages 55 and 78, to test the correctness of:

$$15 \times (65 + 18) \equiv 23 \times (20 + 9), \text{ mod } 7$$

## 3.8 The Number Nine

The number nine has many fascinating properties. They do not stem from some mystic power as numerologists would have one believe. In the main, they stem from the fact that it is the largest integer below the base ten.

One of the interesting characteristics of nine is the fact that any number which is a multiple of nine has a digit sum which is also a multiple of nine.

$$2 \times 9 = 18 \qquad 1 + 8 = 9$$
$$3 \times 9 = 27 \qquad 2 + 7 = 9$$
$$4 \times 9 = 36 \qquad 3 + 6 = 9$$
$$11 \times 9 = 99 \qquad 9 + 9 = 2 \times 9$$

This is a special case of a much more general property. Any number is congruent to the sum of its digits, modulo 9.

$$768 \div 9 = 85, \text{ remainder } 3$$

or

$$768 \equiv 3, \text{ mod } 9$$

but

$$7 + 6 + 8 = 21 \equiv 3, \text{ mod } 9$$

To show that this is true recall that we have shown that congruences may be added and multiplied just as equalities can. If $a \equiv b$ and $c \equiv d$ then $a + c \equiv b + d$ and $a \times c \equiv b \times d$ (all modulo 9). Further, recall that from our system of notation

$$768 = 7 \times 10^2 + 6 \times 10 + 8$$

But since $10 \equiv 1$, mod 9

$$768 \equiv 7 \times 1^2 + 6 \times 1 + 8 = 21 \equiv 3, \text{ mod } 9$$

We note that $21 \equiv 3$ may be obtained by dividing by 9, but we can also apply the original idea to 21 and get $21 \equiv 2 + 1 = 3$.

This process can easily be generalized to any integer. Express the integer in the form

$$a_0 10^n + a_1 10^{n-1} + \dots + a_n$$

then

$$\begin{aligned} a_0 10^n + a_1 10^{n-1} + \dots + a_n &\equiv a_0 1^n + a_1 1^{n-1} + \dots + a^n \\ &= a_0 + a_1 + \dots + a_n \end{aligned}$$

the last expression being the sum of the digits of the original number.

This property shows why the "check of nines" works. We can check addition by adding the digits of each addend (and add the digits of each sum until a one-digit result is reached). The sum of these sums should agree with the sum of the digits in the answer.

*Example:* Add and check (modulo 9):

$$\begin{array}{rl} 786 & \equiv 7 + 8 + 6 = 21 \equiv 2 + 1 = 3 \\ 359 & \equiv 3 + 5 + 9 = 17 \equiv 1 + 7 = 8 \qquad 3 + 8 + 0 + 2 = 13 \\ 243 & \equiv 2 + 4 + 3 = \phantom{0}9 \equiv \qquad\qquad 0 \qquad\qquad \equiv 1 + 3 = 4 \\ 407 & \equiv 4 + 0 + 7 = 11 \equiv 1 + 1 = 2 \qquad\qquad\qquad \uparrow \\ \hline 1795 & \equiv 1 + 7 + 9 + 5 = 22 \equiv 2 + 2 = 4 \leftarrow \end{array}$$

The same principle may be used to check multiplication, but we must multiply residues this time.

*Example:* Multiply and check (modulo 9):

$$\begin{array}{rl} 642 & \equiv 6 + 4 + 2 = 12 \equiv 1 + 2 = 3 \\ 83 & \equiv 8 + 3 = 11 \equiv 1 + 1 = 2 \qquad\qquad 3 \times 2 = 6 \\ \hline 1926 & \qquad\qquad\qquad\qquad\qquad\qquad\qquad \uparrow \\ 5136\phantom{0} & \\ \hline 53286 & \equiv 5 + 3 + 2 + 8 + 6 = 24 \equiv 2 + 4 = 6 \leftarrow \end{array}$$

The check of nines may also be used to check subtraction and division. In subtraction we *subtract* the residues.

*Example:* Subtract and check (modulo 9):

$$\begin{array}{rl} 736 & \equiv 7 + 3 + 6 = 16 \equiv 1 + 6 = \qquad 7 \\ 253 & \equiv 2 + 5 + 3 = 10 \equiv 1 + 0 = \qquad 1 \\ \hline 483 & \equiv 4 + 8 + 3 = 15 \equiv 1 + 5 = 6 \leftrightarrow 6 \end{array}$$

## MULTIPLICATION AND DIVISION

It may happen in subtraction that the residue of the minuend is less than that of the subtrahend. In that case, if we wish to avoid negative numbers we may increase the residue of the minuend by 9, then subtract.

*Example:* Subtract and check (modulo 9):

$$\begin{array}{l} 893 \equiv 8 + 9 + 3 = 20 \equiv 2 + 0 \equiv 2 \equiv 11 \\ \underline{251} \equiv 2 + 5 + 1 = \qquad\qquad 8 = \underline{\ 8} \\ 642 \equiv 6 + 4 + 2 = 12 \equiv 1 + 2 = 3 \leftrightarrow 3 \end{array}$$

When we check division by inverse operations we multiply the quotient by the divisor, then add the remainder to secure the dividend. When the check of nines is used with division it is better to apply the above check, using the residues in the place of the numbers.

*Example:* Divide and check (modulo 9):

```
     49
 17|836
    68
    ---
    156
    153
    ---
      3
```

*Check:*

| | | |
|---|---|---|
| (quotient) | $49 \equiv 4 + 9 = 13 \equiv 1 + 3 = 4$ | |
| (divisor) | $17 \equiv 1 + 7 =$ | $8$ |
| | | $32 \equiv 3 + 2 = 5$ |
| (remainder) | $3$ | $3$ |
| (dividend) | $836 = 8 + 3 + 6 = 17 \equiv 1 + 7 =$ | $8 \leftrightarrow 8$ |

If the division example is checked by performing the direct operations with the residues we have

$$836 \div 17 = 49 + (3 \div 7) \text{ implies}$$
$$8 \div 8 \equiv 4 + (3 \div 8), \text{ but } 3 \div 8 = 6$$
$$\text{because } 6 \times 8 = 48 \equiv 12 \equiv 3.$$
$$1 \equiv 4 + 6 = 10 \equiv 1$$

However, this procedure will not always work.

## THE NUMBER NINE

*Example:* Divide and check (modulo 9)

$$
\begin{array}{rl}
 & \phantom{8}39 \\
21 & \overline{)836} \\
 & 63 \\
 & \overline{206} \\
 & 189 \\
 & \overline{\phantom{2}17}
\end{array}
\qquad\qquad
\begin{array}{r}
836 \equiv 8 \\
21 \equiv 3 \\
\\
39 \equiv 3 \\
17 \equiv 8
\end{array}
$$

The check requires that $8 \div 3 \equiv 3 + (8 \div 3)$. But $8 \div 3$ equals that number which, multiplied by 3, gives a result congruent to 8, and there is no such number. Any number multiplied by 3 gives a result which is congruent to 0, 3, or 6, modulo 9.

As was true of modulo 4, division is not always possible in the modulo 9 system even though division by 0 is not considered.

## EXERCISES

**1.** Each number except 0 on a circle of 7 divisions has a multiplicative inverse. Find the inverse of each of them.

**2.** Start at 0 on a circle of 5 divisions and take steps of 3 units each. What is the smallest number of steps required to stop at 0?

**3.** Start at 0 on a circle of 6 divisions and take steps of four units each. What is the smallest number of steps required to stop at 0?

**4.** Use the table on page 78 to find the following:
(a) $2 \div 5$ (b) $2 \times 3$ (c) $4 \div 6$ (d) $4 \times 6$

**5.** In Exercise 4 (c) and (d) you should have found that $4 \div 6 = 4 \times 6$. We would expect $4 \div 1$ to equal $4 \times 1$. Is this property true of any numbers other than 1 and 6? Explain why it is true of 6?

**6.** Use the addition and multiplication tables, modulo 7, to check the following:
(a) $39 \times 73 \equiv 30 \times 41$, mod 7
(b) $15 \times (37 + 18) \equiv 65 \times (20 + 9)$, mod 7

**7.** Use the addition and multiplication tables, modulo 7, to check for the distributive property with the following:
(a) $4 \times (5 + 3) \equiv 4 \times 5 + 4 \times 3$
(b) $2 \times (6 + 4) \equiv 2 \times 6 + 2 \times 4$

**8.** Add and check (modulo 9):

$$493 + 871 + 639$$

**9.** Multiply and check (modulo 9):
(a) $543 \times 657$
(b) $321 \times 47$

**10.** If we square the numbers 0–8 and express the results as residues, modulo 9, we get $0^2 = 0$, $1^2 = 1$, $2^2 = 4$, $3^2 = 9 \equiv 0$, $4^2 = 16 \equiv 7$, $5^2 = 25 \equiv 7$, $6^2 = 36 \equiv 0$, $7^2 = 49 \equiv 4$, $8^2 = 64 \equiv 1$. We may then conclude that any perfect square will be congruent to 0, 1, 4, or 7, mod 9. Which of the following numbers might possibly be a square?
(a) 183,436 (b) 72,603 (c) 843,675

**11.** Prove that any perfect cube is a multiple of nine, one more than a multiple of nine, or one less than a multiple of nine. *Hint:* Any integer is congruent to 0, 1, 2, 3, 4, 5, 6, 7, or 8, mod 9. Now cube each of these residues.

**12.** Subtract and check (modulo 9):
(a) $18{,}546 - 8328$
(b) $63{,}524 - 3760$

**13.** Construct the modulo 9 multiplication table. What numbers other than zero do not have multiplicative inverses?

**14.** Divide and check (modulo 9); check the direct operation if possible as well as the inverse:
(a) $543 \div 88$
(b) $2974 \div 278$

**15.** Find three numbers that are congruent to 7, modulo 12. Find three numbers that are congruent to 12, modulo 7.

**16.** Find the smallest multiple of 6 which is congruent to 0, modulo 11.

**17.** Give an illustration to demonstrate that congruence is a reflexive, symmetric, and transitive relation.

**18.** Find a modulus for which the following is true:

$$3 + 4 + 6 \equiv 2 \times 7 + 4$$

**19.** Supply the missing numbers:
(a) $15 \times (65 + 18) \equiv 23 \times (20 + 9)$, modulo?
(b) $4 \times 6 \equiv 0$, modulo?
(c) $127 \equiv 7$, modulo?

## 3.9 Division of Integers

We can subtract in the set of positive integers and zero only if the subtrahend (number subtracted) is equal to or less than the minuend. Knowledge of the system of numeration is sufficient to determine when subtraction is possible. We can divide in the set of integers only if the divisor is a factor of the dividend. We know that $12 \div 4 = 3$ because $3 \times 4 = 12$. But $12 \div 5$ is meaningless unless there is an integer $a$ such that $a \times 5 = 12$. It is not as simple a matter to determine whether division of two specific numbers is possible as was the case with subtraction.

We can, of course, determine divisibility by trial. In fact, in its practical application we are as much concerned with division that does not come out even as otherwise. But any time we have a remainder the division is impossible in the sense that we divide two *integers* and get for quotient an *integer*. There are tests for divisibility by small numbers, including all of the one-digit integers except 7, which are easy to apply and which will prove useful.

In Section 3.7 it is shown that the excess of nines in a number is equal to the excess of nines in its digit sum. If a number is divisible by 9 its excess of nines is zero. From this we may infer the rule:

*An integer is divisible by nine if and only if the sum of its digits is divisible by nine.*

We may, of course, apply the rule to the digit sum if necessary. For example, to test 89,783,946 for divisibility by nine we add $8 + 9 + 7 + 8 + 3 + 9 + 4 + 6 = 54$. And we can apply the test to the digit sum of 54: $5 + 4 = 9$. We conclude the original number is divisible by nine because 9 certainly is.

The test is more than a test for divisibility; it gives the remainder upon division by nine in case the number does not have 9 for a factor. For example: 4875 has a digit sum of $4 + 8 + 7 + 5 = 24$ and 24 has a digit sum of $2 + 4 = 6$. Therefore when 4875 is divided by nine the remainder is 6.

Let us see why the familiar rule for divisibility by two applies:

*An integer is divisible by two if and only if its ones digit is divisible by two.*

In applying this rule we merely have to know that 0, 2, 4, 6, and 8 are the one-digit multiples of two. Any two or more digit number may be considered ten times an integer plus the ones digit; for example, $1276 = 10 \times 127 + 6$. Let us express the number $N = 10 \times a + b$ where $a$ is an integer and $b$ a one-digit integer. If 2 is a factor of $N$ it must be a factor of $10 \times a + b$. But 2 is a factor of $10 \times a = 2 \times 5 \times a$. Then by the distributive property 2 must also be a factor of $b$:

$$N = 2[5 \times a + b/2]$$

On the other hand, if $b$ does not have the factor 2, that is, it is odd, $10 \times a$ would have to be odd if $N$ is even. But $10 \times a$ cannot be odd.

The rule for divisibility by five:

*An integer is divisible by five if and only if its ones digit is divisible by five.*

This rule follows from the above argument. Express the number $N = 10 \times a + b$. The term $10 \times a$ having the factor 10 must have the factor 5. Then by the distributive law $N$ has the factor 5 if and only if $b$ does. Then the number must have for ones digit either 5 or 0 if it is divisible by five.

These rules are also rules for determining the remainder upon division by two or five. Any integer is either divisible by two or has remainder one when divided by two. In the case of five the number has the same remainder upon division by five as the ones digit has. This is evident from the fact that the number minus its ones digit must be an exact multiple of five. For example, we know that $86{,}357 \div 5$ has a remainder 2 because $7 \div 5$ has remainder 2.

The rule for divisibility by three:

*An integer is divisible by three if and only if the sum of its digits is divisible by three.*

The test here is analogous to the test for the factor 9. It can be derived in the same manner. We know that 10 has remainder 1 when divided by 3. Or, in the terminology of Section 3.6, $10 \equiv 1$, mod 3. It follows that any integral power of 10 also has remainder $1: 10^n \equiv 1^n = 1$ mod 3, and any multiple $a$ of a power of 10 has remainder $a$:

$$a \times 10^n \equiv a \times 1^n = a, \text{ mod } 3$$

For example, 50 and 5 have the same remainder, 2, upon division by 3. Since an integer is the sum of multiples of powers of 10 it has the same remainder upon division by 3 as does the sum of its digits. If the remainder is zero the number is divisible by 3. For example, 454,326 is a multiple of 3 because $4 + 5 + 4 + 3 + 2 + 6 = 24$ is; and we know 24 is because $2 + 4 = 6$ is. We know that 0, 3, 6, 9 are the one-digit multiples of 3; the test is no help here.

We may derive a test for four patterned after the test for five. Or a slightly different test patterned after the test for three may be developed.

Following the test for five, we have the rule:

*An integer is divisible by four if and only if the number represented by the tens and ones digit is divisible by four.*

This rule follows from the fact that a three-or-more-digit integer is an integral multiple of 100 plus a two-digit integer. For example, $7618 = 100 \times 76 + 18$. The integral multiple of 100 must be divisible by 4 because 100 has the factor 4. The entire number is then divisible by 4 if and only if the two-digit number is. Let $N$ be a three-or-more-digit integer, $a$ an integer and $b$ a two-digit integer. Then

$$N = 100a + b = 4 \times (25a + b/4)$$

and the number in parentheses is an integer if and only if $b$ has 4 for a factor.

If we pattern after the rule for three the test for four becomes:

*An integer is divisible by 4 if and only if the ones digit plus 2 times the tens digit is divisible by 4.*

To establish this rule we note that 10 is 2 more than a multiple of 4:

$$10 \equiv 2, \text{ mod } 4$$

Then $10^2 = 100$ is $2 \times 2$ or 4 more than a multiple of 4. It is a multiple of 4:

$$10^2 \equiv 2^2 = 4 \equiv 0, \text{ mod } 4$$

All higher powers of 10, having $10^2$ for a factor, must be multiples of 4. Then any integer is congruent to 2 times its tens digit plus its ones digit, modulo 4.

*Example:* Test 839,672 for divisibility by 4. By the first rule we may divide $72 \div 4 = 18$ and thus the original number has 4 for a factor.

By the second rule we find $2 \times 7 + 2 = 16$ (and if we wish we may apply the rule to 16, $2 \times 1 + 6 = 8$); since 16 (or 8) is a multiple of 4, so is the original number.

Since $6 = 2 \times 3$ we may combine the tests for 2 and for 3 to obtain a test for divisibility by 6.

*An integer is divisible by 6 if and only if its ones digit is divisible by 2 and the sum of its digits is divisible by 3.*

*Example:* Test 634,254 for divisibility by 6. The ones digit is divisible by 2. The sum of the digits $6 + 3 + 4 + 2 + 5 + 4 = 24$ is divisible by 3. Therefore the number is divisible by 6.

Unlike the other tests, the test for 6 does not indicate the remainder in case the number does not have 6 as a factor. This stems from the fact that we have combined two tests into one.

## MULTIPLICATION AND DIVISION

Each of the rules for divisibility by 4 may be extended to give a test for 8. Since 1000 is a multiple of 8 we have the rule:

*An integer is divisible by 8 if and only if the number represented by the hundreds, tens, and ones digits is divisible by 8.*

Ten being 2 more than a multiple of 8, 100 is $2 \times 2 = 4$ more than a multiple of 8, and 1000 is $2 \times 2 \times 2 = 8$ more than a multiple of 8, that is, it is a multiple of 8.

$$10 \equiv 2, \text{ mod } 8$$
$$10^2 \equiv 2^2 = 4, \text{ mod } 8$$
$$10^3 \equiv 2^3 = 8 \equiv 0, \text{ mod } 8$$

This justifies the rule:

*An integer is divisible by 8 if and only if the ones digit, plus 2 times the tens digit, plus 4 times the hundreds digit is divisible by 8.*

*Example:* Test 867,312 for divisibility by 8. Since $312 \div 8 = 39$ we know that 867,312 is divisible by 8. By the other rule we have $4 \times 3 + 2 \times 1 + 2 = 16$ and $2 \times 1 + 6 = 8$; therefore the original number is a multiple of 8.

The test for divisibility by 11 is known as the skip rule:

*An integer is divisible by 11 if and only if the sum of the odd placed digits, beginning with the ones digit, minus the sum of the even placed digits is divisible by 11.*

*Example:* Test 53,621,348 for divisibility by 11.

$$8 + 3 + 2 + 3 = 16$$
$$4 + 1 + 6 + 5 = 16$$
$$16 - 16 = 0 = 11 \cdot 0$$

Therefore the original number is divisible by 11.

The justification for this rule follows. Since 10 is one less than a multiple of 11 we may express the fact as $10 \equiv -1$, mod 11. Then 100 must be one more than a multiple of 11 since $10^2 \equiv (-1)^2 = 1$, mod 11. But $1000 = 10^3 = 10^2 \times 10$, therefore $10^3 \equiv 1 \times (-1) = -1$, mod 11. Each higher power of 10 has remainder alternately $+1$ and $-1$ upon division by 11, depending on whether the power of ten is even or odd. For example,

$700 = 7 \times 10^2$ has remainder 7 on division by 11, but $7000 = 7 \times 10^3$ has remainder $-7$ (which is equivalent to 4) on division by 11. The rule now follows from the fact that a number is the sum of the numbers represented by its digits, and the sum of the remainders has a remainder equal to the remainder of the sum.

We have given no test for divisibility by seven. One can be developed, using the ideas of congruence but it is easier to divide the number by seven than to apply the test. Note the following congruences:

$$10 \equiv 3, \text{ mod } 7$$
$$10^2 \equiv 3^2 = 9 \equiv 2, \text{ mod } 7$$
$$10^3 = 10^2 \times 10 \equiv 2 \times 3 = 6 \equiv -1, \text{ mod } 7$$
$$10^4 = 10^3 \times 10 \equiv -1 \times 3 = -3, \text{ mod } 7$$
$$10^5 = 10^4 \times 10 \equiv -3 \times 3 = -9 \equiv -2, \text{ mod } 7$$
$$10^6 = 10^5 \times 10 \equiv -2 \times 3 = -6 \equiv 1, \text{ mod } 7$$
$$10^7 = 10^6 \times 10 \equiv 1 \times 3 = 3, \text{ mod } 7$$

The cycle 3, 2, $-1$, $-3$, $-2$, 1, 3 . . . obviously continues. This suggests the rule for divisibility by 7: If the sum of the ones digit, 3 times the tens digit, 2 times the hundreds digit, $-1$ times the thousands digit, and so on, is divisible by 7, the number itself is.

*Example:* Test 83,629 for divisibility by 7.

$$9 + 3 \times 2 + 2 \times 6 + (-1) \times 3 + (-3) \times 8 = 27 - 27 = 0$$

Therefore the number is divisible by 7.

The test for divisibility by 6 combines the tests for 2 and for 3, the factors of 6. In this same fashion, we may devise tests for divisibility by larger numbers. If the number has no repeated factors we may test for divisibility by the factors. For example, a number is divisible by 24 if it is divisible by 3 and by 8. But we may not say it is divisible by 24 if it is divisible by 4 and by 6, since 4 and 6 have the common factor 2. Obviously 36 is divisible by 4 and by 6 but not by 24. A number may be divisible by both 4 and 6 and contain the factor 2 only two times. On the other hand if a number is divisible by 3 and by $8 = 2^3$ it must have the factor 2 three times.

Divisibility by 3 and by 5 constitutes divisibility by 15, but divisibility by 3 and 15 does not constitute divisibility by 45. Divisibility by 15 implies divisibility by 3.

## MULTIPLICATION AND DIVISION

## EXERCISES

1. Test the following for divisibility by 2, 3, 5, 9, and 11; if they are not divisible, find remainders:
   (a) 47,801 (b) 3510
   (c) 635,822 (d) 2970

2. Test the following for divisibility by 2, 4, and 8; if not divisible, find remainders:
   (a) 36,104 (b) 9696
   (c) 8310 (d) 2501

3. Since a number is divisible by 6 if it is divisible by 2 and by 3, why can we not say it is divisible by 8 if it is divisible by 2 and by 4?

4. Using the congruence idea, devise a test for divisibility by 13. The result will be comparable to the test for 7.

5. State a test for divisibility by 12. Apply the test to 10,032.

6. Is it possible for a number to end in 14 and be divisible by 12? By 21? Why?

7. Give a test for divisibility by 22.

8. If a number is divisible by 99 what does this tell us about its digits?

9. Supply the missing digits which will make the following divisible by 2. By 3. By 4. By 5. By 6. By 9. By 11. In each case that is impossible, state why.
   (a) 436–82 (b) 731656–4– (c) 837–61–3

10. How can you tell whether a number is divisible by 25 without dividing by 25? Justify your answer.

## 3.10 Properties of Division

Does division, being the inverse of multiplication, obey the same rules? Until we enlarge our number system to include rational numbers (fractions) the operation is not always possible in the sense that the quotient is an integer. It is never possible if zero is the divisor; it is impossible to enlarge the number system so as to make division by zero possible. However, we can examine the behavior of division in those cases where it is possible.

First, is division commutative? If so, $a \div b = b \div a$. When we examine a specific example, $20 \div 4 = 5$, but $4 \div 20 = ?$ It certainly does not equal 5 because $5 \times 20 = 100$, not 4. It cannot equal any integer, for if it did this would mean that if we use 20 as an addend an integral number of times the sum would be 4. But let us assume that division is commutative and see what conclusion we are forced to accept.

By definition of division, $a \div b = x$ implies $b \times x = a$ and $b \div a = x$ implies $a \times x = b$. Using this value of $b$ in the first implication, we get $a \times x \times x = a$. This implies that $x \times x$ is the multiplication identity element 1 and therefore $x = 1$. But if $a \div b = 1$, then $1 \times b = a$. We conclude that division is commutative only if the dividend and the divisor are identical, and not zero.

Consider continued division such as $(24 \div 6) \div 2$. Does this equal $(24 \div 2) \div 6$? The answer is yes, in this specific case; $(24 \div 6) \div 2 = 4 \div 2 = 2$ and $(24 \div 2) \div 6 = 12 \div 6 = 2$. But this is not an example of commutative division. Neither the 6 nor the 2 plays the role of dividend. They are divisors in both cases. We have not commuted dividend and divisor; we have commuted two division operations, dividing by 6 and dividing by 2.

To show that this property holds for the general case we must show that

$$(a \div b) \div c = (a \div c) \div b$$

To show this let $a \div b = x$. But $a \div b = x$ implies that $b \times x = a$. The left member of the equation becomes $x \div c$. Substituting for $a$ in the right member, the equation becomes

$$x \div c = (b \times x \div c) \div b$$

Consider $x \div c$ as one factor in the parentheses and commute the two factors and we have

$$x \div c = (x \div c) \times b \div b$$

But, as we have seen in Section 3.3, the right member also becomes $x \div c$.

Had we not restricted ourselves to those integers with which exact division is possible, a simpler argument could be used. If we grant that division by an integer is equivalent to multiplication by its reciprocal, that is $a \div b = a \times 1/b$, the following argument could be used:

$$(a \div b) \div c = (a \times 1/b) \times 1/c$$

But since multiplication is both associative and commutative (these properties hold for fractions just as they do for integers) we can say

$$\begin{aligned}(a \times 1/b) \times 1/c &= a \times (1/b \times 1/c) = a \times (1/c \times 1/b) \\ &= (a \times 1/c) \times 1/b = (a \div c) \div b.\end{aligned}$$

We conclude that *in continuous division the order in which the divisors are used is immaterial.*

If division is associative, $(a \div b) \div c = a \div (b \div c)$. A numerical example is sufficient to show that this property does not exist—consider $(24 \div 4) \div 2$ as compared to $24 \div (4 \div 2)$:

$$(24 \div 4) \div 2 = 6 \div 2 = 3 \text{ but } 24 \div (4 \div 2) = 24 \div 2 = 12$$

However, we note that in the successive division $24 \div 4 \div 2 = 3$ we obtain the same result as we do if we *multiply* the successive divisors 4 and 2 and use the product for divisor:

$$24 \div 4 \div 2 = 24 \div (4 \times 2) = 24 \div 8 = 3$$

To show the general case we must show that

$$a \div b \div c = a \div (b \times c)$$

If

$$a \div (b \times c) = x \qquad \text{then} \qquad x \times b \times c = a$$

Replace $a$ in the left member of the equation by $x \times b \times c$ and we get $x \times b \times c \div b \div c = x \times c \times b \div b \div c = x \times c \div c = x$. Then, since both members of the equation equal $x$, we have shown that the equality holds.

Again, a more direct argument results if we admit fractions:

$$a \div b \div c = a \times 1/b \times 1/c = a \times \frac{1}{b \times c} = a \div (b \times c)$$

We conclude from the above that *we may replace successive division with division by the product of the successive divisors.* Or, otherwise stated, *we may divide by each factor of the divisor rather than the divisor itself.* For example:

$$96 \div 8 \div 4 = 96 \div (8 \times 4) = 96 \div 32 = 3$$

$$63 \div 21 = 63 \div (7 \times 3) = 63 \div 7 \div 3 = 9 \div 3 = 3$$

Since multiplication is commutative we know that

$$a \times (b + c) = (b + c) \times a$$

If we apply the distributive law to $a \times (b + c)$ we get

$$a \times (b + c) = a \times b + a \times c$$

Then, commuting the factors in each term,

$$a \times b + a \times c = b \times a + c \times a$$

## PROPERTIES OF DIVISION

The final expression being equal to $(b + c) \times a$ indicates that we can "enter the parentheses through the back door," so to speak. The relationship $a \times (b + c) = a \times b + a \times c$ is properly known as the left-hand distributive law. And the other relationship $(b + c) \times a = b \times a + c \times a$ is known as the right-hand distributive law. Although both properties hold for integers (and other ordinary numbers) they are not necessarily equivalent. There are mathematical systems wherein this is not true.

Numerical examples will indicate that the left distributive law *does not* hold for division but the right does: $96 \div (16 + 32) = 96 \div 48 = 2$ does not equal $(96 \div 16) + (96 \div 32) = 6 + 3 = 9$, as it would if the left-hand distributive law held. However,

$$(16 + 32) \div 4 = 48 \div 4 = 12,$$

and

$$(16 + 32) \div 4 = 16 \div 4 + 32 \div 4 = 4 + 8 = 12$$

In this one case at least, the right-hand distributive law does hold.

To show why the left-hand does not but the right does apply in the general case we reduce the problem to multiplication:

$$c \div (a + b) = c \times \frac{1}{a + b} = \frac{c}{a + b}$$

which is *not* equal

$$c/a + c/b = c \div a + c \div b$$

as required by the distributive law. On the other hand,

$$(a + b) \div c = (a + b) \times 1/c = \frac{a + b}{c}$$

which *does* equal

$$a/c + b/c = a \div c + b \div c$$

as required by the distributive law.

We conclude that *we can distribute the divisor over the terms of the dividend but we cannot distribute the dividend over the terms of the divisor.*

One further property of division follows from the fact that its inverse, multiplication, is commutative. If $a \div b = c$ then $b \times c = a$ and $c \times b = a$, but this implies that $a \div c = b$. In other words, *any division fact, dividend divided by divisor equals quotient, implies another division fact, dividend divided by quotient equals divisor.* We know that if $a \div b = c$ then $a \div c = b$.

In multiplication, if either factor is multiplied by a number the product is multiplied by the same number. For example, $12 \times 5 = 60$ and $12 \times (3 \times 5) = (3 \times 60)$. From this it follows that in division we may *multiply both dividend and divisor by the same number, not zero, without changing the quotient.* For example, since $30 \div 6 = 5$, we know that $(3 \times 30) \div (3 \times 6) = 5$ also. In general, if $a \div b = c$ then $(n \times a) \div (n \times b) = c$. We know that $a \div b = c$ implies $c \times b = a$. Multiplying this by $n$ we get $n \times c \times b = n \times a$, which may be written $c \times (n \times b) = n \times a$. This implies $(n \times a) \div (n \times b) = c$.

We note that $n \times c \times b = n \times a$ can be written $(n \times c) \times b = n \times a$, and this implies $(n \times a) \div b = n \times c$. This establishes the principle *multiplying the dividend by a number produces the same effect on the quotient:*

$$30 \div 6 = 5 \quad \text{implies} \quad (3 \times 30) \div 6 = (3 \times 5)$$

Finally, we wish to determine the effect on the quotient if we multiply the divisor. To this end we divide both sides of the equation

$$c \times n \times b = n \times a$$

by $n$ in order that $a$ be intact. This gives

$$(c \div n) \times (n \times b) = a, \text{ which implies } a \div (n \times b) = c \div n$$

*Multiplying the divisor by a nonzero number divides the quotient by the same number:*

$$100 \div 5 = 20 \quad \text{implies} \quad 100 \div (5 \times 5) = (20 \div 5)$$

The three preceding arguments can be reversed, yielding the same principles with multiplication replaced by division:

| | |
|---|---|
| If | $(n \times a) \div (n \times b) = c$ |
| then | $c \times n \times b = n \times a,$ |
| but this implies | $c \times b = a,$ |
| which implies | $a \div b = c$ |

*We may divide both dividend and divisor by the same nonzero number without changing the quotient.*

In a similar manner we can establish the principle, *dividing the dividend by a nonzero number produces the same effect on the quotient* and *dividing the divisor by a nonzero number multiplies the quotient by the same number:*

$$60 \div 15 = 4 \quad \text{implies} \quad 20 \div 5 = 4$$
$$60 \div 15 = 4 \quad \text{implies} \quad 30 \div 15 = 2$$
$$60 \div 15 = 4 \quad \text{implies} \quad 60 \div 3 = 20$$

Subtraction and division do not behave by the same rules as their inverses addition and multiplication. We have observed a parallel between addition and multiplication of positive integers. Both operations are commutative and associative. The positive integers are closed under both operations, that is, addition and multiplication are always possible. The two operations are related by the distributive law.

A similar parallel exists between subtraction and division. The properties of the two are summarized here:

*Subtraction*

The order of successive subtrahends can be changed:

$$a - b - c = a - c - b$$

Successive subtractions may be performed by subtracting the sum of the subtrahends:

$$a - b - c = a - (b + c)$$

If the same number is added to (or subtracted from) minuend and subtrahend the remainder is unchanged:

$$\begin{aligned} a - b &= (n + a) - (n + b) \\ &= (a - n) - (b - n) \end{aligned}$$

Adding to (or subtracting from) the minuend produces the same change in the remainder:

If $a - b = c$

then $(n + a) - b = n + c$

and $(a - n) - b = (c - n)$

From any subtraction fact another may be obtained by interchanging subtrahend and remainder:

If $a - b = c,$

then $a - c = b$

Multiplication is distributive with respect to subtraction:

$$a \times (b - c) = a \times b - a \times c$$

*Division*

The order of successive divisors can be changed:

$$a \div b \div c = a \div c \div b$$

Successive division may be performed by dividing by the product of the divisors:

$$a \div b \div c = a \div (b \times c)$$

If dividend and divisor are multiplied (or divided) by the same *nonzero* number the quotient is unchanged:

$$\begin{aligned} a \div b &= (m \times a) \div (m \times b) \\ &= (a \div m) \div (b \div m) \end{aligned}$$

Multiplying (or dividing) the dividend produces the same change in the quotient:

If $a \div b = c$

then $n \times a \div b = n \times c$

and $a \div n \div b = c \div n$

From any division fact another may be obtained by interchanging divisor and quotient:

If $a \div b = c,$

then $a \div c = b$

Division obeys only the right-hand distributive law relative to addition (or subtraction):

$$(a + b) \div c = (a \div c) + (b \div c)$$
$$(a - b) \div c = (a \div c) - (b \div c)$$

## EXERCISES

State whether each of the proposed equalities is true. If true, state the principle(s) involved. If the equality holds but represents a special case rather than demonstrates a general principle, so indicate:

1. $28 \div 4 \div 7 = 28 \div 7 \div 4$
2. $5 \times (6 - 3) = 5 \times 6 - 5 \times 3$
3. $125 - 256 = 256 - 125$
4. $3 \times (7 + 6) = 3 + (7 \times 6)$
5. $3 \times (9 + 4) = 3 + (9 \times 4)$
6. $25 \div 5 = 75 \div 15$
7. $(60 \div 12) \div 5 = 60 \div (12 \div 5)$
8. $(25 \div 5) \div 1 = 25 \div (5 \div 1)$
9. $(20 - 5) \div 3 = 20 \div 3 - 5 \div 3$
10. $6 - (30 \div 5) = (30 \div 5) - 6$
11. $48 \div 6 \div 2 = 48 \div 12$
12. $30 \div (6 + 5) = 30 \div 6 + 30 \div 5$
13. $(7 - 3) \times 2 = 7 \times 2 - 3 \times 2$
14. $(3 - 2) \times 3 = 3 \times 2 - 3$
15. $(5 - 3) \times 4 = 5 \times 3 - 4$
16. $36 - 7 - 5 - 4 = 36 - (7 + 5 + 4)$
17. $18 \times 12 \div 18 \times 4 = 12 \div 4$
18. $18 \times (6 \div 3) = (18 \times 6) \div (18 \times 3)$
19. $(25 + 6) - 12 = (13 + 6) - 0$
20. $(48 \div 12) \div (24 \div 12) = 48 \div 12$
21. $13 - (6 - 4) = 13 - (4 - 6)$
22. $42 \div (4 + 3) = 42 \div 4 + 42 \div 3$
23. $(14 + 28) \div 7 = (14 \div 7) + (28 \div 7)$
24. $12 - 8 = 12 - (5 + 2 + 1)$
25. $(29 - 13) - 6 = 29 - (13 - 6)$
26. $17 \times (5 + 8) = (17 \times 5) + (17 \times 8)$

**27.** $96 \div 16 = (96 \div 8) \div 2$

**28.** $(40 - 8) - 12 = 28 - 8$

**29.** $18 - 9 = (72 - 36) \div 4$

**30.** Give an example to illustrate that the left-hand distributive law does not hold for division.

**31.** Which, if any, of the following are correct?
(a) $(36 \div 6) \div 3 = 36 \div (6 \div 3)$
(b) $7 \div (4 + 9) = 7 \div 4 + 7 \div 9$
(c) $(6 + 5) \div 8 = 6 \div 8 + 6 \div 5$
(d) $(3 + 4) \div 14 = 3 \div 14 + 4 \div 14$

**32.** The following is a true relationship:

$$3 \times (9 + 4) = 3 + (9 \times 4)$$

Find other triples of numbers which behave in this way.

# 4 Notation Systems

THERE IS A DIFFERENCE BETWEEN A NUMBER AND ITS NAME. THERE IS ALSO a difference between the name for a number and a nonverbal mathematical symbol which stands for the number. "Twelve" is the name for the number of eggs one gets when he buys a dozen. We apply this same name to the symbol "12" and the symbol "XII."

Number names are chosen in a systematic fashion; so are number symbols. The two systems are quite similar but not identical. We call "23" "twenty-three," but we do not call "13" "onety-three."

"Numeration system" and "notation system" are frequently used interchangeably. However, in this book we wish to make a clear distinction between a system of number names and a system of number symbols. Accordingly, we shall use "numeration system" to mean a system of number names and "notation system" to mean a system of number symbols.

The importance to teacher or student of arithmetic of a thorough understanding of our system of notation cannot be overestimated. The arithmetic algorithms are possible only because of certain properties of our system of notation. The algorithms cannot be understood without corresponding insight into the system of notation. In the past, scant attention was devoted to this topic in the elementary school. This could account for much of the mechanical learning of arithmetic, devoid of meaning and understanding, which has taken place. Yet one of the most remarkable attributes of the system is its simplicity compared to earlier, less efficient ones.

Some kind of notation system has existed since the predawn of civilization. Yet man had to devise one, just as language had to be created. It would be difficult for us to imagine what the world would be like if a notation system had never been invented. But what was primitive man's motivation for such an invention? Our innate number sense is quite limited. We can visualize a set of three or four objects without recourse to some kind of grouping. But if we attempted to identify the number of objects in a set without counting or grouping into subsets we would find that we could not go very far. Even in identifying a set of five we would probably, unconsciously perhaps, visualize either a set of three and a set of two, or two sets of two and a set of one.

If our number requirements were not too great, up to fifteen, for example, we could invent a set of independent names for each number and get along quite well by counting. However, as our number requirements increased, this endless succession of unrelated names would soon become impossibly unmanageable. Furthermore, interpretation of the result of counting would be quite limited for want of a frame of reference. For example, one cannot visualize a set of 175 individual objects without relating it to something else. We can, however, visualize a single set of ten sets of ten, seven sets of ten, and five sets of one.

In this chapter we shall attempt to get a clearer understanding of our system of notation by (1) examining other systems which employ the same grouping into sets of ones, tens, hundreds, and so on, but use a different symbolism to indicate how many of each kind of set; and (2) examining the same system when a different grouping, such as ones, eights, sixty-fours, and so on, is used.

## 4.1 Decimal Systems

Basic to all notation systems is the idea of grouping. In our own system we consider the individual elements of the total set if there are no more than nine objects. If the total consists of ten or more objects we treat a set of ten, not as ten ones, but as a *single* set containing ten ones. Thus, twenty-three is considered to be *two* sets of ten and three sets of one. This is true of both our system of notation and our system of numeration.

A number is an abstraction, the cardinal number *five* is a property common to all sets of things that have the same number of elements as the number of fingers on the normal hand. But when I look at my hand I do not see the number five any more than I see a *red* when I look at a rose. The symbols 5, V, 𝍸 are not numbers, nor are they names for a number. They are nonverbal symbols that are used to represent a number. We call both the word "five" and the symbol 5 numerals.

Our system of notation, the Hindu-Arabic, is decimal; that is, grouping is done by tens. However, a much more important characteristic is the fact that it is *positional*. This means the value of each single symbol in a numeral is determined both by the symbol and by its position in the total numeral. Thus, in 303 the left-hand 3 has position value 100 and total value $3 \times 100 = 300$ while the right-hand 3 has a position value 1 and a total value $3 \times 1 = 3$. Numbers other than ten have been used as base—notably two, five, and twenty—but for obvious anatomical reasons man has shown a decided preference for ten throughout history.

Our system of numeration, that is, system of number names, is also decimal. This is not because it is designed for use with the Hindu-Arabic system of notation. It would be equally appropriate for any other base-ten notation system and inappropriate if the base is not ten even though the system is positional. For example, if we used eight rather than ten as basic grouping number, fifteen would be written "17" rather than "15." Should this be called "seventeen" or "fifteen"?

Unless specifically indicated to the contrary, in this book we shall use the ordinary names when referring to numbers by name. That is, "twelve" will mean this many //////////// regardless of the notation system we are discussing.

## 4.2 Additive Systems

One of the most primitive systems of notation employs different symbols for one, ten, one hundred, and higher powers of ten. The highest power of ten is used as many times as it is contained in the number, similarly for all lower powers of ten. For example, 6083 is expressed by using the symbol for one thousand 6 times, the symbol for ten 8 times, and the symbol for one 3 times. Thus, the values of the individual symbols are added to obtain the number. Note that the symbol for one hundred is not used since the number contains none.

The ancient Egyptian hieroglyphic system is this kind. A vertical staff 𓏺 was used to represent 1, a heel bone 𓎆 stood for 10, a scroll 𓍢 for 100, a flower 𓆼 for 1000, a crooked finger 𓂭 for 10,000, a fish 𓆐 for 100,000 and for 1,000,000 a man in utter amazement at such a number 𓁨. Thus the number 23,154 would be expressed

𓂭𓂭𓆼𓆼𓆼𓍢𓎆𓎆𓎆𓎆𓎆𓏺𓏺𓏺𓏺

In this system, the role of the base ten is evident. Any symbol may be used as many as nine times, but if ten of the particular symbol are needed a new symbol is introduced instead.

The familiar Roman system is the simple additive type with two additional properties incorporated. Here we have

$$1 = \mathrm{I}, \quad 10 = \mathrm{X}, \quad 100 = \mathrm{C}, \quad \text{and} \quad 1000 = \mathrm{M}$$

Inserted midway between each of these we have a symbol to represent five of the one below and half of the one above.

| 1 = I | | 10 = X | | 100 = C | | 1000 = M |
|---|---|---|---|---|---|---|
| | 5 = V | | 50 = L | | 500 = D | |

This is an improvement over the Egyptian method in that the representation of the number is more compact. If we did not have the midway symbols one would express

$$1492 = \mathrm{MCCCCXXXXXXXXXII}$$

But with their aid this is shortened to

$$1492 = \mathrm{MCCCCLXXXXII}$$

The system as we know it includes a subtraction principle. If a basic symbol (I, X, C, M) stands to the left of the next higher one, or the left of the midway symbol (V, L, D) which represents five times as much, then subtraction rather than addition is implied. Thus

CX = 110 *but* XC = 90, and

LX = 60 *but* XL = 40

We would not find 99 expressed as IC, nor would 95 be VC. Using the subtraction principle we get

$$1492 = \mathrm{MCDXCII}$$

The subtraction principle was a relatively late introduction to the system.

## 4.3 The Multiplicative Principle

The Chinese system illustrates the use of mutliplication as a means of shortening the notation. Distinct symbols are used for the numbers one through nine just as they are in our system. But as with the Egyptians, distinct symbols are used for successive powers of ten, that is 10, 100,

1000, and so on. The symbols for one through nine are

| 1 | 2 | 3 | 4 | 5 | 6 | 7 | 8 | 9 |
|---|---|---|---|---|---|---|---|---|
| 一 | 二 | 三 | 四 | 五 | 六 | 七 | 八 | 九 |

Those for ten through one hundred thousand are

| 10 | 100 | 1000 | 10,000 | 100,000 |
|---|---|---|---|---|
| 十 | 百 | 千 | 萬 | 十萬 |

Repetition is avoided by letting the first decade number precede a higher ordered number to indicate the number of times the higher number is taken. For example, 50 is written 五十 or literally 5 times 10. The number 2573 is written

二 千 五 百 七 十 三

Note the symbol 100,000 could be read "ten ten thousands." An alternate form for 10,000 is 十千 or "ten one thousands." Our system of numeration actually more closely parallels this system than it does our own notation.

| two | thousand | five | hundred | seven—ty | (ten) | three |
|---|---|---|---|---|---|---|
| 二 | 千 | 五 | 百 | 七 | 十 | 三 |

When we recall that in the Chinese language a single symbol represents a word rather than a single letter the above symbols could be considered either number symbols 七 = 7 or number names (七 is Chinese for the English word *seven*). As a matter of fact, the above symbols are used in literature and another set of symbols is used in calculation. These, from 1 to 10, are

〡 〢 〣 〤 〥 〦 〧 〨 〩 十

In this system they also have special symbols for 10, 100, 1000, and 10,000; for zero the circle is used.

## 4.4 Computation

Addition is comparatively simple with Egyptian numerals. Let us find 236 + 187. If we place the numerals in the usual way, one over the other, the first step consists of

𓍢𓍢𓎆𓎆𓎆𓏺𓏺𓏺𓏺𓏺𓏺𓏺

𓍢𓎆𓎆𓎆𓎆𓎆𓎆𓎆𓎆𓏺𓏺𓏺𓏺𓏺𓏺

---

𓍢𓍢𓍢𓎆𓎆𓎆𓎆𓎆𓎆𓎆𓎆𓎆𓎆𓎆𓏺𓏺𓏺𓏺𓏺𓏺𓏺𓏺𓏺𓏺𓏺𓏺𓏺

combining like symbols. Below the line we merely have the symbol for one 7 times and then 6 more times, the symbol for ten 8 times and then 3 more times, the symbol for one hundred 1 time and then 2 more times. The final result is then obtained by merely converting ten of any symbol to one of the next higher symbols.

𓍢𓍢𓍢𓍢𓎆𓎆𓏺𓏺𓏺

If this is continued until no symbol appears more than nine times the computation is complete. There is no necessity to know that $6 + 7 = 13$ or $8 + 3 = 11$ or even that $1 + 2 = 3$. We merely have to know how to count to ten.

Multiplication is also quite simple, yet cumbersome. To find $106 \times 23$ we can adapt the usual method to these symbols. We multiply each symbol in the multiplier by each symbol in the multiplicand.

𓍢 𓏺𓏺𓏺𓏺𓏺𓏺

𓎆𓎆 𓏺𓏺𓏺

---

𓍢 𓏺𓏺𓏺𓏺𓏺𓏺

𓍢 𓏺𓏺𓏺𓏺𓏺𓏺

𓍢 𓏺𓏺𓏺𓏺𓏺𓏺

𓆼 𓎆𓎆𓎆𓎆𓎆𓎆

𓆼 𓎆𓎆𓎆𓎆𓎆𓎆

---

𓆼𓆼𓍢𓍢𓍢𓎆𓎆𓎆𓎆𓎆𓎆𓎆𓎆𓎆𓎆𓎆𓎆𓏺𓏺𓏺𓏺𓏺𓏺𓏺𓏺𓏺𓏺𓏺𓏺𓏺𓏺𓏺𓏺𓏺𓏺

These partial products are then combined by converting ten of any symbol to one of the next higher symbol, thus obtaining

𓆼𓆼𓍢𓍢𓍢𓍢𓎆𓎆𓎆𓏺𓏺𓏺𓏺𓏺𓏺𓏺𓏺

To find the partial products it is only necessary to know any symbol times | equals the symbol, any symbol times ∩ equals the next higher symbol, any symbol times e equals the symbol two higher, and so on.

Computation with Roman numerals is somewhat complicated by the presence of the subtractive principle. If we add 49 + 25 the symbols which are to be subtracted can be canceled with

XLIX
XXV
———
LXXIV

the same symbol which is to be added if it is present. The X before the L means "subtract 10." It is canceled with one of the X's in 25. There is no I in 25 to cancel with the I preceding the final X in 49. But it can be entered in the sum preceding the V, indicating it is to be subtracted.

Multiplication with Roman numerals can get rather messy. We illustrate by finding 44 × 16.

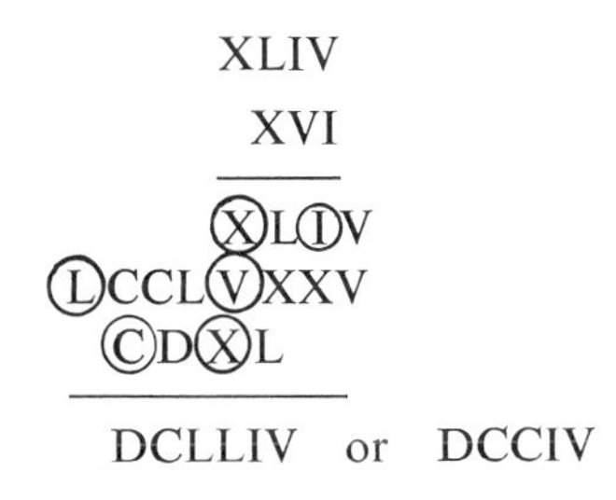


In the partial products, we have resorted to the device of circling the symbols which are to be subtracted. In the first line of partial products we have the product of I times the first factor, which is the first factor. In the second line of partial products we have the product of V times each of the terms of the first factor. Such combinations as V times L = CCL must be known. This particular example avoids many possible difficulties, such as the product of two symbols each of which is in a subtractive position. When this situation arises the partial product must be added rather than subtracted. As we have seen (Section 3.4), the product of two negative numbers is positive.

Computation with Chinese symbols presents problems somewhat similar to those encountered with our own system. However, the presence of symbols for ten, one hundred, and so on, complicates the situation. To add 608 + 537 it is necessary to know the one-digit combinations,

8 + 7 = 15, 0 + 3 = 3, and 6 + 5 = 11. We must combine 一十 (one ten) and 三十 (three tens) equal 四十

| | | | | |
|---|---|---|---|---|
| 六 | 百 | | | 八 |
| 五 | 百 | 三 | 十 | 七 |
| 一千一 | 百 | 四 | 十 | 五 |

(four tens) in carrying the 1 in 8 + 7 = 15. The two symbols for ten (十) are not combined; they merely designate the position value of the one (一) and the three (三). Similarly, when hundreds are combined 六 plus 五 equals 一 十 一 (six + five = one ten and one), but 一 十 一 hundreds must be entered as 千 百 (one thousand one hundred).

In multiplication not only the one-digit combinations but combinations indicating group size (10, 100, and so on) must be known. To multiply 356 × 78 we must find

| | | | | | | | | |
|---|---|---|---|---|---|---|---|---|
| | | 三 | 百 | 五 | 十 | 六 | | 356 |
| | | | | 七 | 十 | 八 | | 78 |
| | 二千八 | 百 | 四 | 十 | 八 | | | 2848 |
| 二萬 | 四千五 | 百 | 二 | 十 | | | | 2492 |
| 二萬 | 七千七 | 百 | 六 | 十 | 八 | | | 27768 |

八 (8) times 六 (6) equal 四十 (4(10)) 八 (8); 八 (8) times 五十 (5(10)) equal 四百 (4(100)); 八 (8) times 三百 (3(100)) equal 二千 (2(1000)) 四百 (4(100)) in the first line of partial products. The 四百 and 四百 have been combined to 八百. In the second line of partial products the multiplier is not 十, it is 七十. We have 七十 (7(10)) times 六 (6) equal 四百 (4(100)) 二十 (2(10)); 七十 (7(10)) times 五十 (5(10)) equal 三千 (3(1000)) 五百 (5(100)); 七十 (7(10)) times 三百 (3(100)) equal 二萬 (2(10000)) 一千 (1(1000)). It is instructive to identify step for step, the steps using Chinese symbols with those using the usual Hindu-Arabic symbols.

## EXERCISES

**1.** Express three thousand two hundred fifty-one in:
(a) Egyptian numerals (b) Roman numerals (c) Chinese numerals.

**2.** Express two thousand nine hundred forty-two in:
(a) Egyptian numerals (b) Roman numerals (c) Chinese numerals.

**3.** Express one thousand one hundred one in:
(a) Egyptian numerals (b) Roman numerals (c) Chinese numerals.

**4.** Write the following in Hindu-Arabic notation:
(a) XLIII (b) MDCCLXXXII (c) CCLVII (d) CMXLVII (e) CMVI

**5.** Write the following in Roman numerals:
(a) 1959 (b) 2001 (c) 1776 (d) 347

**6.** Write the following in Egyptian numerals:
(a) 587 (b) 12,932 (c) 434 (d) 789

**7.** Which of the three systems—Egyptian, Roman, Chinese—would you prefer as a system for writing numbers (not for calculation)? Why?

**8.** Convert the following to Roman numerals, then perform the addition:

$$847 + 164 + 63$$

**9.** Repeat Exercise 8 using (a) Egyptian numerals, (b) Chinese numerals.

**10.** Subtract the following, using Roman numerals:

MCDXCII minus MCCLXVI

**11.** Multiply, using Egyptian numerals:

𓍢∩∩|||| by ∩∩∩∩∩||||||

**12.** Multiply, using Roman numerals:

LXXI by XLIV

**13.** Multiply, using Chinese numerals:

≡ [symbol] [symbol] + )( by − + ≡

**14.** In which, if any, of the systems—Egyptian, Roman, Chinese—can the number zero be written? With which of the three can decimal fractions be written?

**15.** Did the Romans need a symbol for zero? Explain.

**16.** Are Roman numerals of any value today? Why are they used rather than Egyptian or Chinese?

**17.** Could Roman numerals be used to write common fractions? Decimal fractions?

**18.** How many symbols would you need to represent 3648 in Egyptian numerals?

**19.** Compose an addition table using Chinese symbols for the numbers 1 to 10.

**20.** Compose a multiplication table for the numbers 1 to 10 using Roman numerals.

## COMPUTATION

## 4.5 Negative Exponents

In Section 3.3 positive integral exponents were defined as

$$a^b = a \times a \times a \times \ldots \qquad \text{(for } b \text{ factors)}$$

As a consequence of this definition

$$a^b \times a^c = a^{b+c}$$

and, if $b > c$

$$a^b \div a^c = a^{b-c}$$

If the exponent zero is defined as

$$a^0 = 1 \quad a \neq 0$$

these rules of operation will continue to apply, and in the case of division the rule applies when $b = c$. If

$$b = c$$

then

$$a^b \div a^c = a^{b-c} = a^0 = 1$$

When we consider $a$ less than $b$ the rule for division

$$10^a \div 10^b = 10^{a-b}$$

cannot be carried through with natural numbers and zero; $a - b$ is neither a natural number nor zero. However, we know from the definition of natural number exponents

$$10^3 \div 10^5 = \frac{10 \times 10 \times 10}{10 \times 10 \times 10 \times 10 \times 10} = \frac{1}{10 \times 10} = \frac{1}{10^2}$$

In general, if $a$ and $b$ are natural numbers and $a$ is less than $b$

$$10^a \div 10^b = \frac{1}{10^{b-a}}$$

Since the set of integers is closed with respect to subtraction, $a - b$ is an integer if $a$ and $b$ are integers. If $a$ and $b$ are positive integers and $a$ is less than $b$, then $a - b$ is a negative integer.

If we define negative integral exponents as follows:

$$a^{-b} = \frac{1}{a^b}$$

the rules for computing with positive exponents will continue to apply. For example, $10^3 \div 10^5 = 10^{3-5} = 10^{-2}$, which is consistent with the foregoing result:

$$10^3 \div 10^5 = \frac{1}{10^2}$$

Thus, $10^{-1} = \frac{1}{10} = .1$, $10^{-2} = 1/10^2 = .01$, $10^{-3} = 1/10^3 = .0001$, and so on.

We can now express a number as the sum of powers of ten, no power being used more than nine times.

$$347.15 = 3 \times 10^2 + 4 \times 10^1 + 7 \times 10^0 + 1 \times 10^{-1} + 5 \times 10^{-2}$$

$$404.04 = 4 \times 10^2 + 0 \times 10^1 + 4 \times 10^0 + 0 \times 10^{-1} + 4 \times 10^{-2}$$

The value of each digit in the number is obtained by multiplying the digit by the power of ten indicated by the position of the digit in the number. If we start with the ones ($10^\circ$) digit, the exponent of ten increases by one for each position to the left and decreases by one ($-2$ is one less than $-1$) for each position to the right. Thus, the position value of any digit is determined in terms of its position relative to the ones position.

## EXERCISES

**1.** Evaluate the following:
(a) $10^3$ (b) $4^0$ (c) $6^2$ (d) $8^3$ (e) $7^1$ (f) $13^0$ (g) $6^{-3}$ (h) $(\frac{1}{2})^{-2}$ (i) $75^0$ (j) $83^1$ (k) $3^{-2}$

**2.** Compute the following, leaving the result in exponential form:
(a) $5^5 \times 5^4$ (b) $9^5 \div 9^3$ (c) $8^2 \times 8^3 \div 8^2$ (d) $4^2 \div 2^4$

**3.** Express as the sum of multiples of powers of ten:
(a) 468.23 (b) 1003.04 (c) 707.07

**4.** Evaluate:
(a) $2 \times 10^2 + 7 \times 10^1 + 4 \times 10^0$
(b) $6 \times 8^2 + 5 \times 8^1 + 3 \times 8^0$
(c) $4 \times 10^1 + 3 \times 10^0 + 4 \times 10^{-1}$
(d) $5 \times 6^3 + 3 \times 6^1 + 1 \times 6^0 + 4 \times 6^{-1}$

**5.** Evaluate:
(a) $6(10)^3 + 5(10)^2 + 8(10)^1 + 3(10)^0$
(b) $4(10)^2 + 5(10)^0$
(c) $7(10)^3 + 2(10)^2 + 6(10)^0 + 8(10)^{-1}$
(d) $3(10)^2 + 9(10)^0 + 7(10)^{-2}$

## 4.6 The Abacus

The notation systems we have examined lend themselves reasonably well to addition and subtraction. In fact, these operations are at least as simple as with our own system except when the subtractive principal of the Roman system is encountered. But if we attempt multiplication or division the advantage of our own system becomes quite obvious. These systems were not used for computation. The computations were carried out with the aid of an *abacus.* The number symbols were used merely to record the answer.

The abacus played a rather important part in the development of Hindu-Arabic numerals. In the Orient some form of bead abacus was the most popular—in fact, its popularity remains unabated. Shopkeepers and merchants still prefer to use it in making calculations. One of the more popular forms in Europe was the line abacus. It consisted of a series of lines drawn on a flat surface such as a table or a cabinet top. Loose counters were placed either on or between the lines. The counters we find in stores today are so called because of the early practice of using their tops as counting tables.

The lines are used to represent powers of ten: ones, tens, hundreds, and so on. The spaces between the lines represent fives, fifties, five hundreds, and so on. The use of the spaces between the lines is comparable to the use of midsymbols (V, L, and D) in the Roman system. Three counters on the thousands line represent three thousand. Three counters between the hundreds line and the thousands line stand for three five hundreds, and can be changed to one counter on the thousands line and one on the space between it and the hundreds line. Five counters on any line may be exchanged for one in the space above. The one is "carried" to the space—thus the origin of the term "carry" in the addition algorithm. Two counters in any space may be exchanged for one on the line above. When necessary in subtraction the exchange can be reversed; this gives rise to the term "borrow." Thus, when the quantity is expressed in simplest form, there will be not more than four counters on a line and not more than one in a space.

If we wish to add 1753 + 1048, figure (a) indicates the first step: 1753 is recorded on the abacus. In (b) 1048 has been added.

In (c) the final simplified result is shown. Five of the six counters on the 1 line are exchanged for a single counter on the space between the 1 line and the 10 line. This makes two counters in the space. They are exchanged for a single counter on the 10 line. This makes five counters there, which are exchanged for one counter in the space between the 10 line and the

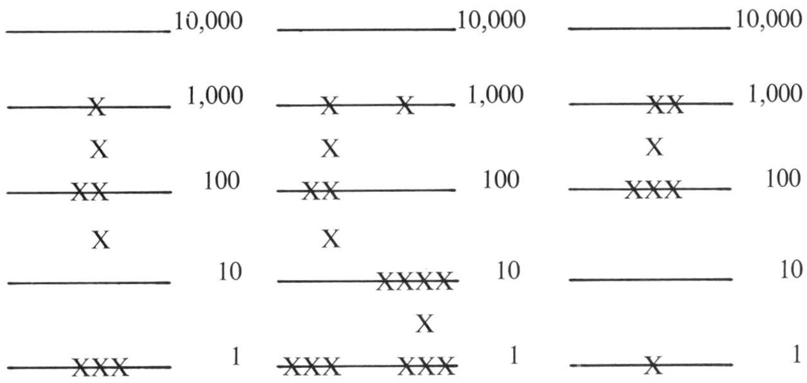

| Line | (a) | (b) | (c) |
|---|---|---|---|
| 10,000 | | | |
| 1,000 | X | X X | XX |
| (space) | X | X | X |
| 100 | XX | XX | XXX |
| (space) | X | X | |
| 10 | | XXXX | |
| (space) | | X | |
| 1 | XXX | XXX XXX | X |

100 line. The two counters in this space are exchanged for one counter on the 100 line. The final result may be read from (c) 2 *thousands*, 1 *five hundred*, 3 *hundreds*, and 1 *one*, or 2801.

Subtraction on the line abacus is, in a very real sense, a "take away" operation. To find 18,436 − 7259 we first enter 18,436 on the abacus, figure (a). In figure (b) 1 *hundred* counter has been exchanged for 2 *fifty* counters, and 1 *ten* counter has been exchanged for 1 *five* counter and 5 *one* counters. It is then possible to remove the counters equivalent to 7,259. The final result is indicated in figure (c).

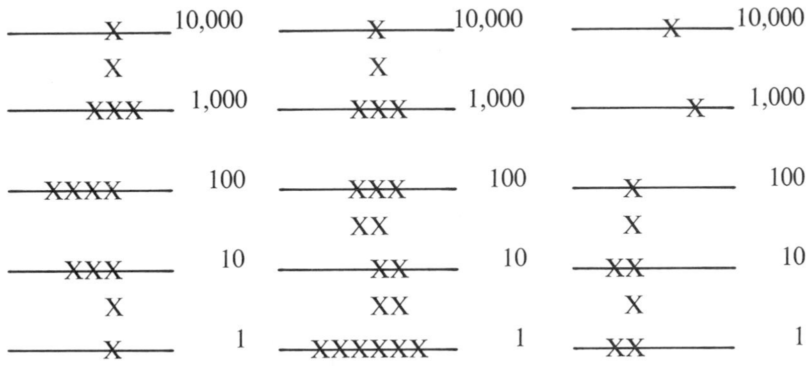

| Line | (a) | (b) | (c) |
|---|---|---|---|
| 10,000 | X | X | X |
| (space) | X | X | |
| 1,000 | XXX | XXX | X |
| 100 | XXXX | XXX | X |
| (space) | | XX | X |
| 10 | XXX | XX | XX |
| (space) | X | XX | X |
| 1 | X | XXXXXX | XX |

On the assumption that the idea of using independent symbols for each of the numbers *one* through *nine* was already employed, it seems inevitable that someone would hit upon the idea of a symbol to indicate an empty space. Then the answer could be recorded by putting in the right *place* the symbol to indicate the number of ones, tens, and so on that there were in the final result, the zero indicating empty places.

### EXERCISES

*By means of drawings show how to perform the following computations on the line abacus:*

**1.** 3421 + 2163

**2.** 555 + 369

**3.** 437 + 1,592 + 382

**4.** 4342 − 2140

**5.** 8634 − 3203

**6.** 1734 − 296

## 4.7 Positional Notation

If in the Chinese system we omit symbols for powers of ten we have our own system, but for one thing. = 千 五 百 七 + ≡ becomes = 五 七 ≡, which translates to 2573. The only thing lacking is a means of showing that a given power of ten (one is a power of ten, $1 = 10^0$) is missing. We need a symbol for zero.

A positional notation system requires that we have a set of independent symbols for the integers one to, but not including, the arbitrarily chosen number which is to be the base. And we must have a symbol to indicate a vacant space. This place holder, zero, enables us to dispense with any symbols to indicate the positive integral powers of ten, as ten, one hundred, one thousand, and so forth. The power of ten is implied by the position occupied by the symbols for the numbers one through nine. The Egyptian ten was ∩; the Roman ten was X; the Chinese ten is +; but in the Hindu-Arabic system we do not have a *single* symbol for ten. The representation of ten as 10 is a compound symbol. The symbol 1 indicates that the base number ten is to be used one time, and the 0 indicates there are no additional ones. This property makes it possible to write a number as large as we please. This was not true in the other systems we have examined. As the numbers continue to get larger there is no end to the different symbols needed in these systems.

The positional system is said to have the "place value property." This merely means the value of each symbol is determined by its position in the numeral, as well as the symbol itself. Thus in 22,032 the extreme left-hand 2 represents 2 ten thousands but the 2 immediately to its right stands for 2 thousands, while the extreme right-hand 2 stands for 2 ones. Any symbol represents ten times as much as the same symbol in the position immediately to the right.

The following representations of the number fourteen thousand thirty-three contrast the three kinds of systems we have discussed. Note that all three systems are decimal.

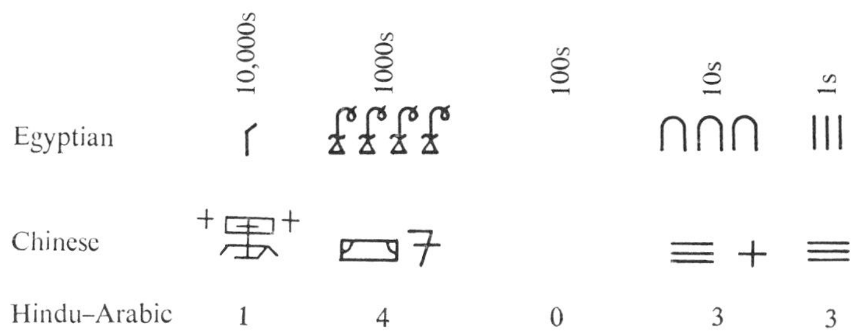

| | 10,000s | 1000s | 100s | 10s | 1s |
|---|---|---|---|---|---|
| Egyptian | 𓂭 | 𓆼𓆼𓆼𓆼 | | ∩∩∩ | III |
| Chinese | 萬 | 四千 | | 三十 | 三 |
| Hindu–Arabic | 1 | 4 | 0 | 3 | 3 |

In the Egyptian scheme each power of ten is indicated by a special symbol. We indicate the number of times the power is used by repeating the symbol that number of times. The Chinese plan also employs different symbols for each power of ten, but the number of times each power is used is indicated by means of the symbols for one through nine. In the Hindu-Arabic system the numbers one through nine are used to indicate the number of times each power of ten is used, but there are no symbols to indicate those powers. The powers of ten are implied by the positions of the one through nine digits.

Other systems have employed the place value principle. The Babylonians used a positional system with sixty as base. However, in forming the primary numbers one through fifty-nine the additive decimal scheme was employed. The Mayan Indians of Central America had a rather highly developed system which used twenty as base, but they too used the additive idea to obtain their first nineteen numbers. This was accomplished by adding dots and dashes; a dot stood for one and a dash for five.

## EXERCISES

**1.** Write the third power of ten in Roman, in Chinese, and in Hindu-Arabic numerals.

2. Evaluate (a) $2 \times 10^2 + 7 \times 10^1 + 4 \times 10^0$
(b) $6 \times 8^2 + 5 \times 8^1 + 3 \times 8^0$
(c) $4 \times 10^1 + 3 \times 10^0 + 5 \times 10^{-1}$

3. Express 876 as multiples of powers of 10, no power to be used more than 9 times.

4. Express 876 as multiples of powers of 8, no power to be used more than 7 times.

5. In what respects is the line abacus similar to the Roman system of notation? In what respects is it similar to Hindu-Arabic notation?

6. Draw a line abacus and show how 3652 is indicated.

7. Show how to add 1739 to the abacus described in Exercise 6.

8. Why is it impossible to have a positional notation system without a symbol for zero?

9. Why is a symbol for zero not needed in the Roman system of notation?

## 4.8 Octonal Notation

Man's predominant preference for ten as base undoubtedly stems from counting on the fingers. The fingers may be used as counters until they are all used. Then we have one handful, one ten, and the fingers are available all over again. The number of handfuls may have been counted by turning down the fingers. In any event, a handful of handfuls would suggest a single something. This does not require the concept of place value or a symbol for zero. It does not even require a system of notation. It is a mistake to assume that our system is unique because it is decimal. In fact it does not derive its superiority from this property, but from its utilization of the principle of place value.

The possibility of using the same positional system we now have but with a base other than ten is well known. In fact there is an organization which devotes its efforts to securing the adoption of twelve as number base. Although binary, base-two, notation is not used, the idea of binary representation of numbers is extensively employed. This is particularly true in the construction of electronic computers. As a matter of fact, any integer greater than one can be used as number base.

Distinct symbols from zero up to but not including the base are needed. This means the invention of more symbols if the base is more than ten and the elimination of some symbols if the base is less than ten. If eight is base the octonal number system requires the symbols 0, 1, 2, 3, 4, 5, 6, 7. In this system 10 represents eight, not ten. It is convenient to have a symbolic means of designating the base when discussing the possibility of using a base other than ten. We shall indicate the base by means of a subscript using the number name. Why could we not indicate the base by means of numerals, using the same base as used to represent the number?

*Example:* $390_{(\text{ten})} = 606_{(\text{eight})}$

The equation states that three hundred ninety is written 390 if ten is base and 606 if eight is base. We may verify this by evaluating $606_{(\text{eight})}$. The 6 in the ones position represents $6 \times 8^{\circ}$ or 6 ones. The 0 in the eights position tells us we use no eights. The 6 in the eight squared or sixty-fours position tells us we have $6 \times 64$ ones. Then $6 + 0 + 384 = 390$. (If no subscript is used it is understood that ten is base.)

Consider the number 84.37. The decimal point separates the whole number 84 from the fraction $\frac{37}{100}$. But more importantly, it *labels the ones position*. Hence, indirectly, it determines the position value of each digit. It is for this reason that division or multiplication by ten or any integral power of ten merely requires a relocation of the decimal point. In 84.37 the 7 is to be multiplied by $10^{-2}$, the 3 by $10^{-1}$, the 4 by $10^{\circ}$, and 8 by $10^{1}$. If we move the decimal point one place to the left, or equivalently leave the decimal point where it is and shift all digits of the number one place to the right, each digit will be multiplied by a power of 10 one less than previously. This is equivalent to dividing the number by 10. In 8.437 the 8 represents only $\frac{1}{10}$ as much as before. Similarly for each digit in the number.

Consider the number 8437. The decimal point is by implication immediately to the right of the 7. Moving the decimal point one place to the left, being equivalent to division by 10, yields 843.7. Hence it is evident that dividing 8437 by 10 will give a quotient 843 and a remainder 7. If we now divide the quotient 843 by 10, the remainder is 3. Continuing in this way, it is evident that successive division by 10 will yield remainders which are the successive digits of the number, starting with the ones digit.

Now consider the number $20365_{(\text{eight})}$. Recall that this means $2 \times 8^{4} + 0 \times 8^{3} + 3 \times 8^{2} + 6 \times 8^{1} + 5 \times 8^{0}$. The scheme for indicating the ones digit, the decimal point, can be used whether the base is ten or any other number. When the base is eight, it is properly called an *octonal point* rather than decimal point. Pointing off one place $20365_{(\text{eight})}$

becomes $2036.5_{(eight)}$ which means $2 \times 8^3 + 0 \times 8^2 + 3 \times 8^1 + 6 \times 8^0 + 5 \times 8^{-1}$. The value of each digit, and hence the value of the number, is $\frac{1}{8}$ as great as before. Thus, if we divide the number by eight, the remainder is the original ones digit. If we now divide $2036_{(eight)}$ by eight, we get $203.6_{(eight)}$. Hence the remainder on the second division is the second or $8^1$ digit. Continuing in this manner, the remainders obtained on successive divisions by eight will produce the successive digits in the base eight representation of the number, beginning with the ones digit. But the remainder obtained when a number is divided by eight is entirely independent of the base of notation. Twenty-five divided by eight will yield three as quotient with remainder one. This fact is true no matter how the numbers are represented. It follows that a number may be converted to a new base by dividing the number and succeeding quotients by the desired base. The successive remainders are the required digits, from lowest to highest placed.

*Example:* Express $8437_{(ten)}$ in base eight.

$$\begin{array}{r}1054\\ 8\overline{)8437}\end{array}\qquad \text{remainder } 5$$

$$\begin{array}{r}131\\ 8\overline{)1054}\end{array}\qquad \text{remainder } 6$$

$$\begin{array}{r}16\\ 8\overline{)131}\end{array}\qquad \text{remainder } 3$$

$$\begin{array}{r}2\\ 8\overline{)16}\end{array}\qquad \text{remainder } 0$$

$$\begin{array}{r}0\\ 8\overline{)2}\end{array}\qquad \text{remainder } 2$$

Hence, $\qquad 8437_{(ten)} = 20365_{(eight)}$
which may be verified by observing that

$$5 \times 8^0 + 6 \times 8^1 + 3 \times 8^2 + 0 \times 8^3 + 2 \times 8^4$$
$$= 5 + 48 + 192 + 8192 = 8437$$

This procedure can be explained in a somewhat different manner. We first note that when we divide by 8 the remainders will always be one of the numbers 0 through 7. When we divide by 8 the quotient tells us how many full sets of 8 we can form, and the remainder tells us how many ones in excess of even eights are in the number. In the example we divide

8437 by 8, giving a quotient 1054 and remainder 5. Then we know that 8437 consists of 1054 complete sets of 8 with 5 left over. Since we are trying to express the number by means of groupings of 8 the 5 left over must be expressed as the ones digit.

The second step, $1054 \div 8$, enables us to find how many sets we can form containing 8 of the sets of 8 obtained in the first step. This is the quotient 131. The remainder 6 tells us how many of the sets of 8 we could not use in forming sets of eight 8's or 64's. Then the 6 occupies the second or $8^1$ position.

In similar fashion, we find from step three we can get 16 sets of 8 of the former sized sets (sets of 64) but 3 of the sets of 64 remain. Thus, a 3 is placed in the next or $8^2$ position. The fourth step, $16 \div 8$, shows that the 16 sets of the previous step may be grouped into 2 sets eight times as large with none of the 16 sets left over. The 16 sets of this step contain $8 \times 8^2$ or $8^3$ ones. Since none were left over we need no $8^3$ and therefore place 0 in that position. Since there are fewer than 8, namely, 2, of the last obtained sets we cannot form them into sets 8 times as large. These last two sets are indicated in the result by a 2 in the $8^4$ position.

The foregoing method enables us to find the digits in the new notation from smallest to largest position, ones, eights, sixty-fours, and so on. We can approach the problem in still another way, finding the highest ordered digit first and working down. Our problem is to express 8437 in terms of powers of 8. We first find the powers of 8 until we reach one which exceeds 8437: $8^0 = 1, 8^1 = 8, 8^2 = 64, 8^3 = 512, 8^4 = 4096, 8^5 = 32{,}768$. We do not need $8^5$ because 32,768 is greater than 8437. But $8^4 = 4096$ is not. We wish to use $8^4$ as many times as we can. We find the number of times by division, $8437 \div 4096$. This gives 2 as quotient and remainder 245. If we place 2 in the $8^4$, or fifth, position we have then expressed all but 245 of the original 8437. We repeat the process with 245. Since it is less than 512 we can use no $8^3$ and therefore place 0 in that position. Next we find how many $8^2$ or 64's there are in 245 by division, $245 \div 64$. This gives 3 for quotient with 53 for remainder. Then we place 3 in the $8^2$ position. Now 53 consists of six 8's plus 5, so we place 6 in $8^1$ position and 5 in ones position.

Using this approach the digits are found as *quotients* rather than remainders, the *remainders* rather than quotients are used in finding succeeding steps, and we find the digits from *highest* to *lowest* rather than lowest to highest.

Each of these methods is perfectly general. Generalizing the first approach, we may find the digits, from right to left, of a number in any base by dividing the number and succeeding quotients by the desired base. The remainders are the required digits.

## OCTONAL NOTATION

For example, if we wish to express $83_{(ten)}$ in base two we divide as follows:

$$
\begin{array}{rll}
 & 41 & \\
2 | & 83 & \text{remainder } 1 \\
 & 20 & \\
2 | & 41 & \text{remainder } 1 \\
 & 10 & \\
2 | & 20 & \text{remainder } 0 \\
 & 5 & \\
2 | & 10 & \text{remainder } 0 \\
 & 2 & \\
2 | & 5 & \text{remainder } 1 \\
 & 1 & \\
2 | & 2 & \text{remainder } 0 \\
 & 0 & \\
2 | & 1 & \text{remainder } 1
\end{array}
$$

and obtain

$$83_{(ten)} = 1010011_{(two)}$$

which may be verified by evaluating

$$1010011_{(two)} = 1 \times 2^6 + 0 \times 2^5 + 1 \times 2^4 + 0 \times 2^3 + 0 \times 2^2 + 1 \times 2^1 + 1 \times 2^0 = 64 + 16 + 2 + 1 = 83$$

The following table shows the base ten, eight, and two representation of the named numbers:

| *Number name* | *Decimal* *base ten* | *Octonal* *base eight* | *Binary* *base two* |
|---|---|---|---|
| one | 1 | 1 | 1 |
| two | 2 | 2 | 10 |
| seven | 7 | 7 | 111 |
| eight | 8 | 10 | 1000 |
| twenty-four | 24 | 30 | 11000 |
| sixty-five | 65 | 101 | 1000001 |
| one hundred eighty-three | 183 | 267 | 10110111 |
| five hundred twelve | 512 | 1000 | 1000000000 |

Some electronic computers employ octonal numbers in conjunction with their use of binary numbers, due to the ease with which one may convert from one base to the other. A number in binary notation can be converted to octonal notation as follows. In binary notation the analogy to digits is "bigits." Electronic engineers have shortened this to "bits." Group the "bits" in threes, starting from the right. For example, one hundred eighty-three in binary notation is

$$10 \quad 110 \quad 111$$

Convert each of the three "bit" numbers thus formed to octonal notation

$$10 = 2, \quad 110 = 6, \quad 111 = 7$$

The result gives the octonal representation

$$10110111_{(two)} = 267_{(eight)}$$

We can move from octonal to binary in the same fashion. Merely write each symbol in binary notation

$$437_{(eight)} = 100\ 011\ 111_{(two)}$$

because

$$4_{(eight)} = 100_{(two)}; \ 3_{(eight)} = 11_{(two)}$$

and

$$7_{(eight)} = 111_{(two)}$$

We can make this same conversion by expressing $437_{(eight)}$ as

$$4 \times 8^2 + 3 \times 8^1 + 7 \times 8^0 = 4 \times 2^6 + 3 \times 2^3 + 7 \times 2^0$$

since $8 = 2^3$. Then expressing the digits in powers of 2 we have

$$\begin{aligned} 437_{(eight)} &= 2^2 \times 2^6 + (2^1 + 2^0)2^3 + (2^2 + 2^1 + 2^0)2^0 \\ &= 2^8 + 2^4 + 2^3 + 2^2 + 2^1 + 2^0 \end{aligned}$$

But this, written in base two, is

$$100011111$$

## EXERCISES

1. Convert $937_{(ten)}$ to base eight.
2. Convert $110011111_{(two)}$ to base eight; to base ten.
3. Convert $732_{(eight)}$ to base ten.
4. Convert $173_{(eight)}$ to base two.
5. Convert $173_{(ten)}$ to base two.

**6.** Convert $374_{(twelve)}$ to base ten.

**7.** Convert $374_{(eight)}$ to base ten.

**8.** Convert $374_{(twelve)}$ to base eight.

**9.** Convert $21022_{(three)}$ to base four.

**10.** Convert $21022_{(four)}$ to base three.

**11.** How many digit symbols are needed for base twelve notation? Why?

## 4.9 Calculations with Octonal Numerals

An algorithm is a schematic device for performing a mathematical operation. When we refer to the division algorithm we refer to the systematic scheme used to carry out the division. The assertion that the Hindu-Arabic system derives its superiority from its utilization of place value, making the algorithms possible, is forcefully illustrated by considering calculation with numbers expressed in positional notation using a base other than ten. The only source of difficulty is unfamiliarity with the symbolism. The mechanics of the algorithms is identical.

If we compute with base eight notation we need new addition and multiplication tables. This is not to say the sums and products will be changed; the only thing that changes is the way they are written.

Addition Facts, Base Eight

| | | | | | | | |
|---|---|---|---|---|---|---|---|
| 0+0=0 | 1+0=1 | 2+0=2 | 3+0=3 | 4+0=4 | 5+0=5 | 6+0=6 | 7+0=7 |
| 0+1=1 | 1+1=2 | 2+1=3 | 3+1=4 | 4+1=5 | 5+1=6 | 6+1=7 | 7+1=10 |
| 0+2=2 | 1+2=3 | 2+2=4 | 3+2=5 | 4+2=6 | 5+2=7 | 6+2=10 | 7+2=11 |
| 0+3=3 | 1+3=4 | 2+3=5 | 3+3=6 | 4+3=7 | 5+3=10 | 6+3=11 | 7+3=12 |
| 0+4=4 | 1+4=5 | 2+4=6 | 3+4=7 | 4+4=10 | 5+4=11 | 6+4=12 | 7+4=13 |
| 0+5=5 | 1+5=6 | 2+5=7 | 3+5=10 | 4+5=11 | 5+5=12 | 6+5=13 | 7+5=14 |
| 0+6=6 | 1+6=7 | 2+6=10 | 3+6=11 | 4+6=12 | 5+6=13 | 6+6=14 | 7+6=15 |
| 0+7=7 | 1+7=10 | 2+7=11 | 3+7=12 | 4+7=13 | 5+7=14 | 6+7=15 | 7+7=16 |

Seven plus six still equals thirteen. Recall (page 103) that we have agreed to use conventional number names when referring to numbers by name. We merely indicate thirteen as 1 eight plus 5 ones.

*Example 1:* Calculate: $437_{(eight)} + 253_{(eight)} + 176_{(eight)}$

*Solution:*

$$\begin{array}{r} 437 \\ 253 \\ \underline{176} \\ 1110 \end{array}$$

We add columnwise precisely as we do when ten is base. In the right-hand column we add 7 + 3 + 6 ones. In the middle column we add 3 + 5 + 7 eights. In the left column 4 + 2 + 1 sixty-fours. From the addition table, 7 + 3 = 12. We proceed with the ones column 12 + 6 by obtaining 2 + 6 = 10 from the table, giving 12 + 6 = 20. Thus 0 is in the ones column and 2 is carried to the eights column. From the table 3 + 5 = 10; and 10 + 7 = 17 since 0 + 7 = 7. Thus 17 + 2 (carried) = 21 because 7 + 2 = 11. This gives the 1 in the eights column with 2 carried to the left-hand, or sixty-fours, column. In the left column 4 + 2 = 6 and 6 + 1 = 7; but 7 + 2 (carried) = 11. Therefore we have 1 in the third column from the right and 1 in the fourth.

*Check:* If we write the addition we have performed in base ten we get:

7 + 3 + 6 = 16 ones in the right column
3 + 5 + 7 = 15 eights in the middle column
4 + 2 + 1 = 7 sixty-fours in the left column

If we total these three subtotals we get:

$$16 + 120 + 448 = 584$$

The base eight answer 1110 expressed in base ten is:

$$1 \times 8^3 + 1 \times 8^2 + 1 \times 8^1 + 0 \times 8^0 = 512 + 64 + 8 + 0 = 584$$

*As a further check:*

$$437_{(\text{eight})} = 4 \times 64 + 3 \times 8 + 7 = 287$$
$$253_{(\text{eight})} = 2 \times 64 + 5 \times 8 + 3 = 171$$
$$176_{(\text{eight})} = 1 \times 64 + 7 \times 8 + 6 = 126$$
$$1110_{(\text{eight})} = 1 \times 512 + 1 \times 64 + 1 \times 8 + 0 = 584$$

Multiplication Facts, Base Eight

| | | | | | | | |
|---|---|---|---|---|---|---|---|
| 0×0=0 | 1×0=0 | 2×0=0 | 3×0=0 | 4×0=0 | 5×0=0 | 6×0=0 | 7×0=0 |
| 0×1=0 | 1×1=1 | 2×1=2 | 3×1=3 | 4×1=4 | 5×1=5 | 6×1=6 | 7×1=7 |
| 0×2=0 | 1×2=2 | 2×2=4 | 3×2=6 | 4×2=10 | 5×2=12 | 6×2=14 | 7×2=16 |
| 0×3=0 | 1×3=3 | 2×3=6 | 3×3=11 | 4×3=14 | 5×3=17 | 6×3=22 | 7×3=25 |
| 0×4=0 | 1×4=4 | 2×4=10 | 3×4=14 | 4×4=20 | 5×4=24 | 6×4=30 | 7×4=34 |
| 0×5=0 | 1×5=5 | 2×5=12 | 3×5=17 | 4×5=24 | 5×5=31 | 6×5=36 | 7×5=43 |
| 0×6=0 | 1×6=6 | 2×6=14 | 3×6=22 | 4×6=30 | 5×6=36 | 6×6=44 | 7×6=52 |
| 0×7=0 | 1×7=7 | 2×7=16 | 3×7=25 | 4×7=34 | 5×7=43 | 6×7=52 | 7×7=61 |

## CALCULATIONS WITH OCTONAL NUMERALS

As with addition, no products have been changed. Five times seven is still thirty-five. But we express thirty-five as 4 eights and 3 ones. Hence $5 \times 7 = 43$.

*Example 2:* Calculate: $263_{(\text{eight})} \times 57_{(\text{eight})}$

$$\begin{array}{r} 263 \\ 57 \\ \hline 2345 \\ 1577\phantom{0} \\ \hline 20335 \end{array}$$

With the aid of the multiplication table we find $3 \times 7 = 25$; we write 5 and carry 2. Then $6 \times 7 = 52$, $52 + 2$ (carried) $=$ 54; we write 4 and carry 5. Next, $7 \times 2 = 16$, $16 + 5$ (carried) $= 23$; we write 23, completing the first line of partial products. Similarly $5 \times 3 = 17$; we write 7 and carry 1. Then $5 \times 6 = 36$, $36 + 1$ (carried) $= 37$; we write 7 and carry 3. Finally, $5 \times 2 = 12$, $12 + 3 = 15$; we write 15.

Adding the partial products, we bring down 5. Then $4 + 7 = 13$; we write 3 and carry 1. Then $3 + 7 + 1 = 13$; we write 3 and carry 1. Next, $2 + 5 + 1 = 10$; we write 0 and carry 1. Finally, $1 + 1 = 2$; we write 2.

*Check:*

$$263_{(\text{eight})} = 2 \times 64 + 6 \times 8 + 3 = 179$$

$$57_{(\text{eight})} = 5 \times 8 + 7 = 47$$

$$20335_{(\text{eight})} = 2 \times 4096 + 3 \times 64 + 3 \times 8 + 5 = 8413$$

and

$$\begin{array}{r} 179 \\ 47 \\ \hline 1253 \\ 716\phantom{0} \\ \hline 8413 \end{array}$$

In similar fashion the inverse operations of subtraction and division may be performed. We illustrate with division.

*Example 3:* Calculate: $472_{(eight)} \div 13_{(eight)}$

$$\begin{array}{r|l} & \phantom{0}34 \\ \hline 13 & 472 \\ & 41 \\ \cline{2-2} & \phantom{0}62 \\ & \phantom{0}54 \\ \cline{2-2} & \phantom{00}6 \end{array}$$

*Check:* $472_{(eight)} = 4 \times 64 + 7 \times 8 + 2 = 314$

$13_{(eight)} = 1 \times 8 + 3 = 11$

$$\begin{array}{r|l} & \phantom{0}28 \\ \hline 11 & 314 \\ & 22 \\ \cline{2-2} & \phantom{0}94 \\ & \phantom{0}88 \\ \cline{2-2} & \phantom{00}6 \end{array}$$

The quotient $34_{(eight)} = 3 \times 8 + 4 = 28$ and the remainder $6_{(eight)} = 6$.

We would proceed in precisely the same manner just set forth if the new base were other than eight. If we use two as base the only addition facts we need are $0 + 0 = 0$, $1 + 0 = 1$, and $1 + 1 = 10$. The multiplication facts are $0 \times 0 = 0$, $1 \times 0 = 0$, and $1 \times 1 = 1$. The advantage of such a system which is derived from the number and simplicity of addition and multiplication facts is offset by the increased number of digits required.

*Example 4:* Use binary notation to find 125 times 89.

*Solution:* Divide 125 and 89 successively by 2 to convert to binary notation.

$$\begin{array}{r|l} & \phantom{0}62 \\ \hline 2 & 125 \\ & 124 \\ \cline{2-2} & \phantom{00}1 \text{ rem.} \end{array} \quad \begin{array}{r|l} & 31 \\ \hline 2 & 62 \\ & 62 \\ \cline{2-2} & \phantom{0}0 \text{ rem.} \end{array} \quad \begin{array}{r|l} & 15 \\ \hline 2 & 31 \\ & 30 \\ \cline{2-2} & \phantom{0}1 \text{ rem.} \end{array} \quad \begin{array}{r|l} & \phantom{0}7 \\ \hline 2 & 15 \\ & 14 \\ \cline{2-2} & \phantom{0}1 \text{ rem.} \end{array} \quad \begin{array}{r|l} & 3 \\ \hline 2 & 7 \\ & 6 \\ \cline{2-2} & 1 \text{ rem.} \end{array}$$

$$\begin{array}{r|l} & 1 \\ \hline 2 & 3 \\ & 2 \\ \cline{2-2} & 1 \text{ rem.} \end{array} \quad \begin{array}{r|l} & 0 \\ \hline 2 & 1 \\ & 0 \\ \cline{2-2} & 1 \text{ rem.} \end{array}$$

Therefore, $125_{10} = 1111101_2$

$$
\begin{array}{ccccc}
\begin{array}{r} 44 \\ 2\overline{)89} \\ 88 \\ \hline 1 \text{ rem.} \end{array} &
\begin{array}{r} 22 \\ 2\overline{)44} \\ 44 \\ \hline 0 \text{ rem.} \end{array} &
\begin{array}{r} 11 \\ 2\overline{)22} \\ 22 \\ \hline 0 \text{ rem.} \end{array} &
\begin{array}{r} 5 \\ 2\overline{)11} \\ 10 \\ \hline 1 \text{ rem.} \end{array} &
\begin{array}{r} 2 \\ 2\overline{)5} \\ 4 \\ \hline 1 \text{ rem.} \end{array}
\end{array}
$$

$$
\begin{array}{cc}
\begin{array}{r} 1 \\ 2\overline{)2} \\ 2 \\ \hline 0 \text{ rem.} \end{array} &
\begin{array}{r} 0 \\ 2\overline{)1} \\ 0 \\ \hline 1 \text{ rem.} \end{array}
\end{array}
$$

Therefore, $89_{(ten)} = 1011001_{(two)}$

$$
\begin{array}{r}
1111101 \\
1011001 \\
\hline
1111101 \\
1111101\phantom{000} \\
1111101\phantom{0000} \\
1111101\phantom{000000} \\
\hline
10101101110101
\end{array}
$$

*Check:* $125 \times 89 = 11{,}125$ and $10101101110101_{(two)} = 1 + 4 + 16 + 32 + 64 + 256 + 512 + 2048 + 8192 = 11{,}125$

Finding the partial products causes no problem here. The addition of the partial products is more complicated. In the fourth column we have $1 + 1 = 10$; we write 0 and carry 1. In the fifth column we have 1 (carried) $+ 1 = 10$, $10 + 0 = 10$, $10 + 1 = 11$; we write 1 and carry 1. In the sixth column we have 1 (carried) $+ 0 = 1$, $1 + 1 = 10$, $10 + 1 = 11$; we write 1 and carry 1. In the seventh column we have 1 (carried) $+ 1 = 10$, $10 + 1 = 11$, $11 + 1 = 100$, $100 + 1 = 101$; we write 1 and carry 10. In the eighth column we have 10 (carried) $+ 0 = 10$, $10 + 1 = 11$, $11 + 1 = 100$; we write 0 and carry 10. In the ninth column we have 10 (carried) $+ 1 = 11$, $11 + 1 = 100$, $100 + 1 = 101$; we write 1 and carry 10. In the tenth column we have 10 (carried) $+ 1 = 11$, $11 + 1 = 100$, $100 + 1 = 101$; we write 1 and carry 10. In the eleventh column we have 10 (carried) $+ 1 = 11$, $11 + 1 = 100$; we write 0 and carry 10. In the twelfth column we have 10 (carried) $+ 1 = 11$; we write 1 and carry 1. In the last column we have 1 (carried) $+ 1 = 10$; we write 10.

## EXERCISES

1. If we let 1, 5, 25, 125 be represented by #, ⊕, ×, □, respectively, we may use these symbols for a simple additive notation system with base five. Express the numbers 27, 131, 33, 252 in this system.
2. If we let 0, 1, 2, 3 be represented by #, ⊕, ×, □, respectively, we may use these symbols for a positional notation system with four as base. Express the numbers 112, 65, 15, 300 in this system.
3. Construct tables showing the needed addition and multiplication facts if five is used as base.
4. Add: $143_{(\text{five})} + 22_{(\text{five})} + 313_{(\text{five})}$
5. Multiply: $321_{(\text{five})} \times 42_{(\text{five})}$
6. Add: $10010_{(\text{two})} + 11001_{(\text{two})} + 10011_{(\text{two})}$
7. Multiply: $1011_{(\text{two})} \times 1101_{(\text{two})}$
8. Add: $635_{(\text{eight})} + 272_{(\text{eight})} + 134_{(\text{eight})}$
9. Multiply: $436_{(\text{eight})} \times 36_{(\text{eight})}$
10. Are there values for $b$ for which $43_b$ is an even number? For which $53_b$ is even? Why?
11. What base is used if $4 \times 4 = 24$?
12. Are there values of $b$ for which $32_b$ is an odd number? For which $42_b$ is odd? Why?
13. Determine the base of notation and the missing digits such that the following addition will be correct:

```
 123
 ...
 111
 323
----
2131
```

14. Find $a + b$ in base eight if $a =$ ten and $b =$ thirteen.
15. Determine the base in which the following multiplication is written, assuming the computation is correct:

```
  432
   54
-----
 3012
3444
-----
41452
```

### CALCULATIONS WITH OCTONAL NUMERALS

**16.** (a) In what base or bases would 53 be an even number?
(b) In what base or bases would 75 be an odd number?
(c) In what base or bases would 42 be an odd number?
(d) In what base or bases would 43 be an even number?

**17.** Fill the blank so that the answer will be correct.
$134_{(\text{five})} + 323_{(\text{five})} + \underline{\qquad\qquad} = 1130_{(\text{five})}$

**18.** Convert $667_{(\text{eight})}$ to base five without going through base ten.

**19.** Add the base eight numbers 276 + 312 + 765.

**20.** Are each of the following numbers even or odd? Why?
(a) $353_{(\text{seven})}$, (b) $432_{(\text{five})}$, (c) $388_{(\text{nine})}$, (d) $425_{(\text{six})}$, (e) $4301_{(\text{seven})}$

**21.** Is a "base one" scale of notation possible? Why?

**22.** Find $321_{(\text{four})} \times 856_{(\text{nine})}$

**23.** Correct the following base four subtraction:

$$\begin{array}{r} 432 \\ 313 \\ \hline 129 \end{array}$$

**24.** In the following additions determine the base and find the missing digits:

$$\begin{array}{r} 13\_ \\ 11\_ \\ 310 \\ \hline 1220 \end{array} \qquad \begin{array}{r} 1\_4 \\ 315 \\ 4\_2 \\ \hline 1163 \end{array}$$

**25.** If forty is written as follows what base is used in each case?
(a) 34 (b) 50 (c) 130 (d) 101000

**26.** Can 321 represent the number forty in any base? If so what base? If not why not?

**27.** Answer question 26 relative to the number one hundred.

## 4.10 Octonal Fractions

Much of the utility of a positional notation system is lost unless the concept of place value is extended to quantities less than one. The utility and the simplicity of decimal fractions is so great it is difficult to appreciate the fact that approximately a thousand years were required to make the extension. With decimal fractions our notation system enables us not only to write a number arbitrarily large but arbitrarily small as well.

We call the fractions decimal, but it is far more important that they are *positional.* A decimal fraction is a fraction whose implied denominator is some power of ten. This is important only because ten is the base of our notation. For example, $.231 = \frac{231}{1000}$ but more significantly $.231 = \frac{2}{10} + \frac{3}{100} + \frac{1}{1000}$.

The idea of a positional fraction (we might call it a basimal fraction) is just as adaptable to a base other than ten as it is to ten.

Just as $73_{(\text{eight})}$ means $7 \times 8 + 3$, so $.73_{(\text{eight})}$ means $\frac{7}{8} + \frac{3}{64}$.

We have said the *position* of a symbol in an integer determines its value. In 1537, the 5 has the value five hundred because it stands in the third or hundreds position. As we move to the left from the decimal point successive digits imply multiplication by 1, 10, $10 \times 10$, and so forth. In precisely the same fashion successive digits to the right of the decimal imply multiplication by $\frac{1}{10}$, $\frac{1}{10} \times \frac{1}{10}$, $\frac{1}{10} \times \frac{1}{10} \times \frac{1}{10}$, and so forth. Then if we shift the decimal point one place to the right we have multiplied the number by ten because the value of each digit is increased tenfold.

Notice that if we multiply .231 by ten we get 2.31 and the integral part of the answer is the first digit of the fraction. If we multiply the new fraction .31 by ten we get 3.1, and the integral part of this result is the second digit of the original fraction. Finally, if we multiply .1 by ten we get 1, an integer, which is the third digit of the original fraction.

In a similar manner, shifting the octonal point one place to the right in a base eight number multiplies the number by eight. For example, $.314_{(\text{eight})}$ means $3 \times \frac{1}{8} + 1 \times \frac{1}{8} \times \frac{1}{8} + 4 \times \frac{1}{8} \times \frac{1}{8} \times \frac{1}{8}$, but $3.14_{(\text{eight})}$ means $3 \times 1 + 1 \times \frac{1}{8} + 4 \times \frac{1}{8} \times \frac{1}{8}$. Now if we multiply $.314_{(\text{eight})}$ by 8 we get the integer 3, which is the first digit of the original number and the fraction $.14_{(\text{eight})}$. If $.14_{(\text{eight})}$ is multiplied by 8 we get $1.4_{(\text{eight})}$ giving the integer 1, which is the next digit of the original number, and the fraction $.4_{(\text{eight})}$. If $.4_{(\text{eight})}$ is multiplied by 8 we get the integer 4, or the last digit of the original $.314_{(\text{eight})}$. But regardless of the base in which $.314_{(\text{eight})}$ might be written, both its value and 8 times its value are unchanged. In other words, 8 times the number will yield the integer 3 plus a fraction which equals $.14_{(\text{eight})}$ regardless of our base of notation.

The foregoing suggests a means of converting a fraction less than one to a new base. We multiply the fraction by the desired base. The integer we obtain is the highest digit in the desired notation. We then multiply the fraction which remains by the desired base and proceed as before, the integer being the next digit of the answer and the fraction being used to obtain the next digit.

## OCTONAL FRACTIONS

*Example 1:* Write $.15625_{(\text{ten})}$ in base eight.

*Solution:*

$$\begin{array}{r} .15625 \\ 8 \\ \hline 1.25000 \end{array} \qquad \begin{array}{r} .25 \\ 8 \\ \hline 2.00 \end{array} \qquad \text{therefore } .15625 = .12_{(\text{eight})}$$

*Check:*

$$.15625_{(\text{ten})} = \frac{15625}{100000} = \frac{5}{32}$$

$$.12_{(\text{eight})} = \frac{1}{8} + \frac{2}{64} = \frac{5}{32}$$

Some fractions when written decimally will terminate, as $\frac{1}{4} = .25$. Others form a repeating cycle, as $\frac{4}{33} = .12\overline{12}\ldots.$ The bar over 12 indicates that it repeats endlessly. Whether a given number will terminate or repeat when expressed as a positional fraction depends upon the base. A number might well terminate in one base and repeat in another.

*Example 2:* Write $.3_{(\text{ten})}$ in base eight.

*Solution:*

| | | |
|---|---|---|
| $.3 \times 8 = 2.4$ | $.4 \times 8 = 3.2$ | $.4 \times 8 = 3.2$ |
| $.4 \times 8 = 3.2$ | $.2 \times 8 = 1.6$ | $.2 \times 8 = 1.6$ |
| $.2 \times 8 = 1.6$ | $.6 \times 8 = 4.8$ | $\ldots$ |
| $.6 \times 8 = 4.8$ | $.8 \times 8 = 6.4$ | $\ldots$ |
| $.8 \times 8 = 6.4$ | | |

$$\therefore\ .3_{(\text{ten})} = (.2314\overline{63146}\ldots)_{(\text{eight})}$$

*Check:*

Base ten to the left of equality signs. Base eight to the right of equality signs.

$$\begin{aligned} \text{Let } n &= .2314\overline{63146}\ldots \\ \text{then } 8n &= 2.314\overline{63146}\ldots \\ \text{and } 8^4 \times 8n = 8^5n &= 23146.\overline{3146}\ldots \\ \text{Subtracting: } 8^5n - 8n &= 23146.\overline{3146}\ldots - 2.\overline{3146}\ldots \\ 32768n - 8n &= 23144 \\ 32760n &= 23144 \end{aligned}$$

$$\text{Hence we see that } n = \frac{23144_{(\text{eight})}}{32760_{(\text{ten})}}$$

and changing the numerator to base ten,

$$n = \frac{9828}{32760} = \frac{3}{10} = .3$$

The same relationship that we observed between octonal and binary representation of a whole number also holds for a fraction. We may change from base two to base eight by grouping the "bits" in threes, starting at the binary point. These three "bit" numbers are the octonal digits.

*Example 3:* Write $.101110111_{(two)}$ in base eight.

*Solution:* $101_{(two)} = 5_{(eight)}$ $110_{(two)} = 6_{(eight)}$ $111_{(two)} = 7_{(eight)}$

$$\therefore .101110111_{(two)} = .567_{(eight)}$$

*Check:* As check we may multiply $.567_{(eight)}$ and succeeding fractions by 2 to convert to base two. Remember, we are using the octonal multiplication table.

| .567 | .356 | .734 | .670 | .560 | .340 | .700 | .600 | .400 |
|---|---|---|---|---|---|---|---|---|
| 2 | 2 | 2 | 2 | 2 | 2 | 2 | 2 | 2 |
| 1.356 | 0.734 | 1.670 | 1.560 | 1.340 | 0.700 | 1.600 | 1.400 | 1.000 |

$$\therefore .567_{(eight)} = .101110111_{(two)}$$

We have not stated why the above relationship works. This will be discussed in Section 7.2, page 195. But granting it for the present, it follows that the fraction will either terminate in both base eight and base two notation or will repeat in both.

As a further check we can convert both the base eight representation and the base two representation to base ten.

$$.567_{(eight)} = \frac{5}{8} + \frac{6}{(8)^2} + \frac{7}{(8)^3} = \frac{5}{8} + \frac{6}{64} + \frac{7}{512} = \frac{375}{512}$$

$$.101110111_{(two)} = \frac{1}{2} + \frac{1}{(2)^3} + \frac{1}{(2)^4} + \frac{1}{(2)^5} + \frac{1}{(2)^7} + \frac{1}{(2)^8} + \frac{1}{(2)^9}$$

$$= \frac{1}{2} + \frac{1}{8} + \frac{1}{16} + \frac{1}{32} + \frac{1}{128} + \frac{1}{256} + \frac{1}{512}$$

$$= \frac{375}{512}$$

Does the number terminate as a positional fraction in base ten?

Finally, if we wish to change the base of notation of a mixed number, we can divide the integral part and its successive quotients by the desired base, and we can multiply the fractional part and succeeding fractions by the desired base.

*Example 4:* Write $376.24_{(\text{eight})}$ in base ten.

*Solution:* We change $376_{(\text{eight})}$ to base ten. The computation, in base eight, is

$$\begin{array}{r} 31 \\ 12\overline{)376} \\ 36 \\ \hline 16 \\ 12 \\ \hline 4 \end{array} \qquad \begin{array}{r} 2 \\ 12\overline{)31} \\ 24 \\ \hline 5 \end{array} \qquad \begin{array}{r} 0 \\ 12\overline{)2} \\ 0 \\ \hline 2 \end{array}$$

$$\therefore\ 376_{(\text{eight})} = 254_{(\text{ten})}$$

We change $.24_{(\text{eight})}$ to base ten. The computation is in base eight.

$$\begin{array}{r} .24 \\ 12 \\ \hline 50 \\ 24 \\ \hline 3.10 \end{array} \qquad \begin{array}{r} .10 \\ 12 \\ \hline 20 \\ 10 \\ \hline 1.20 \end{array} \qquad \begin{array}{r} .20 \\ 12 \\ \hline 40 \\ 20 \\ \hline 2.40 \end{array} \qquad \begin{array}{r} .40 \\ 12 \\ \hline 100 \\ 40 \\ \hline 5.00 \end{array}$$

$$\therefore\ .24_{(\text{eight})} = .3125_{(\text{ten})}$$

$$\therefore\ 376.24_{(\text{eight})} = 254.3125_{(\text{ten})}$$

*Check:*

$$376.24_{(\text{eight})} = 3 \times 8 \times 8 + 7 \times 8 + 6 + 2 \times \tfrac{1}{8} + 4 \times \tfrac{1}{8} \times \tfrac{1}{8}$$

$$= 192 + 56 + 6 + \tfrac{1}{4} + \tfrac{1}{16}$$

$$= 254\tfrac{5}{16} = 254.3125$$

## EXERCISES

**1.** Convert the following to common fractions in base ten:
(a) $.4_{(\text{twelve})}$ (b) $.3_{(\text{six})}$ (c) $.24_{(\text{five})}$ (d) $.21_{(\text{seven})}$

**2.** Convert the following to positional fractions in base eight:
(a) $.32_{(\text{four})}$ (b) $.625_{(\text{ten})}$ (c) $.1101_{(\text{two})}$ (d) $.1101_{(\text{four})}$ (e) $.209_{(\text{twelve})}$

3. Convert the following to base five:
   (a) $.336_{(ten)}$ (b) $.68_{(ten)}$ (c) $.96_{(ten)}$
4. Will a fraction which repeats in base ten also repeat in base eight? Why?
5. Convert $.5625_{(ten)}$ to base eight, and without multiplying, from base eight to base two.
6. Devise a method for converting from base four to base two analogous to the scheme from eight to two.
7. How can one most easily change from base nine to base three?
8. Is it possible for a fraction to terminate in base five but repeat in base ten? If so, find one. If not, explain why.

## 4.11 The Game of Nim

Binary notation has many applications, some useful, some amusing. Unless you have ambitions as a gambler or confidence man, what follows falls in the second category.

Nim is a game for two players. The game begins by placing matches or any convenient counters in several piles. The number of piles is immaterial. Each pile may have any number of counters. The players alternate moves. On each move the player removes from any one pile as many counters as he wishes, anything from one counter to the entire pile. The player removing the last counter wins the game.

There is a system of play, based on binary notation, whereby one is almost certain to win if his opponent does not know the system. In fact, machines for playing the game have been constructed which, given the initial advantage, cannot be beaten.

Obviously, the player who first plays to a single pile wins. The simplest situation which the winner can force on the loser is a single counter in each of two piles; the loser takes one, leaving one for the winner. The player who forces his opponent to play to two counters in each of two piles will win. If the opponent takes one counter, the player takes one counter from the other pile. If the opponent removes one pile the player removes the other. Forcing the opponent to play to three piles containing one, two, and three counters, respectively, constitutes a winning situation. If the opponent takes the pile consisting of one counter, the player takes one from the pile of three.

| | | | |
|---|---|---|---|
| Start | / | // | /// |
| Opponent's play | | // | /// |
| Counter play | | // | // |

THE GAME OF NIM

If the opponent takes one from the pile of two, the player takes all of the pile of three.

| | | | |
|---|---|---|---|
| Start | / | // | /// |
| Opponent's play | / | / | /// |
| Counter play | / | / | |

If the opponent takes all of the pile of two, the player takes two of the pile of three.

| | | | |
|---|---|---|---|
| Start | / | // | /// |
| Opponent's play | / | | /// |
| Counter play | / | | / |

An interchange of the foregoing moves will yield all other possible moves by the opponent and correct countermoves. In other words, regardless of what move the opponent makes, there is a countermove which will leave two identical piles, each having either two counters or one counter.

The system of play can best be described through an example. Suppose we have four piles containing 15, 13, 7, and 5 counters. We write these numbers in binary notation, add the columns, and write the column sums in ordinary base ten notation.

$$\begin{array}{rcr} 15_{(\text{ten})} & = & 1111_{(\text{two})} \\ 13_{(\text{ten})} & = & 1101_{(\text{two})} \\ 7_{(\text{ten})} & = & 111_{(\text{two})} \\ 5_{(\text{ten})} & = & 101_{(\text{two})} \\ \hline & & 2424 \end{array}$$

Each column contains an even number of 1's. This is called an even combination. The player who can first force his opponent to play to an even combination will be the ultimate winner—if he makes no mistakes. Notice that two piles of one each is an even combination $\begin{array}{r} 1 \\ 1 \\ \hline 2 \end{array}$; also two piles of two each is even $\begin{array}{r} 10 \\ 10 \\ \hline 20 \end{array}$; as is three piles of one, two, and three $\begin{array}{r} 1 \\ 10 \\ 11 \\ \hline 22 \end{array}$.

If one or more column sums is an odd number, we have an *odd* combination. The player who plays to an even combination *must* leave an odd combination. In the above situation something must be taken from one and only one pile. This means that a 1 must be removed from at least one column, but nothing else in that column can be disturbed. Since we must remove counters from only one pile at each play only one of the numbers 15, 13, 7, and 5 can be changed. For instance, if one counter is taken from the pile of 13, the right-hand column will have only three 1's and a 1 cannot be taken from any other pile. If two are taken from the seven pile a single counter remains in the second column from the right and neither of the zeros in this column can be changed to ones because we can change the count in only one pile. When playing to an even situation the player must leave the situation odd. But when playing to an odd situation the player *can*, if he knows how, leave the situation even. The winning system consists of forcing the opponent to play to an even situation every time.

The following example shows how one can play to an odd situation and leave it even. Suppose we have 15, 13, 5, and 1 counters. We write these numbers in the binary scale:

15—1111
13—1101
5— 101
1— 1

The two middle columns are odd. If we make an even situation we must make the highest odd column even. There are three counters in the third column from the right. Then we must take four counters from either the 15, the 13, or the 5 pile. If subsequent columns are already even we leave them intact. This is true of the right-hand column. If subsequent columns are odd, we replace counters in case our pile has a zero in that column. If our pile has a one in the column being considered, we remove it. There are three possible ways to make the above situation even. We can take six from the pile of 15. We would then have the even situation:

9 — 1001
13 — 1101
5 — 101
1 — 1

We can also remove two from the pile of 13. This amounts to removing four and replacing two. We would then have the even situation:

15 — 1111
11 — 1011
5 — 101
1 — 1

Or, finally, we can remove two from the pile of five. Again, this amounts to taking four and giving two back. This move gives the even situation:

| | |
|---:|---:|
| 15 — | 1111 |
| 13 — | 1101 |
| 3 — | 11 |
| 1 — | 1 |

The player who is forced always to play to an even situation can never pick up the last counter.

## 4.12 Russian Peasant Multiplication

Another application of the notion of binary notation is involved in Russian peasant multiplication. If you happen to know a Russian who never heard of this kind of multiplication it could be because he is not a peasant. In any event the method probably had its origin with the ancient Egyptians, who used a method that is very close to this one. We can best describe the method through an example.

*Example 1:* Use the Russian peasant method to multiply 375 by 48

*Solution:* In parallel columns we double one of the factors and halve the other, ignoring remainders. Continue until one is reached in the halved column.

| | |
|---:|---:|
| ~~375~~ | 48 |
| ~~750~~ | 24 |
| ~~1500~~ | 12 |
| ~~3000~~ | 6 |
| 6000 | 3 |
| 12000 | 1 |
| 18000 | |

Then, in the doubled column we strike out all numbers which lie opposite even numbers in the halved column. Add the remaining numbers in the doubled column. This sum is the required product.

If we write 48 in base two it becomes apparent why the above method works.

*Example 2:* Convert $48_{(\text{ten})}$ to base two.

*Solution:*

$2\,\underline{|48}$ 24 rem. 0 $\quad 2\,\underline{|24}$ 12 rem. 0 $\quad 2\,\underline{|12}$ 6 rem. 0 $\quad 2\,\underline{|6}$ 3 rem. 0

$2\,\underline{|3}$ 1 rem. 1 $\quad 2\,\underline{|1}$ 0 rem. 1

$$\therefore 48_{(\text{ten})} = 110000_{(\text{two})}$$

The numbers in the doubled column are actually $375 \times 1$, $375 \times 2$, $375 \times 4$, $375 \times 8$, $375 \times 16$, and $375 \times 32$.

Comparison of Example 2 with the halved column in Example 1 shows that we have used 375 multiplied by those powers of two that we must add to get 48.

$$\begin{aligned} 6000 &= 375 \times 16 \\ 12000 &= 375 \times 32 \\ \hline 18000 &= 375 \times 16 + 375 \times 32 = 375(16 \times 32) = 375 \times 48 \end{aligned}$$

Obviously, it makes no difference which factor is doubled.

*Example 3:* Find $375 \times 48$ by doubling and halving 375.

*Solution:*

| | |
|---:|---:|
| 375 | 48 |
| 187 | 96 |
| 93 | 192 |
| 46 | ~~384~~ |
| 23 | 768 |
| 11 | 1536 |
| 5 | 3072 |
| 2 | ~~6144~~ |
| 1 | 12288 |
| | 18000 |

Here we have

$48 \times 1 + 48 \times 2 + 48 \times 4 + 48 \times 16 + 48 \times 32 + 48 \times 64 + 48 \times 256 = 48(1 + 2 + 4 + 16 + 32 + 64 + 256) = 48 \times 375.$

RUSSIAN PEASANT MULTIPLICATION

## EXERCISES

**1.** If $.13 + .56 = 1.02$, what base of notation is used?

**2.** What is wrong with the following?

$$\begin{array}{r} 3.42_{(\text{five})} \\ 1.34_{(\text{five})} \\ \hline 10.26_{(\text{five})} \end{array}$$

**3.** Convert the following to base ten by evaluating each symbol and adding:
(a) $1011.11_{(\text{two})}$ (b) $63.15_{(\text{eight})}$ (c) $.75_{(\text{eight})}$ (d) $.1111_{(\text{two})}$

**4.** Change to base eight by dividing the integer and multiplying the fraction by eight, as illustrated in Section 4.10.
(a) $176.8_{(\text{ten})}$ (b) $1101.11101_{(\text{two})}$

**5.** Will a fraction that terminates in base two also terminate in base eight? Base ten? Why?

**6.** Will a fraction that terminates in base ten also terminate in base eight? Will one that terminates in base eight terminate in base ten?

**7.** Is the first play an advantage or disadvantage in a game of Nim in which there are piles of 19, 21, and 6 counters?

**8.** State three correct plays if faced with 16, 25, and 23 counters in a game of Nim.

**9.** State the system of play if the objective of the game of Nim is changed so that the loser picks up the last counter.

**10.** Will the Russian peasant method work with decimal fractions? Try the method on $23.46 \times 12.5$.

**11.** Will the Russian peasant method work with octonal numbers? Try it with $137_{(\text{eight})} \times 23_{(\text{eight})}$. Remember the computation is in base eight.

**12.** Use the Russian peasant method to find $975 \times 96$. Convert the entire problem to base two. In the new notation what determines when we get remainders in the halved column?

**13.** Multiply $345_{(\text{seven})} \times 53_{(\text{seven})}$ by the Russian peasant method.

**14.** In a game of Nim there are six piles of counters containing 12, 8, 2, 5, 7, and 18 counters. Who has the advantage, and what is the most appropriate move?

**15.** Distribute 20 counters into three piles so as to make an even combination in a game of Nim.

## 4.13 Algorithms

The common multiplication and division algorithms are the result of an evolutionary process. Russian peasant multiplication is only one of many schemes that have been employed in the past. An algorithm is a schematic device used in performing a mathematical computation. The arithmetic algorithms utilize the positional nature of our notation system and the properties of cardinal numbers listed on page 69. To illustrate this with multiplication consider the product

$$\begin{array}{r} 34 \\ 24 \\ \hline 136 \\ 68\phantom{0} \\ \hline 816 \end{array}$$

The product is found by adding the two products $34 \times 4$ and $34 \times 20$. This is an application of the distributive property.

$$34 \times 24 = 34 \times (20 + 4) = 34 \times 20 + 34 \times 4$$

The fact that $34 \times 4$ is found first is an application of the fact that addition is commutative

$$34 \times 20 + 34 \times 4 = 34 \times 4 + 34 \times 20$$

Finding of these partial products requires the use of the commutative and distributive properties, and where "carrying" is involved, the associative property.

$$34 \times 4 = 4 \times 34 = 4 \times (30 + 4) = 4 \times 30 + 4 \times 4 = 4 \times 4 + 4 \times 30$$

$$4 \times 4 + 4 \times 30 = 16 + 120 = 6 + (10 + 120) = 6 + 130 = 130 + 6 = 136$$

Notice that the indenting device in the algorithm reduces $34 \times 20$ to $[34 \times 2] \times 10$.

When the partial products are combined the addition algorithm is brought into play. In finding the sum $136 + 680$ the addition by columns is an application of the commutative and associative principles

$$\begin{aligned}136 + 680 &= (100 + 30 + 6) + (600 + 80)\\ &= (100 + 600) + (30 + 80) + 6\\ &= 700 + 110 + 6\\ &= 700 + 100 + 10 + 6\\ &= 800 + 10 + 6\\ &= 816\end{aligned}$$

The division algorithm also depends on place value and the properties of number. The algorithm

$$\begin{array}{r} 26\\ 32\overline{)835}\\ 64\\ \hline 195\\ 192\\ \hline 3\end{array}$$

depends upon the fact that division obeys the right-hand distributive law.

$$\begin{aligned}835 \div 32 &= (640 + 192 + 3) \div 32\\ &= 640 \div 32 + 192 \div 32 + 3 \div 32\\ &= 20 + 6 + \tfrac{3}{32}\\ &= 26\tfrac{3}{32}\end{aligned}$$

## EXERCISES

*Perform the following computations. Justify the process in terms of positional notation and the properties of cardinal numbers.*

**1.** Add: $237 + 194 + 36$

**2.** Subtract: $437 - 289$

**3.** Multiply: $47 \times 23$

**4.** Divide: $643 \div 56$

## NOTATION SYSTEMS

# 5 Number Theory

THE NATURAL NUMBERS ARE THE "BUILDING BLOCKS" OF MATHEMATICS. In contrast to the set of rational numbers, the set of natural numbers is discrete. That is, there is no natural number between 4 and 5. There is always a next natural number following any natural number. But there is no next rational number greater than 4, because there are always rational numbers between any two rational numbers.

The set of integers is also discrete. The essential difference between the set of integers and the set of natural numbers is the fact that there is always a next number *less than* any integer as well as a next number greater than any integer.

In this chapter we wish to examine some of the properties peculiar to the set of integers, that is, properties of the set of integers that are not properties of the set of rational numbers. Most of these properties will also apply to the set of natural numbers.

## 5.1 Even and Odd Numbers

All integers belong to one of two classes, even integers and odd integers.

> An integer is *even* if it is 2 times an integer. That is, $a$ is an even integer if $a = 2b$ and $b$ is an integer.

For example, 6 is an even integer because $6 = 2 \times 3$ and 3 is an integer. Notice however, that the definition does not require anything of $b$ except that it be an integer; $8 = 2 \times 4$, hence 8 is an even integer because 4 is an integer. The fact that 4 is also an even integer has no bearing on the question. Under this definition is zero an even integer? That is, if $a = 0$ can we find an integer $b$ such that $a = 2 \times b$? If $0 = 2 \times b$ then $b = 0$. In this case we have an integer equal 2 times itself. But this satisfies the definition; being 2 times itself, zero is certainly equal 2 times an integer.

| An integer that is not even is an *odd* integer. |
| --- |

This definition forces us to conclude that each integer is either even or odd and cannot be both. In the language of sets, if $E =$ the set of even integers, $0 =$ the set of odd integers, and $I =$ the set of integers,

$$E \cup 0 = I \text{ and } E \cap 0 = \varnothing$$

Can we prove that every odd integer is an integer of the form $2n + 1$, where $n$ is an integer? That is, $a$ is an odd integer if

$$a = 2b + 1$$

and $b$ is an integer. Since $a$ must be either even or odd, let us assume it is even and see what conclusion we must accept. If $a = 2b + 1$ is even, then by the distributive property $a = 2(b + \frac{1}{2})$ and $b + \frac{1}{2}$ is an integer. But if $b$ is an integer $b + \frac{1}{2}$ cannot be. We conclude that $a = 2b + 1$, where $b$ is an integer, cannot be an even integer; hence it must be an odd integer.

If $n^2$, the square of a number $n$, is even can we infer whether $n$ is even or odd? This is a special case of the more general question as to how even and odd numbers behave under multiplication. A few examples would indicate that the product of two odd numbers is an odd number.

$$3 \times 5 = 15 \quad 7 \times 9 = 63 \quad 13 \times 17 = 221$$

Is the product of any two odd numbers an odd number? If $a$ is an odd integer then $a = 2b + 1$ and $b$ is an integer. Similarly, if $c$ is odd, $c = 2d + 1$ and $d$ is an integer. The product is $a \times b = (2b + 1)(2d + 1)$ and by the distributive principle

$$(2b + 1)(2d + 1) = (2b + 1)2d + (2b + 1)$$

Apply the associative principle and we have

$$(2b + 1)2d + (2b + 1) = ((2b + 1)2d + 2b) + 1$$

Finally, if we apply the distributive property to the first term we have

$$((2b + 1)2d + 2b) + 1 = 2((2b + 1)d + b) + 1$$

Since the integers are closed with respect to addition and multiplication $((2b + 1)d + b)$ is an integer. Hence, $a \times c$ is shown to be 2 times an integer plus 1; $a \times c$ is an odd integer.

If $a$ is an even integer $a \times c$ is even whether $c$ is even or odd. Let $a = 2b$ with $b$ an integer. Then $a \times c = 2b \times c = 2(b \times c)$. But since the integers are closed with respect to multiplication $b \times c$ is an integer. Hence, $a \times c$, being 2 times an integer, is an even integer. We summarize these results in the table

| $\times$ | $E$ | 0 |
|---|---|---|
| $E$ | $E$ | $E$ |
| 0 | $E$ | 0 |

Since the product of two even numbers is even and the product of two odd numbers is odd, we must conclude that any integer $n$ and its square $n^2$ agree; they are both even or both odd.

How do odd and even numbers behave under addition? We have seen that if either factor, $a$ or $b$, is even the product $ab$ is even. If either addend, $a$ or $b$, is even does this mean the sum $a + b$ is even? Two examples are sufficient to show that the sum is not necessarily even or odd: $4 + 6 = 10$, an even sum; and $4 + 3 = 7$, an odd sum. However, these same examples would suggest that the sum of *two* even addends is even, and the sum of an even addend and an odd addend is odd. What about the sum of two odd addends? $3 + 5 = 8$, an even sum. Can we say the sum of two odd addends is even?

If $a$ and $b$ are even integers then $a = 2c$ and $b = 2d$ when $c$ and $d$ are integers. And $a + b = 2c + 2d = 2(c + d)$. Thus, the sum $a + b$, being 2 times the integer $c + d$, is an even integer.

If on the other hand both $a$ and $b$ are odd integers, then $a = 2c + 1$ and $b = 2d + 1$ when $c$ and $d$ are integers. Hence $a + b = 2c + 1 + 2d + 1 = 2(c + d + 1)$, an even integer since it is 2 times $c + d + 1$, an integer.

If one addend, $a$, is even and the other, $b$, is odd the sum is odd. Let $a = 2c$ and $b = 2d + 1$. Then $a + b = 2c + 2d + 1 = 2(c + d) + 1$, an odd integer since $c + d$ is an integer.

The results are summarized in the table

| + | $E$ | 0 |
|---|---|---|
| $E$ | $E$ | 0 |
| 0 | 0 | $E$ |

**EXERCISES**

1. Recall that 0 is the addition identity because for any number $a, a + 0 = a$. In the arithmetic of even and odd is there an addition identity? If so, what is it? Why?
2. In the arithmetic of even and odd what is the multiplication identity?
3. What is the additive inverse of an even number in the arithmetic of even and odd? What is the additive inverse of an odd number?
4. In the arithmetic of even and odd does an odd number have a multiplicative inverse? Does an even number have an inverse?
5. If the sum of a set of addends is even what, if anything, does this tell us about the number of addends that are even? Odd?
6. Answer question 5 if the sum is odd.
7. If the product of a set of factors is even what, if anything, does this tell us about the number of factors that are even? Odd?
8. Answer question 7 if the product is odd.
9. Is it possible for $2b + 3$, $b$ an integer, to be an odd integer? An even integer? Why?
10. Is it possible for $7b + 5$, $b$ an integer, to be an odd integer? An even integer? Why?
11. Can $a^2 + a - 1$, $a$ an integer, be even? Can it be odd?
12. Can $a^2 + 4a - 1$, $a$ an integer, be even? Can it be odd?

## 5.2 Figurate Numbers

Number theory has its beginnings with the Greek mathematicians of the pre-Christian era. The Greeks investigated many properties of classifications of numbers called *figurate numbers*. These are numbers that can be represented by geometric arrays of dots. For example, *triangular numbers* are numbers that can be represented by arrays of dots forming equilateral triangles.

The above arrays represent the first five triangular numbers, 1, 3, 6, 10, 15.

What must be added to the first triangular number to produce the second? What must be added to the second to produce the third? Examination of the above dot arrays indicates that any triangle can be obtained from the next larger one by removing the bottom row of dots. Or put the other way around, any array can be obtained from the one that precedes it by adding one more row of dots. The added row will contain one more dot than the preceding one. Thus, the sixth triangular number is obtained by adding 6 to the fifth triangular number.

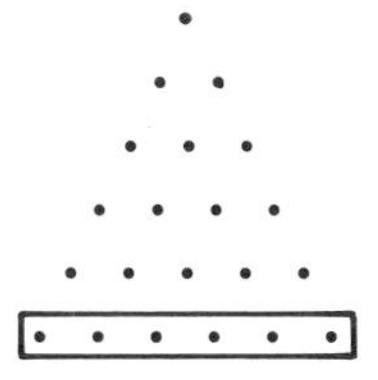

Since the first triangular number is 1 and we add 2 to this to get the second, and add 3 to the second to get the third, we can express the third as $1 + 2 + 3$. Or in general, the $n$th triangular number is the sum of the first $n$ integers.

Suppose we want to find the 100th triangular number. Is it necessary to find the 99th then add 100? That is, is it necessary to add $1 + 2 + 3 + \ldots + 100$? Indicate the 100th triangular number by $S$. Then

$$S = 1 + 2 + 3 + \ldots + 99 + 100$$

and

$$S = 100 + 99 + 98 + \ldots + 2 + 1,$$

then by addition we have

$$2S = 101 + 101 + 101 + \ldots + 101 + 101$$

How many addends of 101 are there on the right? Since there are 100 addends in the sum $1 + 2 + 3 + \ldots + 100$ we have 100 addends of 101. Hence

$$2S = 100 \times 101$$
$$S = 50 \times 101 = 5050$$

We can devise a similar result for the $n$th triangular number for any $n$. Let the $n$th triangular number be $S$, then

$$S = 1 + 2 + 3 + \ldots + n$$

and

$$S = n + (n - 1) + (n - 2) + \ldots + 1,$$

and by addition

$$2S = (n + 1) + (n + 1) + (n + 1) + \ldots + (n + 1)$$

for $n$ terms.

$$S = \frac{n(n + 1)}{2}$$

The $n$th triangular number is the sum of the first $n$ integers

$$\frac{n(n + 1)}{2}$$

Since $S$ is $\frac{1}{2}$ of the integer $n(n + 1)$ how can we be sure $S$ is an integer? If $n$ is even then $n/2$ is an integer. But suppose $n$ is odd? How do we know that $n + 1$ is even, and hence $(n + 1)/2$ is an integer?

Another type of figurate number is the square number. A square number is one that can be represented by a square array of dots.

As indicated by the above arrays, the first five square numbers are 1, 4, 9, 16, and 25. The $n$th square number is pictured by a square array of dots, $n$ dots on a side. Hence the $n$th square number is $n \times n = n^2$.

Do you see any connection between the sequence of triangular numbers and the sequence of square numbers?

1, 3, 6, 10, 15, 21, 28, 36, 45, ... $\frac{n(n+1)}{2}$

1, 4, 9, 16, 25, 36, 49, 64, 81, ... $n^2$

The spacing of the numbers in each sequence suggests that any square number after 1 is the sum of two consecutive triangular numbers. A square array can be divided into two triangular arrays, as indicated in the diagram.

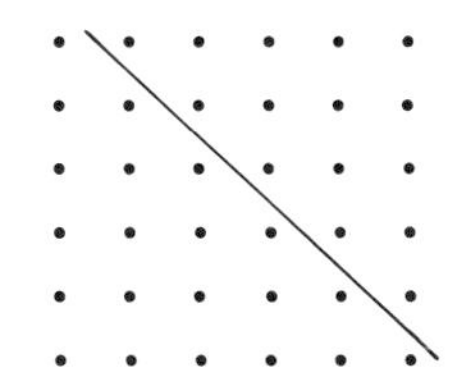

Notice that to the right of the diagonal we have the fifth triangular number represented and to the left the sixth triangular number represented. Can we conclude that the $n$th square number, $n^2$, is the sum of the $n$th and $(n-1)$th triangular numbers?

We wish to show that

$$\frac{(n-1)n}{2} + \frac{n(n+1)}{2} = n^2$$

$$\frac{(n-1)n}{2} + \frac{n(n+1)}{2} = \frac{(n-1)n + n(n+1)}{2}$$

$$\frac{(n-1)n + n(n+1)}{2} = \frac{n^2 - n + n^2 + n}{2}$$

$$\frac{n^2 - n + n^2 + n}{2} = \frac{2n^2}{2}$$

$$\frac{2n^2}{2} = n^2$$

Hence we may conclude

$$\frac{(n-1)n}{2} + \frac{n(n+1)}{2} = n^2$$

| The sum of two consecutive triangular numbers, the $(n-1)$th and $n$th, is equal to the $n$th square number. |
|---|

If each square number is subtracted from the next greater square number we get the sequence shown below the sequence of squares

$$\begin{array}{ccccccccc} 1, & 4, & 9, & 16, & 25, & 36, & 49, & 64, & \ldots \\ & 3, & 5, & 7, & 9, & 11, & 13, & 15, & \ldots \end{array}$$

Can you recognize this sequence? Since 1 is both the first square number and the first odd number, and the difference sequence is the sequence of odd numbers greater than 1, it seems that the sum of the first $n$ odd numbers is a square number, $n^2$. Examination of consecutive square arrays shows that

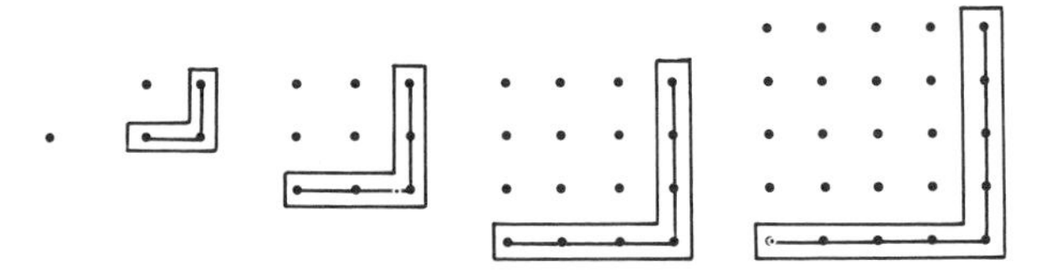

the next square can be obtained from the preceding one by adjoining the border indicated in the diagram. In each case this border consists of $2n + 1$ dots where $n^2$ is the number of dots in the original array. But $2n + 1$ is an odd number, in fact the $(n + 1)$th positive odd number. We may conclude that the $(n + 1)$th square number is obtained from the $n$th square number by adding the $(n + 1)$th odd number. If, beginning with 1, we construct the sequence of square numbers in this way we may conclude that any square number, $n^2$, is equal to the sum of the first $n$ odd numbers.

*Example:* $5^2 = 25$ is the sum of the first 5 odd numbers:

$$1 + 3 + 5 + 7 + 9 = 25.$$

$10^2 = 100$ is the sum of the first 10 odd numbers:

$$1 + 3 + 5 + 7 + 9 + 11 + 13 + 15 + 17 + 19 = 100$$

A cubic number is one that can be represented by dots forming a cube. This is a three-dimensional representation. The first four cubic numbers 1, 8, 27, and 64. They are $1^3$, $2^3$, $3^3$, and $4^3$.

## NUMBER THEORY

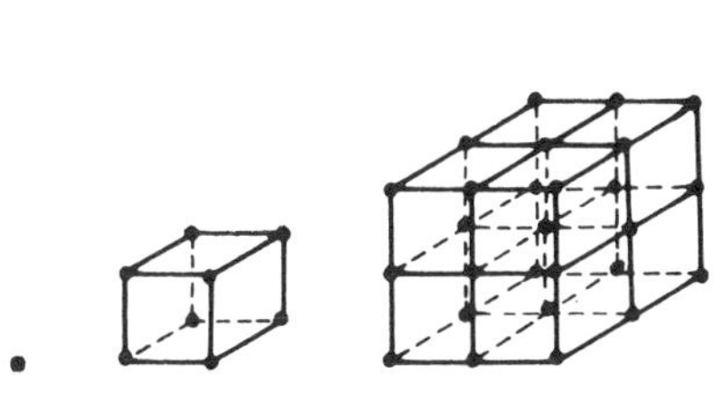

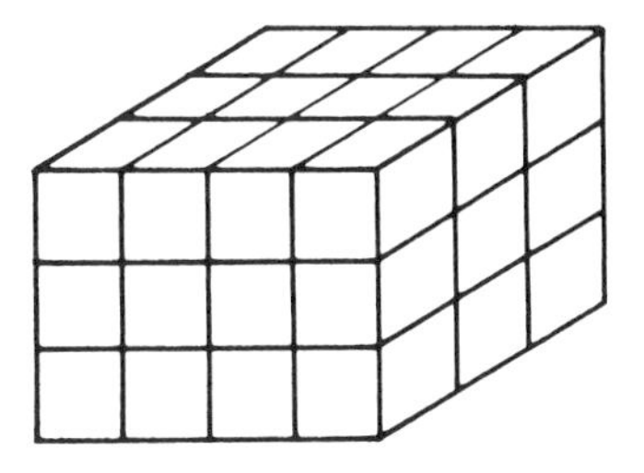

The $n$th cubic number $n^3$ is represented by a cube, $n$ dots on each edge, $n^2$ dots on each face. The 4th cubic number $4^3$ is pictured by showing only that part of a solid cube which is visible from one position, three of its six faces.

In the sequence of cubic numbers 1, 8, 27, 64, 125, 216, 343, 512, . . . $n^3$ find the sum of the first two terms, the sum of the first three terms, first four terms, and so on. This will produce a new sequence, beginning with, 1, 9, 36, 100, 225, 441, 784, 1296, . . . .

One might not recognize the last few terms, but certainly the first few are recognizable as square numbers. A little verification will show all the terms that are written here are square numbers. The same sequence can be written as $1^2$, $3^2$, $6^2$, $10^2$, $15^2$, $21^2$, $28^2$, $36^2$. What kind of pattern is involved here? Do you recognize the sequence of numbers that are squared?

1, 3, 6, 10, 15, 21, 28, 36

This turns out to be our old friend, the sequence of triangular numbers. What we seem to have discovered here is that the sum of the first $n$ cubic numbers is the *square of* the sum of the first $n$ integers. In other words $1^3 + 2^3 + \ldots + n^3 = (n(n + 1)/2)^2$.

Can we prove that this is true for any $n$? It is not easy to do so if we use a geometric approach such as we used in showing the sum of the first $n$ odd numbers is equal to $n^2$. Nor is there readily available the kind of trick that was used in showing the $n$th triangular number is equal to $n(n + )/2$. However, the result can be established by using a little more sophisticated approach. But we must be sure to make the right start.

One of the basic assumptions governing the natural numbers is a principle called the *Principle of Finite Induction.* Suppose we have a set, $N$, of numbers, and it is agreed that *if* some particular natural number, $k$, is a member of $N$ then $k + 1$ is also a member of $N$. It is further agreed that the natural number 1 is a member of $N$. Would you accept the conclusion that all natural numbers are members of $N$? In other words, we are asked to grant that 7 being in $N$ is sufficient evidence to conclude that 8 is too; 119 being in $N$ is sufficient evidence to conclude that 120 is also;

any natural number $k$ being in $N$ is sufficient reason to conclude that the next natural number, $k + 1$, is also in $N$. We are further asked to accept the fact that 1 is a member of $N$. The principle of finite induction is a basic assumption that, whenever the two conditions (1) if $k$ is a member of $N$ then $k + 1$ is a member of $N$ and (2) 1 is a member of $N$ are fulfilled, all natural numbers are members of $N$. This seems reasonable, it is hoped, but we cannot prove it.

| Principle of Finite Induction<br>Given a set $N$ such that (1) if $k \in N$ then $k + 1 \in N$<br>(2) $1 \in N$<br>Then all natural numbers are members of $N$. |
|---|

We wish to use the principle of finite induction to prove the proposition that the sum of the first $n$ cubic numbers equals the square of the $n$th triangular number (the $n$th triangular number being the sum of the first $n$ natural numbers). In other words

$$1^3 + 2^3 + \ldots n^3 = \left(\frac{n(n+1)}{2}\right)^2$$

First, we wish to show that if there is some number $k$ for which the statement is true it will have to be true for $k + 1$.

We assume

$$1^3 + 2^3 + \ldots + k^3 = \left(\frac{k(k+1)}{2}\right)^2 \tag{1}$$

and want to show that as a consequence

$$1^3 + 2^3 + \ldots + k^3 + (k+1)^3 = \left[\frac{(k+1)(k+2)}{2}\right]^2 \tag{2}$$

If we add $(k + 1)^3$ to both sides of Equation (1) we have

$$1^3 + 2^3 + \ldots + k^3 + (k+1)^3 = \left[\frac{k(k+1)}{2}\right]^2 + (k+1)^3$$

Then the first part of the proof is complete if we can show that

$$\left[\frac{(k+1)(k+2)}{2}\right]^2 = \left[\frac{k(k+1)}{2}\right]^2 + (k+1)^3$$

This can be shown by algebraic manipulation. You may find it tedious, but it is perfectly straightforward. Just remember that $k$ is simply some number and evaluate each side independently.

$$\left[\frac{(k+1)(k+2)}{2}\right]^2 = \left[\frac{k(k+1)}{2}\right]^2 + (k+1)^3$$

$$\left[\frac{k^2+3k+2}{2}\right]^2 = \left[\frac{k^2+k}{2}\right]^2 + k^3 + 3k^2 + 3k + 1$$

$$\frac{k^4 + 9k^2 + 4 + 6k^3 + 4k^2 + 12k}{4} = \frac{k^4 + k^2 + 2k^3}{4} + k^3 + 3k^2 + 3k + 1$$

$$\frac{k^4 + 6k^3 + 13k^2 + 12k + 4}{4} = \frac{k^4 + k^2 + 2k^3 + 4k^3 + 12k^2 + 12k + 4}{4}$$

$$\frac{k^4 + 6k^3 + 13k^2 + 12k + 4}{4} = \frac{k^4 + 6k^3 + 13k^2 + 12k + 4}{4}$$

We have shown that, $N$ being the set of numbers for which the statement is true, if $k \in N$ then $k + 1 \in N$.

But the statement is surely true if $n = 1$ because $1^3 = 1^2$. Hence, by the principle of finite induction the statement is true for all natural numbers.

## EXERCISES

**1.** Use the principle of finite induction to prove that the sum of the first $n$ positive integers is $\frac{n(n+1)}{2}$.

**2.** Use the formula in Exercise 1 to find the sum of the first 150 positive integers.

**3.** Find the sum of the integers 100 through 200.

**4.** An arithmetic series is a sum of numbers such that the difference between any two consecutive terms is constant. For example, $1 + 4 + 7 + 10 + 13 + 16$ is an arithmetic series with common difference 3. Adapt the argument for the sum of the first $n$ integers, page 145, to find the sum $1 + 4 + 7 + \ldots + 31$.

**5.** If the first term of an arithmetic series is $a$, the common difference $d$, and the number of terms is $n$, the sum is

$$\frac{n(2a + (n-1)d)}{2}$$

Use this formula to check the result found in Exercise 4.

**6.** Find the first ten terms of the arithmetic series

$$7 + 11 + 15 + \ldots.$$

## FIGURATE NUMBERS

7. Prove that the $n$th term of an arithmetic series with first term $a$ and common difference $d$ is equal to $a + (n - 1)d$.

8. Use the principle of finite induction to prove the formula in Exercise 5 is correct.

9. Use finite induction to prove the sum of the first $n$ positive odd numbers is equal to $n^2$.

## 5.3 Divisibility

In Chapter 4 several tests for divisibility by a particular number were developed. Here, we wish to investigate some of the general properties of divisibility.

We say that 30 is divisible by 6 because 6 divides 30 evenly, that is, with no remainder: $30 \div 6 = 5$. Hence, 6 is a *factor* of 30.

> The integer $a$ is a factor of the integer $b$ if and only if $a$ divides $b$ evenly, $b \div a = k$ where $k$ is an integer. This is expressed as $a \mid b$ and is read "$a$ divides $b$."

When two or more numbers are multiplied, as $3 \times 4 \times 5$, the result, 60, is their product, and the numbers multiplied are factors. Thus, 3, 4, and 5 are factors of 60. But they are not the only factors of 60. Since $60 \div 30 = 2$, $60 \div 15 = 4$, $60 \div 6 = 10$, we conclude that 30, 15, and 6 are also factors of 60.

If $a \mid b$ and $a \mid c$ then $a \mid (b + c)$. This fact was employed in Chapter 4 a number of times in developing divisibility tests. As a specific example of the principle: $4 \mid 12$ and $4 \mid 16$, hence $4 \mid 28$. To prove the general case: If $a \mid b$ then $b = ak_1$ where $k_1$ is an integer, and if $a \mid c$ then $c = ak_2$ where $k_2$ is an integer. Then by addition $b + c = ak_1 + ak_2$. By the distributive principle $b + c = a(k_1 + k_2)$. Since $k_1$ and $k_2$ are integers $k_1 + k_2$ is an integer. Hence $a \mid (b + c)$.

The relation "is a factor of" is transitive. That is, if $a \mid b$ and $b \mid c$ then $a \mid c$. For example, 3 divides 12 and 12 divides 60; hence 3 divides 60. To show that $a \mid b$ and $b \mid c$ implies $a \mid c$: if $a \mid b$ then $b = ak_1$, $k_1$ an integer. If $b \mid c$ then $c = bk_2$, $k_2$ an integer. Substituting $ak_1$ for $b$, we have $c = ak_1k_2$. But $k_1k_2$ is an integer, hence $a \mid c$. We repeat the argument using specific values for $a$, $b$, and $c$. To show that $7 \mid 21$ and $21 \mid 42$ implies $7 \mid 42$: if $7 \mid 21$ then $21 = 7 \times 3$. If $21 \mid 42$ then $42 = 21 \times 2$. Substituting $7 \times 3$ for 21, we have $42 = 7 \times 3 \times 2 = 7 \times 6$; hence $7 \mid 42$.

The relation "is a factor of" is reflexive. That is, $a \mid a$. For any $a \neq 0$, $a \div a = 1$, hence $a \mid a$. Incidently, $a \mid b$ has meaning only if $a \neq 0$, for in no case does $0 \mid b$. Zero cannot divide $b$ evenly because $b \div 0$ is undefined for any $b$.

"Is a factor of" is not an equivalence relation; it is not symmetric. The symmetric property requires that if $a \mid b$ then $b \mid a$. But this is not true unless $a = b$.

We have seen that if $a \mid b$ and $a \mid c$ then $a \mid (b + c)$. Is it also true that if $a \mid (b + c)$ then $a \mid b$ and $a \mid c$? Consider the example, $5 \mid (17 + 13)$ because $17 + 13 = 30$ and $30 = 5 \times 6$. But it is not true that $5 \mid 17$ or that $5 \mid 13$.

Is it true that if $a \mid (b + c)$ and $a \mid b$ then $a \mid c$? For example, $7 \mid 63$ and $7 \mid 14$; hence $7 \mid 49$. In the general case, $a \mid (b + c)$ implies $b + c = ak_1$ and $a \mid b$ implies $b = ak_2$. Subtracting the second equality from the first, we have

$$b + c - b = ak_1 - ak_2$$
$$c = ak_1 - ak_2$$

and by the distributive property

$$c = a(k_1 - k_2)$$

Since $k_1$ and $k_2$ are integers, $k_1 - k_2$ is an integer. Hence $a \mid c$.

Any integer is divisible by 1; $1 \mid a$, $a$ any integer. This is true because $a \div 1 = a$. Any nonzero integer is also divisible by itself; $a \mid a$, $a \neq 0$. This is true because $a \div a = 1$, $a \neq 0$.

Any negative integer may be considered $-1$ times a positive integer. The positive integer, $a$, is *composite* if it has factors other than 1 and $a$. For example, $7 \mid 63$ and $9 \mid 63$; hence 63 is composite. But although $1 \mid 13$ and $13 \mid 13$ no other number $a$ divides 13. Hence 13 is not composite. Any integer greater than 1 that is not composite is a *prime number*. Hence, every positive integer is one and only one of the following: 1, prime, composite.

Prime numbers play an important role in number theory. There are many unanswered questions regarding prime numbers. No algebraic formula for all primes has ever been devised. In fact, no formula which always yields a prime has been devised. The formula $n^2 + n + 41$, when $n = 0$ is the prime 41. When $n = 1$, $n^2 + n + 41 = 43$, a prime. Obviously no value of $n$ will produce a prime less than 41. So the formula will not produce all primes. But it will not even produce a prime for all $n$. Although each value of $n$ through $n = 40$ produces a prime number, when $n = 41$ we have $n^2 + n + 41 = 41^2 + 41 + 41 = 43 \times 41$, a composite number.

All prime numbers less than a given number can be isolated by means of a simple device known as the Sieve of Eratosthenes. We shall illustrate the method by finding the prime numbers less than 20. First write down the integers 2 through 20. Two is a prime, so we circle it. We next cross out every second number after two, that is 4, 6, 8, . . . . Three is a prime; we circle it. We then cross out every third number after three, 6, 9, 12, . . . . Some of them will have been crossed out already but they are counted in getting every third number.

As we continue, the first number remaining in the sequence is always a prime. Five is a prime and every fifth number after 5 has already been crossed out. Obviously the remaining numbers 11, 13, 17, 19 are prime because the eleventh number after 11 goes beyond 20.

When we test a number for prime factors it is sufficient to test only those primes whose squares are equal to or less than the given number. For example, suppose we wish to determine whether 97 is a prime. We test and find that neither 2, 3, 5, 7, nor 11 is a factor. We need go no further because $11 \times 11$ is greater than 97 and if 97 had a prime factor greater than 11 it would have to have one less than 11 also.

## EXERCISES

1. Use the Sieve of Eratosthenes and find all positive prime numbers less than 100.

2. Verify that $n^2 - n + 41$ is a prime for $n = 3, 5, 6$, and 10.

3. Tabulate the number of primes in each decade through 100. Can you draw any conclusion as to their distribution?

4. Determine the primes between 100 and 110; between 110 and 120.

5. A number of the form $2^{2^n} + 1$ is known as a Fermat number. The French mathematician de Fermat thought numbers of this type are always primes. This later proved to be wrong. Find the Fermat numbers for $n = 1, 2$, and 3. Are they primes?

6. The numbers 5, 15, 25 are all divisible by 5. If the sequence is continued (numbers ending in 5) do the numbers continue to be divisible by 5?
   The numbers 3, 13, 23 are all primes. If the sequence is continued (numbers ending in 3) do the numbers continue to be prime?

7. The definition of prime numbers excludes the number 1. Can you think of reasons why this is done? Can you think of reasons why it would be better to include 1 as a prime?

## 5.4 The Euclidean Algorithm

Any two positive integers $a$ and $b$ have a *greatest common divisor*, $d > 0$.

> If $d$ divides both $a$ and $b$ ($d \mid a$, $d \mid b$), and every divisor $c$ of both $a$ and $b$ is a divisor of $d$ ($c \mid d$), then $d$ is the greatest common divisor of $a$ and $b$.

*Example:* The greatest common divisor of 105 and 189 is 21; $21 \mid 105$ and $21 \mid 189$. Furthermore, the common divisors of 105 and 189 are 1, 3, 7, and 21; and $1 \mid 21$, $3 \mid 21$, $7 \mid 21$, and $21 \mid 21$.

The greatest common divisor of $a$ and $b$ can be expressed in the form $d = Ma + Nb$ where $M$ and $N$ are integers, one of which may be negative. Let $d$ be the *smallest* positive value of $Ma + Nb$ for any $M$ and $N$ (since $a$ and $b$ are positive at least one of $M$ and $N$ must be positive).

For example, the greatest common divisor of 105 and 189 is $21 = 2 \times 105 + (-1) \times 189$.

We must show that $d = Ma + Nb$ divides $a$. By division we know that

$$a = qd + r, \quad 0 \le r < d$$

This equation merely asserts that $a \div d$ has a quotient $q$ and remainder $r$. Solving for $r$, we have

$$r = a - qd$$

and substituting for $d$

$$\begin{aligned} r &= a - q(Ma + Nb) \\ &= a(1 - qM) + b(-qN) \end{aligned}$$

Now $r$ is a number of the form $Ma + Nb$, but $r$ is less than $d$. Hence, since $d$ is the smallest positive number of this form, $r = 0$ and from $r = a - qd$ we conclude that $a = qd$. But this means that $d$ divides $a$. By a similar argument we can show that $d$ divides $b$.

We must also show that any divisor, $c$, of $a$ and $b$ is a divisor of $d$. If $c$ divides $a$ then $a = k_1c$, $k_1$ an integer. If $c$ divides $b$ then $b = k_2c$, $k_2$ an integer. Then $d = Mk_1c + Nk_2c = (Mk_1 + Nk_2)c$ and hence $c$ is a divisor of $d$.

The above argument shows any two positive integers $a$ and $b$ have a greatest common divisor of the form $Ma + Nb$, $M$ and $N$ integers. But it gives no clue as to how to find the greatest common divisor of two given positive integers. It can be found by a method known as the Euclidean Algorithm. We shall first illustrate the method with an example.

*Example:* Find the greatest common divisor of the integers 368 and 1081. Divide 1081 by 368

```
       2
368|1081
     736
     ---
     345
```

Divide the divisor 368 by the remainder 345

```
      1
345|368
    345
    ---
     23
```

Divide the divisor 345 by the remainder 23

```
    15
23|345
   23
   ---
   115
   115
   ===
```

The last nonzero remainder, 23, is the greatest common divisor.

The method consists of dividing the larger of the two original integers by the smaller, then on each succeeding step, dividing the previous divisor by the previous remainder.

If two integers have no common factor except 1 they are *relatively prime*. If in applying the Euclidean Algorithm, a remainder 1 is reached, the next step must yield a remainder zero. The greatest common divisor is 1 and the numbers are relatively prime.

## NUMBER THEORY

*Example:* Show that 391 and 113 are relatively prime.

$$
\begin{array}{rrrrrr}
3 & 2 & 5 & 1 & 3 & 2 \\
113\overline{)391} & 52\overline{)113} & 9\overline{)52} & 7\overline{)9} & 2\overline{)7} & 1\overline{)2} \\
\underline{339} & \underline{104} & \underline{45} & \underline{7} & \underline{6} & \underline{2} \\
52 & 9 & 7 & 2 & 1 & 0
\end{array}
$$

Hence the greatest common divisor of 391 and 113 is 1; 391 and 113 are relatively prime.

We shall examine the first example to discover why the method works. Since in the last division the remainder is zero we know that 23 is a divisor of 345. The division in the second step shows that $368 = 1 \times 345 + 23$. Since 23 divides 345 it divides $1 \times 345 + 23$ and hence 23 divides 368. Furthermore, 23 is the greatest common divisor of 368 and 345.

The division in the first step shows that

$$1081 = 2 \times 368 + 345$$

Since 23 is the greatest common divisor of 368 and 345 it must divide 1081 and hence is the greatest common divisor of 368 and 1081.

The algorithm can also be used to express the greatest common divisor as $Ma + Nb$. From the first step we have

$$345 = 1081 - 2 \times 368$$
$$345 = 1081 + (-2) \times 368$$

From the second step, we have

$$23 = 368 - 1 \times 345$$
$$23 = 368 + (-1) \times 345$$
$$23 = 368 + (-1)[1081 + (-2) \times 368]$$
$$23 = 3 \times 368 + (-1) \times 1081$$

the required form.

The form $Ma + Nb$ for the greatest common divisor is useful in establishing other properties. For example, if $p$ is a prime and $p \mid (a \times b)$, $p \mid a$ or $p \mid b$. That is, if $p$ divides the product $a \times b$ it must divide at least one of the factors $a$ and $b$. Suppose that $p$ does not divide $a$. Then

$$Ma + Np = 1$$

for some integers $M$ and $N$; then multiplying by $b$, we have

$$Mab + Npb = b$$

But since $p \mid ab$ we have $p \mid (Mba + Npb)$, and hence

$$p \mid b$$

*Example:* Since 13, a prime number, divides $520 = 65 \times 8$ and 13 does not divide 8, it follows that 13 must divide 65.

*Counter Example:* Although 8, a composite number, divides $168 = 28 \times 6$, it does not divide either 28 or 6.

The *Fundamental Theorem of Arithmetic* asserts that any positive integer greater than one may be factored into primes in essentially one way. That is, the order of the primes may differ but the same primes must be present. For example: $24 = 3 \times 8 = 4 \times 6$ but 8, 4, and 6 are not prime. If they are factored into primes we get

$$24 = 3 \times 2 \times 2 \times 2 = 2 \times 2 \times 3 \times 2$$

and the two representations of 24 in prime factors differ only in the order in which the primes appear. This theorem is as important as it seems obvious. But the obviousness of a statement has no necessary relationship to the ease with which it can be proved. For that matter, history is filled with "obvious facts" that have been disproved. In the following proof we designate the integer to be factored as $a$. If $a$ is prime, the truth of the theorem follows from the definition of prime numbers. If $a$ is not prime it can be expressed as the product of two factors, $a = b \times c$, with $b$, $c$ each less than $a$. If $b$ and $c$ are prime $b \times c$ is the required factorization. If $b$ is composite it can be expressed as the product of two factors less than $b$; similarly for $c$. Repetition of this argument a finite number of times produces prime factors, for there are only a finite number of positive integers less than $a$. This shows that any integer $a$ may be expressed as a product of primes. To show the primes are the same for any factorization consider $a$ factored into two sets of primes.

$$a = p_1 \times p_2 \times p_3 \times \ldots = q_1 \times q_2 \times q_3 \times \ldots$$

Since $p_1$ is a factor of $a$ it is also a factor of $q_1 \times q_2 \times q_3 \times \ldots$. But the $q$s are prime, therefore $p_1$ must equal some one of the $q$s. We may now apply the cancellation principle and get the product $p_2 \times p_3 \times \ldots =$ the product of the remaining $q$s. By a repetition of the same argument we can show there is a $q$ equal to $p_2$, and similarly for all the $p$s. Having eliminated all $p$s, we have on that side of the equation 1, and on the other side a product of the remaining $q$s. But since the $q$s are all integers we know they have been canceled and 1 remains on that side. It follows that the products $p_1 \times p_2 \times p_3 \times \ldots$ and $q_1 \times q_2 \times q_3 \times \ldots$ differ only in the order in which the factors appear.

### EXERCISES

**1.** Use the Euclidean algorithm to find the greatest common divisor of 180 and 252.

**2.** Use the Euclidean algorithm to show that 76 and 207 are relatively prime.

**3.** Express the greatest common divisor, $d$, of 468 and 546 as $468M + 546N$ where $M$ and $N$ are integers.

**4.** Illustrate the fundamental theorem of arithmetic with

$$40 \times 63 = 35 \times 72$$

**5.** The lowest common multiple of two numbers, as the name implies, is the smallest number that is an exact multiple of each. For example, 60 is the lowest common multiple of 12 and 15. Use the fundamental theorem of arithmetic to find the lowest common multiple of 144 and 216.

**6.** Are two distinct prime numbers relatively prime? Illustrate.

**7.** Are two relatively prime numbers necessarily primes? Illustrate.

**8.** What is the lowest common multiple of two prime numbers?

**9.** What is the greatest common divisor of two prime numbers?

## 5.5 More About Primes

Although there are many unanswered questions concerning prime numbers, one question that was answered long ago concerns the number of primes. In Euclid's *Elements* there is a beautiful proof that there are an infinite number of primes. The argument is a classic example of indirect proof.

We wish to prove there are infinitely many prime numbers, assume there are only a finite number of primes:

$$p_1, p_2, p_3, \ldots, p_n \qquad (n = \text{a finite number})$$

Consider the product of the $n$ primes plus 1:

$$q = p_1 \times p_2 \times p_3 \times \ldots \times p_n + 1$$

The number $q$ is either a prime number or a composite number. If it is a prime number it is certainly different from any of the $n$ primes which were assumed to be all of the primes. Our assumption that there are only a finite number of primes is false. If $q$ is composite it must have prime factors. But none of the $n$ primes will divide $q$, since there will be a remainder 1 when any of the $n$ primes is used as divisor. Hence, once again the assumption that there are only a finite number of primes is shown false. We must conclude that there are infinitely many prime numbers.

The properties of prime numbers have intrigued mathematicians for centuries. Although the study of primes has yielded rich rewards in number theory, there are still many unanswered questions concerning them. The absence of a formula for all primes, or even a formula that always yields a prime, have already been mentioned.

If you examine the prime numbers less than 100 you will notice the frequent occurrence of primes that differ by 2, for instance, 11 and 13, 17 and 19, 29 and 31, 41 and 43. These are known as twin primes. It has been known for a long time that there are infinitely many primes. Are there infinitely many pairs of twin primes? As yet nobody knows.

Can any even integer greater than 2 be expressed as the sum of two primes? For example, $50 = 19 + 31$; $34 = 17 + 17$. Nobody has found an even number that could not be so expressed, yet it has not been proved that it can always be done. This question is known as Goldbach's conjecture.

The distribution of primes over a relatively small range of integers appears to be quite uneven. However, it has been proved that as the number of integers increases without limit the relative number of primes approaches a constant. In view of this fact the two following facts which have also been proved seem all the more startling: (1) It is possible to find an interval of integers containing any specified number of primes. (2) It is possible to find an interval of any specified number of integers which does not contain a single prime.

## EXERCISES

**1.** The product of the first $n$ primes plus 1 is either a prime or it has prime factors other than that the first $n$ primes. For example, $2 + 1 = 3$, a prime; $2 \times 3 + 1 = 7$, a prime; $2 \times 3 \times 5 + 1 = 31$, a prime. Continue the process until a composite number is obtained. Find the prime factors of the result.

2. Find all the pairs of twin primes less than 100.

3. Express the following integers as the sum of two primes in as many ways as you can: 34, 50, 76, 88, 100.

4. Goldbach's conjecture can be stated: Any even number greater than 4 is the sum of two odd primes. Show that this is equivalent to the statement in Section 5.5.

# 6 Rational Numbers

IN CHAPTERS 2 AND 3 WE SAW THAT THE CARDINAL NUMBERS, OR NATURAL numbers and zero, are closed with respect to addition and multiplication. But they are not closed with respect to subtraction or division. The motive for the creation of negative numbers was to produce a system closed with respect to subtraction. The set of integers—positive, negative, and zero—is such a set. The existence of additive inverse elements, or opposites, is equivalent to closure for subtraction. We have seen that subtraction of an integer is equivalent to addition of its opposite.

The integers are not closed under division, even with division by zero excluded. In this chapter we shall make another extension of number to produce a system that is closed with respect to division, except that division by zero is not permissible. The set of rational numbers is such a set.

## 6.1 Ratios

Jim has 6 marbles and Tom has 18. The ratio of Jim's marbles to Tom's marbles is 6:18. The marbles are sold in packages of six. In terms of packages of marbles, the ratio of Jim's to Tom's marbles is 1:3.

The packages sell for 5 cents each. Then in terms of cost the ratio is 5:15. These ratios 6:18, 1:3, and 5:15 are an illustration of *equivalent ratios*.

Before we define equivalent ratios we should decide what a ratio is. Suppose Sam has 24 marbles. The ratio of Jim's to Tom's to Sam's is 6:18:24. In terms of the number of packages of marbles it is 1:3:4. A ratio does not necessarily consist of only two numbers. In the illustration we have used a ratio to indicate the relative measure of two sets, 6:18, then three sets, 6:18:24. We can compare in this way as many sets as we wish.

A ratio is an $n$-tuple of numbers
$a_1:a_2:a_3: \ldots :a_n$
indicating $n$ comparable measures.

We have said that 6:18, 1:3, and 5:15 were equivalent ratios. Each tells the same story by way of comparing the two sets, Jim's marbles and Tom's marbles. The three ratios are related such that each of the numbers in any ratio can be multiplied by some number $k$ to produce any other of the ratios. For example, if we multiply the 1 and the 3 in the ratio 1:3 by 5 we get 5:15. If we multiply each of the members of 6:18 by $\frac{1}{6}$ we get 1:3. The same holds for the equivalent ratios 1:3:4 and 6:18:24; if each member of the first ratio is multiplied by 6 we get the second ratio.

Two ratios are equivalent,
$a_1:a_2:a_3:a_4 \ldots :a_n$ is equivalent to $b_1:b_2:b_3:b_4: \ldots :b_n$ if and only if $a_1 = kb_1$; $a_2 = kb_2$; $a_3 = kb_3$; $a_4 = kb_4$; $a_n = kb_n$ and $k \neq 0$.

In the definition of equivalent ratios no limitation is placed on the numbers except that $k$ cannot be zero. For example, $\frac{1}{2}:\frac{3}{7}$ is a ratio and $\frac{1}{7} \times \frac{1}{2}: \frac{1}{7} \times \frac{3}{7}$ is a ratio equivalent to it.

The idea of equivalent ratios can be used to advantage in both the analysis and solution of many problems.

*Example:* Mr. Jones, Mr. Smith, and Mr. Brown formed a partnership. Mr. Jones put up \$10,000; Mr. Smith put up \$15,000; and

Mr. Brown operated the business. In dividing the profits it was agreed that Mr. Brown's contribution was to be evaluated at \$25,000. Determine the share each should receive from a profit of \$1200.

*Solution:* The ratio of investments of Jones: Smith: Brown: Total is 10,000: 15,000: 25,000: 50,000. If we multiply each member of the ratio by $\frac{1}{5000}$ we have the equivalent ratio 2:3:5:10. Or in general, $2k:3k:5k:10k$ is an equivalent ratio for any $k \neq 0$. We are required to find $k$ such that we have $2k:3k:5k:1200$. That is, $10k = 1200$. Hence $k = 120$. Jones' share is $2k =$ \$240, Smith's share is $3k =$ \$360, and Brown's share is $5k =$ \$600.

## EXERCISES

**1.** In each of the following fill the blanks so as to make the ratios equivalent:
(a) 3:__, 5:$8\frac{1}{3}$, __:15
(b) 2:3:7, 4:__:14, 6:__:__, __:12:__
(c) 1:3:5, __:__:25, __:12:__, 4:__:__

**2.** Which of the following sets have as elements equivalent ratios?
(a) {1:2, 2:3, 3:4, 4:5, 5:6}
(b) {2:3, 4:6, 5:15, 20:30}
(c) {3:5, 9:15, 6:10, 24:40}
(d) {4:8, 3:6:7, 9:18, 6:12:14:25}
(e) {9:6, 12:8, 30:20, 27:18}

**3.** For what values of $k$ are each of the following pairs of ratios equivalent?
(a) 2:3:7 and $2k:3k:21$
(b) 50:75:90 and $10:5k:18$
(c) 6:7:9 and $2k:21:3k$
(d) 2:3:5:10 and $2k:3k:5k:25$

*Use equivalent ratios to solve each of the following:*

**4.** Mr. Brown made an automobile trip of 235 miles in 5 hours. At this same rate how far can he travel in 7 hours? How long will a trip of 530 miles require at the same rate?

**5.** Jim is paid \$2 per hour, Tom is paid \$3 per hour, and Bob is paid \$5 per hour. If they work the same number of hours how much does each earn when their total earnings come to \$150?

**6.** At the same time that a 6-ft fence post casts a shadow 8 ft long a flag pole casts a shadow 44 ft long. How high is the flag pole?

**7.** A fuel mixture requires 3 lb of fuel $A$ to 5 lb of fuel $B$ to 7 lb of fuel $C$. How many pounds of each fuel are required to make 1500 lb of the mixture?

## RATIONAL NUMBERS

## 6.2 Equivalence Classes

According to the definition of cardinal numbers on page 34, the cardinal number 2 is the set of all sets equivalent to $\{0, 1\}$. Since it is the set of *all* equivalent sets it is called an *equivalence class*. A somewhat different approach could have been used in defining negative numbers. We have seen that a negative number is actually an implied subtraction. Negative numbers can be defined as equivalence classes. If this approach were used $-3$ would be the class of all differences equivalent to $3 - 6$. There are infinitely many such differences, so the equivalence class is an infinite set. But under what circumstances are such differences equivalent? We cannot find $3 - 6$ in the set of natural numbers. By definition, if $a$ is less than $b$, the difference $a - b$ is equivalent to $c - d$ if and only if $b - a = d - c$. Using this approach

$$-3 = \{(1 - 4), (2 - 5), (3 - 6), (4 - 7), \ldots\}$$

where it is understood that the three dots imply not merely an endless set, but all such equivalent differences.

In Section 6.1 equivalent ratios were defined. The *class* of equivalent ratios $\{4k:2k\}$ is the set of *all* ratios equivalent to the ratio 4:2. Each possible value of $k$ determines an element of the set of ratios.

If we confine our consideration to ratios of two numbers the notation $a/b$ can be used instead of $a:b$. If we restrict ratios to ratios of integers we can now define rational numbers.

> A rational number is an equivalence class of ratios of pairs of integers $ka/kb$, $b \neq 0$.

According to this definition, the equivalence class

$$\{\tfrac{1}{2}, \tfrac{2}{4}, \tfrac{3}{6}, \tfrac{4}{8}, \ldots, k/2k, \ldots\}$$

is a rational number. We need a more convenient way to indicate the number. We take as representative element of the set the simplest ratio $\frac{1}{2}$. Hence $\frac{1}{2}$ is both a ratio 1:2 and a rational number. Any other element of the equivalence class can also be used to represent the rational number. Thus $\frac{4}{8}$ is just another way to write the rational number $\frac{1}{2}$.

Two ratios $a/b$ and $c/d$ are two names for the same rational number if and only if they are equivalent ratios, that is, if and only if $a = kc$ and

$b = kd$, where $k \neq 0$. Since $b = kd$ is equivalent to $kd = b$ we can multiply these equal numbers by the equal numbers $a = kc$ and obtain $akd = bkc$. Since $k$ cannot be zero we can divide both sides by $k$ and obtain $ad = bc$. Hence the rational numbers $a/b$ and $c/d$ are the same number if and only if $ad = bc$.

We should make a distinction between a *fraction*, a *ratio*, and a *rational number*. The word "fraction" has to do with the form of a number. Although $\frac{8}{4} = 2$, 2 is not a fraction, but $\frac{8}{4}$ is a fraction. A fraction is a number that has two parts, a numerator and a denominator. It is an implied division, numerator divided by denominator. The fraction $\frac{8}{4}$ means $8 \div 4$. It is by no means always possible to carry through the division; in fact it is not necessary for either numerator or denominator to be an integer. For example, $1/\sqrt{2}$ and $\sqrt{2}/\sqrt{3}$ are fractions.

A ratio is simply a set of comparable measures of some kind. A ratio is not restricted to two numbers, nor are the numbers restricted to integers. For example, $1:\sqrt{2}:-5$ is a ratio. For this reason we cannot say in general that a ratio is an implied division. If a ratio were always an implied division how would we interpret 8:4:2? Does it mean $(8 \div 4) \div 2 = 2 \div 2 = 1$ or does it mean $8 \div (4 \div 2) = 8 \div 2 = 4$? In truth, it means neither. It merely states a comparison of three comparable measures; the first is twice as large as the second and the second is twice as large as the third.

However, *if the ratio compares only two magnitudes*, the second of which is not zero, it can be considered as an implied division. We may think of $8 \div 4 = 2$ in the sense that 8:4 and 2:1 are equivalent ratios.

We have technically defined a rational number as an equivalence class of ratios of two integers, $a:b$, with the restriction that $b \neq 0$. However, we agree that any element of the equivalence class may be used as a symbol for the rational number. Thus $\frac{1}{2}$ and $\frac{2}{4}$ are but two symbols for the same rational number.

Then what is $\frac{1}{2}$, or for that matter $a/b$, where $a$ and $b$ are integers and $b \neq 0$? It may be interpreted as a fraction, numerator $a$ and denominator $b$, meaning $a \div b$. It may also be interpreted as a ratio $a:b$. Finally, it may be interpreted as a symbol for a rational number. We must develop the properties of rational numbers in a manner consistent with this triple interpretation.

It is to this end that we exclude $b = 0$ from the rational number $a/b$. We *want* the rational number to mean an implied division, and division by zero is excluded as a possible operation. It is of interest to note that the fraction $\frac{5}{0}$ is meaningless because a fraction is an implied division. But there is nothing wrong with the ratio 5:0. The Yankees have scored 5 runs and the Giants no runs. What is the ratio of their scores? It is 5:0. No inconsistency would result from the concept of a ratio 0:0, but it is a rather useless concept. No other ratio is equivalent to it.

### EXERCISES

1. Why is no other ratio equivalent to 0:0?
2. What is the distinction, if any, between an equivalence class and an infinite set of equivalent elements?
3. If the elements of an equivalence class of ratios are considered implied divisions what is the simplest way to designate the equivalence class $\{\frac{8}{4}, \frac{16}{8}, \ldots, 2k/k, \ldots\}$?
4. In the light of Exercise 3 is 2 a rational number? Are all rational numbers fractions?
5. Give an example of a fraction that is not a rational number.
6. Give an example of a ratio that is not a rational number.
7. Is it possible for the ratio of two numbers, not necessarily integers, not to be a symbol for a rational number? Illustrate.
8. Write five elements of the equivalence class of which $\frac{2}{5}$ is representative element.
9. Is $12 \div 5$ a rational number? Discuss.
10. If 3 is a rational number what ratio is implied? The ratio implies what division? Why can we not then say that 3 is a fraction?
11. Interpreted as a fraction, what does $\frac{3}{4}$ mean? Interpreted as a ratio, what does it mean? Interpreted as a rational number, what does it mean?

## 6.3 Operations with Rational Numbers

We wish to change our point of view slightly from that in the previous section. If $a$ and $b$ are integers and $b \neq 0$, we wish to say that by definition $a/b$ is a rational number. This is simply more convenient than to say $a/b$ is a symbol whereby we may identify the rational number (equivalence class of ratios) of which $a/b$ is a member.

Furthermore, we may refer to two equal rational numbers when we have two ratios from the same equivalence class. Thus, $a/b = c/d$ if and only if $ad = bc$.

Next, we wish to determine how to multiply and add rational numbers. In doing so we shall be guided by three principles.

(1) The properties of the integers—the closure, associative, commutative, distributive, identity, and additive inverse properties—shall be preserved.

(2) Since we want closure for division by nonzero numbers, we want the rational number $a/b$ to mean $a \div b$.

(3) We want all nonzero rational numbers to have multiplicative inverses. This will assure closure of nonzero rational numbers under division. Specifically, we want $a$ times the inverse of $b$ to mean $a/b$.

We shall follow the same procedure as was used in determining the rules of signs for addition and multiplication of integers. We shall not define addition and multiplication of rational numbers. We shall assume that the properties listed are satisfied by the rational numbers; and we shall derive the rules for addition and multiplication as a consequence of this assumption.

## 6.4 Multiplication of Rational Numbers

We have assumed the existence of a multiplication inverse for each nonzero integer. The inverse of the integer $a$ is written $1/a$. Hence

$$a \times 1/a = 1$$

Note parenthetically that this is in keeping with our earliest contact with fractions. The child learns early in life that "one half of" means the same thing as "divided by two." Multiplying by $\frac{1}{2}$ has the same effect as dividing by 2, and $2 \times \frac{1}{2} = 1$.

Before proceeding to the general problem of multiplying two rational numbers, let us investigate the product $1/b \times 1/d$. We know that

$$b \times 1/b = 1, \ d \times 1/d = 1,$$

and

$$(b \times d) \times \frac{1}{(b \times d)} = 1$$

This follows from the meaning of the multiplicative inverse of an integer. But multiplying the first two equalities, we have

$$(b \times 1/b) \times (d \times 1/d) = 1 \times 1 = 1$$

and since the associative and commutative properties must hold for rational numbers

$$(b \times d) \times (1/b \times 1/d) = 1 \qquad (1)$$

We may conclude that both $\frac{1}{(b \times d)}$ and $(1/b \times 1/d)$ are the multiplicative inverse of $b \times d$. That is, they are equal:

$$\boxed{1/b \times 1/d = \frac{1}{(b \times d)}} \qquad (2)$$

We wish to derive a rule for finding $a/b \times c/d$, the product of two rational numbers. Since $a/b$ means $a \div b$ and $c/d$ means $c \div d$ we have

$$(a \div b) \times (c \div d) = (a \times 1/b) \times (c \times 1/d) \qquad (3)$$

or

$$(a \times 1/b) \times (c \times 1/d) = (a \times c) \times (1/b \times 1/d) \qquad (4)$$

And from Equation (2)

$$(a \times c) \times (1/b \times 1/d) = (a \times c) \times \frac{1}{(b \times d)} \qquad (5)$$

But this means

$$(a \times 1/b) \times (c \times 1/d) = (a \times c) \div (b \times d) = \frac{a \times c}{b \times d} \qquad (6)$$

Combining Equations (1) through (6), we have the rule for multiplication of rational numbers.

> If $a$, $b$, $c$, $d$ are integers and neither $b$ nor $d$ is zero, the product of two rational numbers $a/b$ and $c/d$ is
>
> $$a/b \times c/d = \frac{a \times c}{b \times d}$$

This is, of course, the usual rule for multiplication of fractions. The numerator of the product is the product of the numerators and the denominator of the product is the product of the denominators.

The question was raised in the Exercises in Section 6.2 as to whether an integer is also a rational number. In the strict sense of the word it is not, whether we follow the definition in Section 6.2 or the alternate statement in the first paragraph of Section 6.3. From the point of view of an equivalence class of ratios, 5 cannot be the representative element of any such class simply because 5 is not a ratio. Similarly, if a rational number is a symbol $a/b$ where $a$ and $b$ are integers and $b \neq 0$, 5 cannot qualify as a rational number.

On the other hand, we have said a rational number must mean an implied division. Now there are infinitely many pairs of integers whose quotient is 5. If we interpret the elements of the equivalence class of ratios

$$\{5:1, 10:2, 15:3, \ldots, 5k:k, \ldots\}$$

as fractions each one of them will equal 5. The representative element of this equivalence class is $\frac{5}{1}$. Therefore we certainly can call $\frac{5}{1}$ a rational number. The question seems to reduce itself to this—must the division which a rational number implies remain merely implied if we are to continue to call it a rational number?

Exactly the same kind of problem arises when integers are defined as implied subtractions of natural numbers. Since $5 - 2$ is an implied subtraction it defines an integer. Strictly speaking, the difference 3 is not an integer, it is a natural number. The difference $5 - 2$ defines the integer $+3$. But the positive integers and the natural numbers behave in a perfectly consistent manner. In the set of natural numbers $3 + 2 = 5$ and in the set of positive integers $(+3) + (+2) = (+5)$. Also, in the set of natural numbers $3 \times 2 = 6$ and in the set of positive integers $(+3) \times (+2) = (+6)$. For purposes of computation, we need make no distinction between the set of positive integers and the set of natural numbers. The principle exhibited here is called *isomorphism*. The set of natural numbers and the set of positive integers are *isomorphic*.

We wish to establish this same relationship between the set of rational numbers of the form $a/1$, where $a$ is an integer, and the set of integers. Does the definition of multiplication preserve this relationship? Since $2 \times -3 = -6$ we should get the result $\frac{2}{1} \times -\frac{3}{1} = -\frac{6}{1}$ when we multiply the rational numbers $\frac{2}{1}$ and $-\frac{3}{1}$. This is precisely what the definition requires.

$$\frac{2}{1} \times \frac{-3}{1} = \frac{2 \times (-3)}{1 \times 1} = \frac{-6}{1}$$

This is true in the general case also. If $a$ and $b$ are integers and $a \times b = c$ then

$$\frac{a}{1} \times \frac{b}{1} = \frac{a \times b}{1 \times 1} = \frac{c}{1}$$

When we investigate the addition of rational numbers we shall see that this property also applies to addition. Then we need make no distinction between the integer $a$ and the rational number $a/1$.

**RATIONAL NUMBERS**

Do the rational numbers have a multiplication identity? That is, is there a rational number by which any rational number $a/b$ may be multiplied such that the product is $a/b$? We would certainly expect the rational number equivalent to the multiplication identity for integers, namely 1, to be the multiplication identity.

$$\frac{a}{b} \times \frac{1}{1} = \frac{a}{b}$$

However, if $c$ is any integer different from zero, $c/c$ is an element of the same equivalence class as $1/1$.

$$\frac{a}{b} \times \frac{c}{c} = \frac{a \times c}{b \times c}$$

Here we find the product is not $a/b$, but it is a member of the same equivalence class as $a/b$. That is $a/b = (a \times c)/(b \times c)$. We conclude that the multiplication identity is 1 in the sense that the integer $c$ is the same as the rational number $c/1$. But the multiplication identity may appear as $\frac{3}{3}$, $\frac{5}{5}$, $\frac{9}{9}$, or any rational number $c/c$.

## EXERCISES

**1.** Prove that the rational numbers are closed with respect to multiplication.

**2.** Demonstrate that multiplication of rational numbers is commutative by applying the rule for multiplication of rational numbers to each side of the following equalities.
(a) $\frac{5}{6} \times (\frac{2}{7} \times \frac{3}{5}) = (\frac{2}{7} \times \frac{3}{5}) \times \frac{5}{6}$
(b) $2/b \times c/5 = c/5 \times 2/b$
(c) $-3/7 \times 2/-5 = 2/-5 \times -3/7$
(d) $2x/y \times x/2y = x/2y \times 2x/y$

**3.** Demonstrate that multiplication of rational numbers is associative by applying the rule for multiplication of rational numbers to each of the following equalities:
(a) $(\frac{2}{3} \times \frac{5}{6}) \times a/2b = \frac{2}{3} \times (\frac{5}{6} \times a/2b)$
(b) $-3 \times (-\frac{2}{5} \times \frac{1}{7}) = (-3 \times -\frac{2}{5}) \times \frac{1}{7}$
(c) $(a/b \times \frac{4}{7}) \times b/a = a/b \times (\frac{4}{7} \times b/a)$
(d) $(\frac{6}{5} \times \frac{2}{3}) \times \frac{5}{6} = \frac{6}{5} \times (\frac{2}{3} \times \frac{5}{6})$

**4.** Prove that the following pairs of rational numbers are equal:
(a) $-a/b$; $a/-b$
(b) $-6/-2$; $3$
(c) $1/-5$; $-\frac{1}{5}$
(d) $-7/-3$; $\frac{7}{3}$
(e) $\frac{0}{7}$; $\frac{0}{5}$

**5.** Prove that any two rational numbers whose numerator is zero are equal.

**6.** Justify "cancellation" in multiplication of the fractions

$$\frac{\overset{1}{\cancel{3}}}{\underset{2}{\cancel{4}}} \times \frac{\overset{1}{\cancel{2}}}{\underset{3}{\cancel{9}}} = \frac{1}{6}$$

in terms of the development in this chapter.

**7.** Prove that the product of any rational number times a rational number whose numerator is zero is a rational number whose numerator is zero.

## 6.5 Addition of Rational Numbers

As we seek to establish the rule for addition of rational numbers, the usual rule for addition of fractions is, of course, our objective. We wish to show that this rule is a logical consequence of the properties of rational numbers.

The rule for multiplication emerges naturally because a rational number is an implied division, and division is the inverse of multiplication.

If we express the sum $a/b + c/d$ so as to indicate the division involved we have

$$\frac{a}{b} + \frac{c}{d} = (a \div b) + (c \div d)$$

And this can be changed to

$$\frac{a}{b} + \frac{c}{d} = a \times \frac{1}{b} + c \times \frac{1}{d}$$

by using the multiplication inverses of $b$ and $d$. Here we have both addition and multiplication involved, which indicates the use of the distributive property. But in order that this can be done we must find equivalent forms for $a/b$ and $c/d$ such that they have a common factor.

$$\frac{a}{b} = \frac{a \times c}{b \times c} \qquad \text{and} \qquad \frac{c}{d} = \frac{a \times c}{a \times d}$$

Hence

$$\frac{a}{b} + \frac{c}{d} = \frac{a \times c}{b \times c} \times \frac{a \times c}{a \times d} = (a \times c)\frac{1}{b \times c} + (a \times c) \times \frac{1}{a \times d}$$

$$= (a \times c)\left(\frac{1}{b \times c} + \frac{1}{a \times d}\right)$$

We have used the distributive property, yet we are still confronted with the necessity of adding two fractions. We can find equivalent fractions in another way.

$$\frac{a}{b} = \frac{a \times d}{b \times d} \quad \text{and} \quad \frac{c}{d} = \frac{b \times c}{b \times d}$$

Hence

$$\frac{a}{b} + \frac{c}{d} = \frac{a \times d}{b \times d} + \frac{b \times c}{b \times d} = (a \times d) \times \frac{1}{(b \times d)} + (b \times c) \times \frac{1}{(b \times d)}$$

which, by the commutative property, yields

$$\frac{a}{b} + \frac{c}{d} = \frac{1}{(b \times d)} \times (a \times d) + \frac{1}{(b \times d)} \times (b \times c)$$

and, employing the distributive property,

$$\frac{a}{b} + \frac{c}{d} = \frac{1}{b \times d} \times (a \times d + b \times c) = \frac{a \times d + b \times c}{b \times d}$$

Hence we have derived the rule for addition of rational numbers.

> If $a/b$ and $c/d$ are any two rational numbers
>
> $$\frac{a}{b} + \frac{c}{d} = \frac{a \times d + b \times c}{b \times d}$$

This should be recognized as the usual method for addition of fractions. To find $\frac{3}{4} + \frac{7}{5}$ we first reduce to a common denominator

$$\tfrac{3}{4} + \tfrac{7}{5} = \tfrac{15}{20} + \tfrac{28}{20}$$

then write the sum of the numerators over the common denominator.

$$\tfrac{15}{20} + \tfrac{28}{20} = \tfrac{43}{20}$$

But following the above rule, we do essentially the same thing.

$$\frac{3}{4} + \frac{7}{5} = \frac{3 \times 5 + 4 \times 7}{4 \times 5} = \frac{15 + 28}{20} = \frac{43}{20}$$

Are sums preserved when we identify the rational number $a/1$ with the integer $a$? Since $2 + 3 = 5$, we should have $\frac{2}{1} + \frac{3}{1} = \frac{5}{1}$. When we apply the definition of addition we have

$$\frac{2}{1} + \frac{3}{1} = \frac{1 \times 2 + 1 \times 3}{1 \times 1} = \frac{2 + 3}{1} = \frac{5}{1}$$

and in the general case

$$\frac{a}{1} + \frac{b}{1} = \frac{1 \times a + 1 \times b}{1 \times 1} = \frac{a + b}{1}$$

Since the rational numbers of the form $a/1$ behave precisely as the integers $a$, we shall make no distinction between them, and consider any integer $a$ as a rational number.

Accordingly, does the rational number 0 serve as the addition identity? That is, does $a/b + \frac{0}{1} = a/b$? Applying the definition, we have

$$\frac{a}{b} + \frac{0}{1} = \frac{1 \times a + 0 \times b}{b \times 1} = \frac{a}{b}$$

## EXERCISES

**1.** Prove that the rational numbers are closed with respect to addition.

**2.** Verify that addition of rational numbers is commutative by evaluating independently each side of the following equations:

(a) $\frac{1}{3} + \frac{2}{5} = \frac{2}{5} + \frac{1}{3}$

(b) $\dfrac{-2}{7} + (\frac{1}{4} + \frac{5}{6}) = (\frac{1}{4} + \frac{5}{6}) + \dfrac{-2}{7}$

(c) $-a/5 + \dfrac{3}{2b} = \dfrac{3}{2b} + -a/5$

(d) $(\frac{1}{3} + 5) + \frac{1}{4} = \frac{1}{4} + (\frac{1}{3} + 5)$

**3.** Verify that addition of rational numbers is associative by evaluating independently each side of the following equations:

(a) $\frac{3}{4} + \left(\dfrac{1}{5} + \dfrac{-6}{2}\right) = (\frac{3}{4} + \frac{1}{5}) + \dfrac{-6}{2}$

(b) $-a/b + (\frac{1}{2} + a/b) = (-a/b + \frac{1}{2}) + a/b$

(c) $\left(-5 + \dfrac{-2}{3}\right) + \frac{2}{3} = -5 + \left(\dfrac{-2}{3} + \dfrac{2}{3}\right)$

(d) $a/2b + (2/b + 2a/b) = (a/2b + 2/b) \times 2a/b$

**4.** Verify that multiplication of rational numbers is distributive over addition by evaluating independently each side of the following equations:

(a) $\frac{2}{5} \times (\frac{1}{3} + \frac{1}{4}) = \frac{2}{5} \times \frac{1}{3} + \frac{2}{5} \times \frac{1}{4}$

(b) $a/b \times (1/c + d) = a/b \times 1/c + a/b \times d$

(c) $-4 \times \left(\frac{-2}{3} + \frac{-1}{6}\right) = -4 \times \frac{-2}{3} + -4 \times \frac{-1}{6}$

(d) $-1/a \times (2 + -1/b) = -1/a \times 2 + -1/a \times -1/b$

**5.** Prove that if addition of rational numbers were defined as $a/b + c/d = (a + c)/(b + d)$ addition would be associative and commutative.

**6.** Prove that if addition of rational numbers were defined as in Exercise 5 and multiplication were defined in the usual way multiplication would be distributive over addition.

**7.** In the light of Exercises 5 and 6 why is the definition in Exercise 5 not acceptable as a rule for addition of rational numbers?

**8.** The rule for addition of rational numbers given on page 173 does not require finding the lowest common denominator. Explain why the results are comparable to the lowest common denominator method.

## 6.6 The Inverse Operations

Negative integers were created in order that each integer $a$ will have an additive inverse $-a$. Can this be extended to rational numbers? Either the numerator $a$ or the denominator $b$ of the rational number $a/b$ may be negative. For that matter both may be negative. Without regard to the signs of $a$ and $b$ if $-(a/b)$ is the additive inverse of $a/b$ then $a/b + -(a/b) = 0$. On the other hand, the rule for the addition of rational numbers gives

$$\frac{a}{b} + \frac{-a}{b} = \frac{a + (-a)}{b} = \frac{0}{b} = 0$$

Hence

$$-\left(\frac{a}{b}\right) = \frac{-a}{b}$$

Since the subtraction of rational numbers is the inverse of addition, subtraction and addition of the additive inverse should give the same result.

$$\frac{a}{b} - \frac{c}{d} = \frac{a}{b} + \frac{-c}{d} = \frac{a \times d + b \times (-c)}{b \times d} = \frac{a \times d - b \times c}{b \times d}$$

> If $a/b$ and $c/d$ are any two rational numbers
>
> $$\frac{a}{b} - \frac{c}{d} = \frac{a \times d - b \times c}{b \times d}$$

This is consistent with the usual rule for subtraction of fractions. To find $\frac{5}{8} - \frac{1}{3}$ first change to a common denominator

$$\frac{5}{8} - \frac{1}{3} = \frac{15}{24} - \frac{8}{24}$$

then write the difference of the numerators over the common denominator.

$$\frac{15}{24} - \frac{8}{24} = \frac{7}{24}$$

The above rule requires essentially the same thing

$$\frac{5}{8} - \frac{1}{3} = \frac{5 \times 3 - 8 \times 1}{8 \times 3} = \frac{7}{24}$$

Every rational number $a/b$ other than zero has a multiplicative inverse $b/a$ since

$$\frac{a}{b} \times \frac{b}{a} = \frac{a \times b}{b \times a}$$

But $\frac{a \times b}{b \times a} = \frac{a \times b}{a \times b}$ is equivalent to the multiplication identity $\frac{1}{1}$.

> The multiplicative inverse of $\frac{a}{b}$, $ab \neq 0$, is $\frac{b}{a}$

Since division is the inverse of multiplication, division by the rational number $c/d$ should give the same result as multiplication by the multiplicative inverse $d/c$.

$$\frac{a}{b} \div \frac{c}{d} = \frac{a}{b} \times \frac{d}{c} = \frac{a \times d}{b \times c}$$

> If $a/b$ and $c/d$ are rational numbers and $cd \neq 0$
>
> $$\frac{a}{b} \div \frac{c}{d} = \frac{a \times d}{b \times c}$$

Every rational number $c/d$ other than zero has a multiplicative inverse $d/c$. The definition of rational numbers excludes zero. The inverse of

$0/a$ would be $a/0$, but since a rational number is an implied division this would mean division by zero.

The rule for division is consistent with the interpretation of a rational number as an implied division.

$$\tfrac{18}{3} \div \tfrac{4}{2} = (18 \div 3) \div (4 \div 2) = 6 \div 2 = 3$$

and by the rule for division

$$\tfrac{18}{3} \div \tfrac{4}{2} = \tfrac{18}{3} \times \tfrac{2}{4} = \tfrac{36}{12} = 3$$

In the general case, the rule can be established by using the division principle which permits multiplying both dividend ana divisor by the same number without changing the quotient.

$$\frac{a}{b} \div \frac{c}{d} = \frac{a}{b} \times \frac{d}{c} \div \frac{c}{d} \times \frac{d}{c}$$

$$\frac{a}{b} \div \frac{c}{d} = \frac{a}{b} \times \frac{d}{c} \div 1$$

$$\frac{a}{b} \div \frac{c}{d} = \frac{a}{b} \times \frac{d}{c}$$

## EXERCISES

1. Prove that the rational numbers are closed with respect to subtraction.
2. Prove the nonzero rational numbers are closed with respect to division.
3. Verify that subtraction of rational numbers is not commutative by evaluating the following pairs of expressions:
   (a) $\frac{3}{5} - \frac{1}{2}$; $\frac{1}{2} - \frac{3}{5}$
   (b) $(\frac{1}{4} + \frac{2}{3}) - \frac{5}{6}$; $\frac{5}{6} - (\frac{1}{4} + \frac{2}{3})$
   (c) $a/b - 1/c$; $1/c - a/b$
4. Verify that subtraction of rational numbers is not associative by evaluating the following pairs of expressions:
   (a) $\frac{1}{4} - (\frac{2}{3} - \frac{1}{6})$; $(\frac{1}{4} - \frac{2}{3}) - \frac{1}{6}$
   (b) $2/a - (3/b - 1/(a \times b))$; $(2/a - 3/b) - 1/(a \times b)$
   (c) $\frac{1}{5} - (-\frac{2}{3} - \frac{1}{4})$; $(\frac{1}{5} - -\frac{2}{3}) - \frac{1}{4}$
5. Verify that division of rational numbers is not commutative by evaluating the following pairs of expressions:
   (a) $\frac{2}{5} \div \frac{3}{7}$; $\frac{3}{7} \div \frac{2}{5}$

THE INVERSE OPERATIONS

(b) $1/a \div 1/b$; $1/b \div 1/a$
(c) $(-\frac{5}{6} \div 2/-3) \div \frac{1}{2}$; $-\frac{5}{6} \div (2/-3 \div \frac{1}{2})$

**6.** Evaluate each of the following pairs of expressions:
(a) $\frac{2}{5} \div \frac{3}{4}$; $(\frac{2}{5} \div \frac{1}{3}) \div (\frac{3}{4} \div \frac{1}{3})$
(b) $\frac{1}{7} \div \frac{2}{9}$; $(\frac{1}{7} \times \frac{9}{2}) \div (\frac{2}{9} \times \frac{9}{2})$
(c) $\frac{3}{8} \div \frac{2}{5}$; $(\frac{3}{8} \times \frac{5}{2}) \div (\frac{2}{5} \times \frac{5}{2})$
What generalization does this suggest?

**7.** The following are written in base eight. Compute in base eight.
(a) $\frac{2}{5} + \frac{2}{11}$
(b) $\frac{5}{14} \times \frac{1}{10}$
(c) $\frac{11}{12} \div \frac{3}{24}$
(d) $\frac{5}{11} - \frac{2}{3}$

**8.** Convert each of the parts of Exercise 7 to base ten and evaluate. Convert the answers obtained in Exercise 7 to base ten and compare with the answers obtained here.

**9.** Are there any integers $a$ and $b$ for which $1/a + 1/b = 1/(a + b)$? If so, what are they?

**10.** Find the additive inverse and the multiplicative inverse of each of the following:

(a) $\dfrac{-3}{4}$ (b) $-\dfrac{-3}{5}$ (c) $\frac{2}{5}$ (d) $a/2b$ (e) $-b/2a$

**11.** Is there a rational number whose additive inverse is its multiplicative inverse. If so, what is it; if not, why not?

## 6.7 Comparing Rational Numbers

In Section 6.2 we saw that "fraction" has to do with the form of a number. A fraction has a numerator and denominator and is an implied division, numerator divided by denominator. If the numerator and denominator are both integers the fraction is a *simple fraction.* If numerator or denominator, or both, are themselves fractions it is a *complex fraction.* If the numerator is smaller that the denominator the fraction is called a *proper fraction.* If the numerator is equal to or greater than the the denominator the fraction is an *improper fraction.*

*Examples:* $\frac{2}{3}$, $\frac{7}{4}$, $\frac{5}{5}$ are simple fractions, but not all of them are proper fractions. The fractions

$$\frac{\frac{1}{2}}{\frac{2}{5}}, \quad \frac{1}{\frac{4}{7}}, \quad \frac{\frac{3}{8}}{5}$$

are complex fractions, but not all of them are improper fractions;

$$\tfrac{3}{4},\ \frac{\frac{1}{2}}{5},\ \tfrac{2}{7}$$

are proper fractions, but not all of them are simple fractions;

$$\tfrac{5}{5},\ \frac{\frac{1}{2}}{\frac{2}{5}},\ \frac{3}{\frac{3}{4}}$$

are improper fractions, but not all of them are complex.

An improper fraction may always be reduced to an integer or a *mixed number* by carrying out the implied division.

*Examples:* $\frac{28}{7} = 4$ because $28 \div 7 = 4$

$\frac{30}{7} = 4\frac{2}{7}$ because $30 = 4 \times 7 + 2$

A mixed number, such as $4\frac{2}{7}$, is actually an integer plus a proper fraction: $4\frac{2}{7}$ means $4 + \frac{2}{7}$.

What is the relationship between rational numbers and fractions? Every rational number can be expressed as a simple fraction, either proper or improper. If a complex fraction has numerator and denominator which are obtained by adding, subtracting, and multiplying simple fractions then it may be considered a fraction having a simple fraction as numerator and denominator. This is because rational numbers are closed with respect to addition, subtraction, and multiplication. Since such a complex fraction is an implied division it also represents a rational number if the denominator is not zero. We know this because, except for division by zero, the rational numbers are also closed with respect to division. Hence, with this one exception of division by zero, any fraction consisting exclusively of integers, added, subtracted, multiplied, and divided, represents a rational number.

In Section 1.5 the relation "greater than" was briefly mentioned. We have a clear intuitive notion of this relation. The statement "10 is greater than 5" is probably acceptable because we agree that a set of 10 elements has more elements than does a set of 5 elements. Or, to reduce the concept to more primitive considerations, if the elements of the set of 5 are placed in correspondence with the elements of the set of ten, when the elements of the first set are exhausted there will still be elements of the second unpaired. But this idea of "greater than" is not of much help when we attempt to compare $-5$ with $\frac{1}{3}$.

## COMPARING RATIONAL NUMBERS

"Greater than" is an order relation. We can define the relation for all rational numbers. The symbol for "greater than" is $>$. Thus "$a$ is greater than $b$" is written $a > b$. In the above paragraph the intuitive notion of "greater than" as applied to positive integers can be expressed in terms of subtraction. Consider sets $A$ and $B$ with $n(A) = a$ and $n(B) = b$. If there is a distinct element of $A$ to pair with each element of $B$ but not an element of $B$ to pair with each element of $A$ we say that $a > b$. But this is precisely the condition under which $a - b$ is a positive number. We take this as the definition of $>$ for any two rational numbers.

> If $a$, $b$ are rational numbers
>
> $$a > b$$
>
> if and only if $a - b$ is a positive number.

Any two rational numbers $a$ and $b$ are related in one of three ways.

$$a = b, \; a > b, \text{ or } b > a$$

We know that if $a = b$ then $a - b = 0$. If $a > b$ then $a - b$ is positive. If $b > a$ then $b - a$ is positive, and consequently $a - b$ is negative.

Is $-10 > -2$? If I owe \$10 and you owe \$2 my debt is certainly larger than yours. However, since $(-10) - (-2) = -8$ we must conclude from the definition that $-2 > -10$. In fact, if $a$ and $b$ are positive and $a > b$ then $-b > -a$. For if $a > b$ then $a - b$ is positive. But

| | |
|---|---|
| $a - b = a + (-b)$ | $b$ and $-b$ are additive inverses |
| $a + (-b) = (-b) + a$ | addition is commutative |
| $-b + a = (-b) - (-a)$ | $a$ and $-a$ are additive inverses |

Hence $(-b) - (-a)$, being equal to $a - b$, is positive and it follows $-b > -a$.

When the integers are placed on the number line

$$-4 \quad -3 \quad -2 \quad -1 \quad 0 \quad 1 \quad 2 \quad 3 \quad 4$$

$a > b$ if and only if the point indicating $a$ is farther to the right than the point indicating $b$.

All rational numbers can be represented on the number line. If the rational number is a proper fraction it is represented on the line as a point between 0 and 1. If it is an improper fraction, expressed as a mixed number, the integer $a$ plus a proper fraction, the point on the number line is found between $a$ and $a + 1$ just as the same proper fraction is found between 0 and 1.

*Example:* Find on the number line points corresponding to $\frac{2}{5}$ and $\frac{23}{7}$.

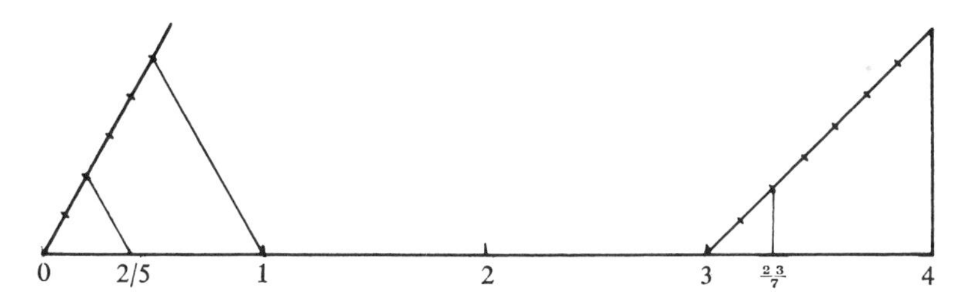


Any convenient line is drawn through the point 0. On this line 5 equal segments are laid off. Join the end of the fifth segment and the point 1. At the end of the second segment draw a parallel to this line. The parallel will cut the number line at the required point $\frac{2}{5}$. To find $\frac{23}{7}$ change to the corresponding mixed number $3\frac{2}{7}$. We now proceed as before except that we begin at the point 3 and use 7 equal segments rather than 5.

The generality of the method used in the example is evident. To locate the point on the number line corresponding to the proper fraction $a/b$ we lay off $b$ equal segments and draw the parallel at the end of the $a$th segment.

As with the integers, if $a$ and $b$ are rational numbers $a > b$ if and only if the point representing $a$ on the number line is to the right of the point representing $b$.

However, it is not necessary to locate the numbers on the number line to determine which is the greater. If $a$, $b$, $c$, $d$ are integers and $b \times d \neq 0$ (Why does this mean neither $b$ nor $d$ is zero?) by definition $a/b > c/d$ if and only if $a/b - c/d$ is positive. But let us examine $a/b - c/d$ more closely.

If $a/b$ is expressed as $ab/b^2$ the denominator must be positive. Similarly for $c/d = cd/d^2$. Hence

$$\begin{aligned} a/b - c/d &= ab/b^2 - cd/d^2 \\ &= abd^2/b^2d^2 - b^2cd/b^2d^2 \\ &= \frac{abd^2 - b^2cd}{b^2d^2} \end{aligned}$$

## COMPARING RATIONAL NUMBERS

The denominator $b^2d^2$ is positive. Then the fraction is positive if and only if the numerator $abd^2 - b^2cd$ is positive. But $abd^2 - b^2cd$ is positive if and only if $abd^2 > b^2cd$. We conclude that $a/b > c/d$ if and only if $abd^2 > b^2cd$ is positive.

*Example:* Determine which is the greater: $\frac{-5}{6}$ or $-2/-7$

$$-5 \times 6 \times -7 \times -7 = -1470$$

$$-2 \times -7 \times 6 \times 6 = 540$$

Since $540 > -1470$ it follows that

$$\frac{-2}{-7} > \frac{-5}{6}$$

The relation "greater than" enables one to determine which of two given numbers is the greater. There is an important difference between the ordering of the integers and the ordering of the rational numbers. There is always a next integer after any given one. This is not true of the rational numbers. Between any two rational numbers there is always an infinite number of others. The rational numbers are *dense*. For example, if

$$a/b > c/d$$

then

$$a/b > \frac{ad + bc}{2bd} > c/d$$

## EXERCISES

**1.** Classify each of the following as simple or complex and as proper or improper:

(a) $\frac{7}{6}$ (b) $\frac{\frac{1}{2}}{5}$ (c) $\frac{2}{\frac{2}{3}}$ (d) $\frac{4}{9}$

**2.** Express each of the following as a simple fraction:

(a) $\dfrac{\frac{1}{2} + \frac{1}{3}}{\frac{1}{4}}$ (b) $\dfrac{\frac{2}{5} \times \frac{3}{4}}{\frac{1}{2} - \frac{2}{3}}$

**3.** Find on the number line:

(a) $\frac{-3}{-5}$ (b) $\frac{32}{6}$ (c) $\frac{-3}{4}$ (d) $\frac{-25}{6}$

**4.** Prove that if $a$, $b$, $c$, and $d$ are positive

$$a/b > c/d \text{ if and only if } a \times d > b \times c$$

**5.** Prove that if two positive fractions have the same numerator the one with the smaller denominator is the greater. That is, $a/b > a/d$ if and only if $d > b$.

**6.** Arrange the following from the smallest to largest:

$$\tfrac{2}{3}, \tfrac{20}{31}. \tfrac{21}{31}, \tfrac{21}{30}, \tfrac{3}{5}, \tfrac{5}{7}$$

**7.** Find a rational number between $\frac{3}{7}$ and $\frac{2}{5}$, that is, larger than the smaller of the two and smaller than the larger of the two.

**8.** Prove: If $a/b > c/d$
then

$$\frac{a}{b} > \frac{ad + bc}{2bd} > \frac{c}{d}$$

**9.** Prove that if $a$ is any positive number $a > 0$.

**10.** Prove that any positive number is greater than any negative number. That is, if $a$, $b$ are positive $a > -b$.

# 7 The Real Numbers

THE SET OF ALL RATIONAL NUMBERS IS CLOSED WITH RESPECT TO ADDITION, subtraction, multiplication, and, except for division by zero, division. Hence, for many practical purposes, the set of rational numbers is sufficient. However, from the theoretical point of view, this is not the case. For example, although it is possible to find a rational number whose square differs from 2 by less than any prescribed number, there is no rational number $a$ whose square, $a^2 = 2$. Although there is a point on the number line corresponding to each rational number, there is not a rational number corresponding to each point on the line.

In this chapter we shall extend the set of numbers to the *real* numbers. The deficiencies just mentioned do not apply to the set of real numbers. There is a real number whose square is equal to any non-negative rational number, or for that matter, any non-negative real number. Also there is a one-to-one correspondence between the set of points on a line and the set of real numbers.

## 7.1 Decimal Fractions

A decimal fraction is a fraction whose denominator is an integral power of ten. Thus $\frac{1}{4}$ is not a decimal fraction but $\frac{25}{100}$ is. Now, $\frac{1}{4}$ and $\frac{25}{100}$ are each elements of the same equivalence class of equal ratios; they are two names for the same rational number. Evidently then, reference to a decimal fraction has to do with the *form* in which a rational number is expressed. Not all rational numbers can be expressed in this form: $\frac{2}{3}$ does not equal $\frac{6}{10}$ or $\frac{66}{100}$ or $\frac{666}{1000}$ or any other rational number whose denominator is an integral power of 10.

If a rational number can be expressed as a decimal fraction the positional notation system can be employed to express it. For example, since

$$\begin{aligned}\frac{625}{1000} &= \frac{600 + 20 + 5}{1000} \\ &= \frac{1}{1000}(600 + 20 + 5) \\ &= \frac{600}{1000} + \frac{20}{1000} + \frac{5}{1000} \\ &= \frac{6}{10} + \frac{2}{100} + \frac{5}{1000}\end{aligned}$$

it can be written as .625.

When the term "decimal fraction" is used positional notation is usually implied. Even though $\frac{75}{100}$ is a decimal fraction "the decimal fraction seventy-five hundredths" usually implies the form .75.

The algorithms employed in computing with decimals are merely extensions of the corresponding algorithms with integers. [The only new problem in the matter of "pointing off" the result.] A decimal fraction can always be expressed as an integer multiplied by an integral power of ten. If this is done the rules for "pointing off" become apparent.

*Example:* Find the sum $.37 + .056 + .872$

*Solution:* Express each decimal fraction as an integral power of ten.

$$.37 + .056 + .872 = 37 \times 10^{-2} + 56 \times 10^{-3} + 872 \times 10^{-3}$$

Make the power of ten in each factor the same by adjoining the necessary zeros to the integer to compensate for the change in the exponent of ten. Here, we want $10^{-3}$ as a factor of the first term. Changing $10^{-2}$ to $10^{-3}$ is equivalent to dividing by 10. Hence we change 37 to 370, which is equivalent to multiplying by 10.

$$\begin{aligned}&37 \times 10^{-2} + 56 \times 10^{-3} + 872 \times 10^{-3} = \\ &\qquad 370 \times 10^{-3} + 56 \times 10^{-3} + 872 \times 10^{-3}\end{aligned}$$

Now applying the distributive property

$$\begin{aligned}&370 \times 10^{-3} + 56 \times 10^{-3} \\ &\qquad + 872 \times 10^{-3} = (370 + 56 + 872) \times 10^{-3} \\ &\qquad\qquad = 1298 \times 10^{-3} \\ &\qquad\qquad = 1.298\end{aligned}$$

You can readily see that the usual column addition algorithm accomplishes the same purpose as the method in the above example.

$$\begin{array}{r} .37 \\ .056 \\ .872 \\ \hline 1.298 \end{array}$$

The column alignment of the decimal points in effect makes the integral power of ten the same in each addend and in the sum.

Subtraction of decimal fractions is essentially the same as addition. In fact, we can consider subtraction as addition of the additive inverse.

*Example:* Find the difference

$$.834 - .0562$$

*Solution:*

$$\begin{aligned} .834 - .0562 &= .834 + -.0562 \\ &= 834 \times 10^{-3} + (-562) \times 10^{-4} \\ &= 8340 \times 10^{-4} + (-562) \times 10^{-4} \\ &= [8340 + (-562)] \times 10^{-4} \\ &= 7778 \times 10^{-4} \\ &= .7778 \end{aligned}$$

The rule for pointing off the product in multiplication can be derived in a manner similar to that of addition.

*Example:* Find the product

$$.123 \times .42$$

*Solution:* $.123 \times .42 = 123 \times 10^{-3} \times 42 \times 10^{-2}$

Since multiplication is associative

$$\begin{aligned} 123 \times 10^{-3} \times 42 \times 10^{-2} &= 123 \times 42 \times 10^{-3} \times 10^{-2} \\ &= 123 \times 42 \times 10^{-5} \\ &= 5166 \times 10^{-5} \\ &= .05166 \end{aligned}$$

From the example it is easy to see that, when each factor is expressed as an integer multiplied by an integral power of ten, the exponent in the product is the sum of the exponents in the factors. Consequently, the rule: The number of decimal places in the product is the sum of the numbers of decimal places in the factors.

In division, there are several rules for placing the decimal point in the quotient. Any one of them can be rationalized within the framework of the following example:

*Example:* Find the quotient

$$.00783 \div 4.35$$

*Solution:*

$$\begin{aligned} .00783 \div 4.35 &= 783 \times 10^{-5} \div (435 \times 10^{-2}) \\ &= 7830 \times 10^{-6} \times \frac{1}{435} \times \frac{1}{10^{-2}} \\ &= 7830 \times \frac{1}{435} \times 10^{-6} \times \frac{1}{10^{-2}} \\ &= (7830 \div 435) \times (10^{-6} \div 10^{-2}) \\ &= 18 \times 10^{-4} \\ &= .0018 \end{aligned}$$

Notice that $783 \times 10^{-5}$ is changed to the equivalent form $7830 \times 10^{-6}$. This was necessary because, in order to complete the division, .00783 is changed in the usual algorithm to .007830.

## EXERCISES

**1.** Determine whether each of the following can be written as a decimal fraction. That is, with an integral numerator and denominator an integral power of ten.
(a) $\frac{1}{15}$ (b) $3\frac{1}{5}$ (c) $\frac{18}{21}$ (d) $\frac{3}{64}$ (e) $\frac{5}{8}$ (f) $\frac{5}{30}$ (g) $\frac{13}{65}$ (h) $\frac{7}{25}$

**2.** Devise a rule for determining whether a given common fraction can be written as a decimal.

**3.** Find the following sum by first changing each addend to an integer multiplied by an integral power of ten. Then apply the distributive property so that the sum will be the sum of integers times an integral power of ten.

$$3.15 + .0051 + 32.07 + 1.834$$

**4.** Show why the procedure in Exercise 3 must give the same result as column addition with the decimal points aligned in a column.

**5.** Find the following product by first changing each factor to an integer times an integral power of ten. Then apply the associative property so that the product is a product of integers times a product of integral powers of ten.

$$.035 \times 41.3 \times 3.6$$

**6.** Show why the procedure in Exercise 5 places the decimal in the product in the same position as does the rule: the number of decimals in the product is equal to the sum of the number of decimals in the factors.

**7.** Find each of the following as a quotient of integers times a quotient of integral powers of ten:

(a) $.00221 \div 1.7$ (b) $2.21 \div .0013$

(c) $.0221 \div .017$ (d) $22.1 \div 1.3$

**8.** State a rule for "pointing off" the quotient in division that is consistent with the results of Exercise 7.

## 7.2 Repeating Decimals

Since a rational number is an implied division, any rational number $a/b$ can be expressed as a decimal by carrying through the division $a \div b$. In some cases the division terminates. For example, $\frac{3}{4} = .75$. But in other cases the division cannot be completed in a finite number of steps. If we attempt to carry through the division necessary to express $\frac{2}{3}$ decimally the division $2 \div 3$ will not come out even; we get an endless succession of 6's; $2 \div 3 = .6666\ldots.$ The three dots at the right are used to indicate that the fraction continues endlessly.

If a decimal terminates it can be considered an endless decimal with an endless succession of zeros following the last nonzero digit. Thus, .75 may be considered .75000. . . .

Not all rational numbers have a single digit as their repeating cycle:

$$\frac{1}{11} = .090909\ldots$$

Here the two-digit cycle 09 repeats endlessly. Nor does the repeating cycle always begin with the decimal point:

$$\frac{1}{6} = .1666\ldots$$

The cycle consists of the single digit 6 and begins at the second digit to the right of the decimal point.

A rational number, which incidentally may be greater than one, may have any finite number of digits preceding its repeating cycle. The cycle may begin before or after the decimal point: The repeating cycle of $21\frac{7}{33} = 21.2121\ldots$ is 21. But the cycle of $21\frac{11}{90} = 21.122\ldots$ is the single digit 2.

To show that every rational number, when expressed in decimal form, either repeats or terminates we first examine an example. To convert $\frac{3}{7}$

to decimal form we divide

```
      .428571
   7|3.000000
     28
    ---
     ②0
      14
      --
      ⑥0
       56
       --
       ④0
        35
        --
        ⑤0
         49
         --
         ①0
           7
          --
          ③
```

For emphasis we have circled the remainders which were obtained each time a quotient digit times divisor product was subtracted. If a remainder zero were ever obtained after all nonzero digits of the quotient had been used this would mean the division terminates. And, under the earlier interpretation of repeating zeros, we then have a repeating decimal. In this illustration it is possible to have only six different nonzero remainders, namely the numbers 1 through 6. Otherwise we have made a mistake. Since the divisor is 7, each remainder must be an integer less than 7. Then after not more than 6 steps have been completed we must be faced with some dividend figure for the second time. In this particular case the maximum number of steps was required. Every possible remainder appeared in the order 2, 6, 4, 5, 1, 3. Since the first step required 30 $\div$ 7 it is evident that the same sequence of remainders, and consequently the same sequence of digits in the quotient, will appear again and again endlessly:

$$\tfrac{3}{7} = .428571428571\ldots$$

As we shall see presently, every repeating decimal is also a rational number. For example, .428571717171 . . . is also a rational number, the repeating cycle being the two-digit cycle 71. It is the rational number 212143/495000. The three dots after the number indicate that the number does not terminate, but we need a means of identifying what the sequence of digits is that is to repeat. This may be done by drawing a bar over the repeating cycle. Thus we write:

$$\tfrac{3}{7} = .\overline{428571}\ldots$$
$$\tfrac{1}{6} = .1\overline{6}\ldots$$
$$\tfrac{1}{5} = .2\overline{0}\ldots$$
$$\tfrac{1}{11} = .\overline{09}\ldots$$

We return to the proposition that every rational number when expressed decimally either terminates or repeats. If after the digits of the dividend have been used we obtain a remainder zero the decimal terminates. Otherwise, after a sequence of steps not more in number than one less than the divisor we must obtain some remainder for a second time. The digits of the quotient which were obtained between the first and second occurrence of this remainder will repeat endlessly.

*Example:* Represent $\frac{61}{13}$ decimally. The digits of 61 will be used in the first step. We know that from that point on we can have not more than 12 different nonzero remainders. The repeating cycle *may have* as many as 12 digits.

```
       4.692307
   13)61.000000
      52
      --
      (9)0
       78
      ---
      120
      117
      ---
        (3)0
         26
         --
         (4)0
          39
          ---
          100
           91
          ---
           (9)
```

The first remainder after the digits of 61 were used (subsequent dividends will then merely be the remainder with zeros attached) was 9. After six steps the remainder 9 reappeared. Then the digits of the quotient, 6, 9, 2, 3, 0, 7, will repeat because the remainders 9, 12, 3, 4, 1, 10 will also repeat:

$$\tfrac{61}{13} = 4.\overline{692307}\ldots$$

It does not follow that every repeating decimal is a rational number simply because every rational number is a repeating decimal. It is nonetheless true.

First let us consider the decimal whose repeating cycle is zero, in other words a terminating decimal. It is evident that this is a rational number since it is the ratio of the integer indicated by the digits to the power of ten indicated by their position. For example, $.175 = \frac{175}{1000}$. The fact that this can be reduced to lower terms has no bearing on its being a rational number. Sometimes the result cannot be reduced to lower terms. The decimal .33 does not equal $\frac{1}{3}$ but it does equal $\frac{33}{100}$, which cannot be reduced. We have said that $\frac{1}{3} = .3\bar{3}\ldots$. We discover this to be true by carrying through the division implied by $\frac{1}{3}$. Now let us show that $.3\bar{3}\ldots = \frac{1}{3}$. If we designate the number $.3\bar{3}\ldots$ as $N$ we get

$$N = .3\bar{3}\ldots$$

and multiplying by 10

$$10N = 3.\bar{3}\ldots$$

Then, if we subtract the top equation from the bottom, we get

$$10N - N = 3.33\bar{3}\ldots - .33\bar{3}\ldots$$

or

$$9N = 3$$

$$N = \tfrac{3}{9} = \tfrac{1}{3}$$

It is evident that the repeating decimal 2.00 . . . is equal to the rational number $\frac{2}{1}$. Let us inquire what rational number $1.9\bar{9}\ldots$ equals.

Let $\quad N = 1.9\bar{9}\ldots$

then $\quad 10N = 19.9\ldots$

and $\quad 10N - N = 19.9\bar{9}\ldots - 1.9\bar{9}\ldots$

$$9N = 18$$

$$N = 2$$

Since they both equal 2 we may say

$$2.00\bar{0}\ldots = 1.99\bar{9}\ldots$$

(Of course, for any *finite* number of 9s, 1.999 does not quite equal 2.)

The two different decimal representations of 2 should cause no surprise. We have already seen a variety of ways to write 2, such as $5 - 3$, $1 + 1$, $\frac{4}{2}$, $2 \times 1$. However, the fact that $2 = 1.\bar{9}\ldots$ suggests the possibility of expressing a rational number which terminates decimally as a repeating decimal without the necessity of a repeating cycle of zeros.

We found $\frac{3}{4} = .75\bar{0}\ldots$. Let us find what rational number $.74\bar{9}\ldots$ equals:

| | |
|---|---|
| Let | $N = .749\bar{9}\ldots$ |
| Then | $100N = 74.9\bar{9}\ldots$ |
| and | $1000N = 749.\bar{9}\ldots$ |

Subtracting, $1000N - 100N = 749.\bar{9}\ldots - 74.\bar{9}\ldots$

$$900N = 675$$

$$N = \tfrac{675}{900} = \tfrac{3}{4}$$

Any terminating decimal is equivalent to the repeating decimal obtained from the former by reducing the last digit of the former by one, then adding an endless sequence of 9s:

$$17.35 = 17.34\bar{9}\ldots$$

This follows at once from the fact that

$$1.\bar{0}\ldots = .\bar{9}\ldots$$

| | |
|---|---|
| Let | $.9\bar{9}\ldots = N$ |
| then | $9.9\bar{9}\ldots = 10N$ |
| and subtracting | $9 = 9N$ or $N = 1$ |

Let us find $.45\overline{23}\ldots$ as the ratio of two integers

| | |
|---|---|
| Let | $N = .45\overline{23}\ldots$ |
| then | $100N = 45.\overline{23}\ldots$ |
| and | $10{,}000N = 4523.\overline{23}\ldots$ |
| Subtracting, | $9900N = 4478$ |
| | $N = \frac{4478}{9900} = \frac{2239}{4950}$ |

This example illustrates the general procedure. First, if the cycle does not begin with the decimal point multiply by the necessary power of ten to bring the decimal point immediately to the left of the cycle. In the above example this was accomplished when we multiplied by 100

$$100N = 45.\overline{23}\ldots$$

Next we multiply by the power of ten corresponding to the number of digits in the repeating cycle. In the example the cycle has two digits, so we multiply by $10^2$ or 100 giving

$$10{,}000N = 4523.\overline{23}\ldots$$

These two steps will always yield two numbers, each greater than one, which have the same repeating cycle for fractional part. Then if we subtract these two numbers we get an integer for difference. But this integer must be an integral multiple of the original number, $N$. Therefore $N$ is the ratio of these two integers.

The fact that all rational numbers are either terminating or repeating decimals does not in and of itself make decimal notation either a time-saver or a convenience. There would not be much profit in converting a common fraction to decimal form even though it terminates—after 175 digits. If the fraction is a repeating decimal we use a terminating approximation to it for purposes of decimal computation. We frequently use for $\frac{1}{3}$ the decimal approximation .33 and for $\frac{2}{3}$ the decimal approximation .67.

We have seen that a repeating decimal will have not more than one less digit in its repeating cycle than the denominator of the corresponding common fraction. There are six digits in the cycle of $\frac{3}{7}$. There can be no more than 22 digits in the cycle of $\frac{6}{23}$. There can be no more than 20 digits in the cycle of $\frac{7}{21}$. However, we can place a further restriction. The above criterion applies to the common fraction when reduced to lowest terms. There can be no more than two digits in the cycle of $\frac{7}{21}$ since it is equal to $\frac{1}{3}$. Of course, we know there is only one digit in its cycle, but the denominator 3 tells us there can be no more than two.

We now consider the question "Under what condition will a common fraction terminate when expressed decimally?" Again let us consider the common fraction in lowest form. All factors common to numerator and denominator have been cancelled. Although we think of decimal fraction in terms of a new kind of notation, far more significant is the fact that it is a fraction whose denominator is an integral power of 10. Then if a common fraction is to be a terminating decimal it must be possible to express it as the ratio of an integer to an integral power of 10.

Consider the fraction $\frac{4}{15}$. It is in lowest terms, we may write it in factored form as

$$\frac{2 \times 2}{3 \times 5}$$

The only factors of 10 are 2 and 5. Therefore we must get rid of the factor 3 in the denominator. If we divide the denominator by 3 we must also divide the numerator by 3. But the numerator does not have the factor 3. We may conclude from this that if the denominator contains any factor other than 2 or 5 it is not a terminating decimal. On the other hand, if the denominator consists of 2s and/or 5s exclusively we can always multiply the numerator and denominator by the power of 2 or 5 that is necessary for the 2 and 5 to be raised to the same power and make the denominator that power of 10. For example,

$$\frac{11}{80} = \frac{11}{2^4 \times 5}$$

If we multiply numerator and denominator by $5^3$ we get

$$\frac{11 \times 5^3}{2^4 \times 5^4} = \frac{11 \times 5^3}{10^4} = \frac{1375}{10{,}000} = .1375$$

Then, in answer to our question, a common fraction in lowest terms will terminate if and only if the factors of its denominator consist exclusively of 2s and 5s.

Whether or not a common fraction terminates as a decimal is not a property of the number alone. It is also a function of the system of notation. *Twelve* has *four* as a factor. This is a property of the number. It is independent of the system of notation employed. But the statement "a number has four for a factor if and only if the ones digit is a multiple of four" is true or false depending on the system of notation. It is false if ten is base and true if eight is base. The denominator of the fraction must consist exclusively of 2s and 5s because 2 and 5 are the factors of the base 10.

In Chapter Four we observed that a fraction may terminate in one base and repeat in another, terminate in both, or repeat in both. We can generalize the foregoing discussion. Regardless of the base in which we write, a fraction in lowest terms will terminate when written as a positional fraction if and only if all prime factors of the denominator are prime factors of the base of notation. It is for this reason that a fraction will either terminate in both base eight and base two notation or will repeat in both. Since two is the only prime factor of eight the fraction will terminate in either base only when its denominator is an integral power of two.

## THE REAL NUMBERS

*Example:* Convert $\frac{1}{5}$ to a positional fraction in base two and in base eight.

*Solution:* We express $\frac{1}{5}$ decimally as .2. To convert it to base two we multiply by 2. The integer of the product is the first digit of the fraction. The process is then repeated with the fractional part of the product. See page 130.

| .2 | .4 | .8 | .6 | .2 | .4 | .8 | .6 |
|---|---|---|---|---|---|---|---|
| 2 | 2 | 2 | 2 | 2 | 2 | 2 | 2 |
| 0.4 | 0.8 | 1.6 | 1.2 | 0.4 | 0.8 | 1.6 | 1.2 |

$$\therefore \quad .2_{(\text{ten})} = .0011\overline{0011}\ldots_{(\text{two})}$$

We may verify this result by using the same technique used in base ten.

Let $\quad N = .0011\overline{0011}\ldots$

then $\quad 10{,}000N = 11.\overline{0011} \quad (10{,}000N = \text{sixteen } N)$

Subtracting, $1111N = 11$

$$N = \tfrac{11}{1111}$$

But $11_{(\text{two})} = 3_{(\text{ten})}$ and $1111_{(\text{two})} = 15_{(\text{ten})}$

$$\therefore \left(\tfrac{11}{1111}\right)_{(\text{two})} = \left(\tfrac{3}{15}\right)_{(\text{ten})} = \left(\tfrac{1}{5}\right)_{(\text{ten})}$$

To express $\frac{1}{5}$ in base eight we proceed as before.

| .2 | .6 | .8 | .4 | .2 |
|---|---|---|---|---|
| 8 | 8 | 8 | 8 | 8 . . . |
| 1.6 | 4.8 | 6.4 | 3.2 | 1.6 |

$$\therefore \quad .2_{(\text{ten})} = (.\overline{1463}\ldots)_{(\text{eight})}$$

We may verify the correctness of the result by employing the principle developed on page 131. The sum of the first three binary digits gives the first octonal digit, the sum of the second three binary digits gives the second octonal digit, and so on.

$$001_{(\text{two})} = 1_{(\text{eight})}, \quad 100_{(\text{two})} = 4_{(\text{eight})}, \quad 110_{(\text{two})} = 6_{(\text{eight})},$$
$$011_{(\text{two})} = 3_{(\text{eight})}$$

$$\therefore \quad (.001\ 100\ 110\ 011)_{(\text{two})} = (.1463)_{(\text{eight})}$$

Note that the repeating cycle .0011 in base two was needed three times in order to establish the cycle in base eight. We can convert from base two to base eight in the above manner because eight is two to the third power. We say that $.111_{(\text{two})} = .7_{(\text{eight})}$. This is evident if we write the expression in base ten: $111_{(\text{two}} = \frac{1}{2} + \frac{1}{4} + \frac{1}{8} = \frac{4}{8} + \frac{2}{8} + \frac{1}{8} = \frac{7}{8}$. The numerators

4, 2, and 1 are expressed in base two as 100, 10, and 1. Or when we add the numerators $4 + 2 + 1$ the sum, written in base two, is 111. Then if the base two digits are added in groups of three we obtain the base eight digits.

A fraction will terminate in both of two bases only if the prime factors of its denominator are prime factors of both bases. From this it follows that no fraction can terminate in each of two bases which are relatively prime. For example, no fraction can terminate in both base five and base six. The factors of the denominator of $\frac{1}{30}$ include the factors of both bases but it has factors not found in each. Therefore it will not terminate in either base. Since it does not terminate in base ten we must convert it to the new base and divide in order to find its cycle. We first convert to base five, $(\frac{1}{30})_{(ten)} = (\frac{1}{110})_{(five)}$.

The following division is done in base five:

```
       .00404
   110|1.0000
        440
       ----
         1000
          440
          ---
           10
```

Therefore $(\frac{1}{30})_{(ten)} = (.0\overline{04}\ldots)_{(five)}$.

Next, we convert to base six, $(\frac{1}{30})_{(ten)} = (\frac{1}{50})_{(six)}$. The division is now in base six:

```
      .011
    50|1.00
        50
       ---
        100
         50
         --
         10
```

Therefore $(\frac{1}{30})_{(ten)} = (.0\overline{1}\ldots)_{(six)}$.

By contrast $\frac{1}{18}$, which does not terminate in base ten, does in base six and base twelve.

$$(\tfrac{1}{18})_{(ten)} = (\tfrac{1}{30})_{(six)}$$

Dividing in base six, we get

```
      .02
    30|1.00
       1 00
       ====
```

## THE REAL NUMBERS

Hence $(\frac{1}{30})_{(six)} = .02_{(six)}$.

$$(\tfrac{1}{18})_{(ten)} = (\tfrac{1}{16})_{(twelve)}$$

Dividing in base twelve, we get

$$\begin{array}{r|l} & .08 \\ \hline 16 & 1.00 \\ & 1\ 00 \\ \hline\hline \end{array}$$

Hence $\frac{1}{16}_{(twelve)} = .08_{(twelve)}$.

We may check the correctness of each of the above by observing that

$$.02_{(six)} = \tfrac{2}{36}_{(ten)},\ .08_{(twelve)} = \tfrac{8}{144}_{(ten)},\ \text{and}\ \tfrac{2}{36} = \tfrac{8}{144} = \tfrac{1}{18}$$

## EXERCISES

**1.** Show that the terminating decimal .25 is equivalent to the repeating decimal $.24\overline{9}\ldots$.

**2.** Find the common fraction to which .123 is equal. Find the common fraction to which $.\overline{123}\ldots$ is equal.

**3.** Show that $.\overline{123}\ldots = .1\overline{231}\ldots$.

**4.** Find the repeating cycle of the fraction $\frac{1}{7}$.

**5.** Multiply the result of Exercise 4 by 3 and compare your answer with the repeating cycle of $\frac{3}{7}$ on page 189.

**6.** The number 142,857 is called a revolving number because, if it is multiplied by any integer 2 through 6, the same cyclic arrangement of digits is obtained. Verify this.

**7.** Attempt to determine, without actually multiplying out, $142857 \times 7$. Verify your answer by multiplication. Explain the result.

**8.** Find the repeating cycle of $\frac{1}{81}$. Multiply by 45. Explain the result.

**9.** Which of the following will terminate when written decimally: $\frac{1}{16}$, $\frac{3}{17}$, $\frac{9}{40}$, $\frac{1}{9}$, $\frac{10}{128}$?

**10.** Which of the fractions in Exercise 9 will terminate when written as a positional fraction in base twelve? base five?

**11.** Convert $.39453125_{(ten)}$ to base eight.

**12.** Convert the answer to Exercise 11 to base two.

**13.** If a fraction is a terminating decimal, how can one determine in advance of the division the number of digits in its decimal expansion?

**14.** If $5.0\overline{0}\ldots = 4.99\overline{9}\ldots$, does $4.88\overline{8}\ldots = 4.77\overline{7}\ldots$? Prove your answer.

**15.** Will the following fractions terminate or repeat when reduced to decimals? $\frac{4}{7}$; $\frac{2}{5}$; $\frac{5}{6}$.

**16.** Select a base greater than ten in which each of the fractions in Exercise 15 will terminate.

**17.** Find the repeating cycle for each of the following: $\frac{1}{7}$; $\frac{1}{13}$; $\frac{1}{11}$; $\frac{1}{17}$.

**18.** How does the number of digits in the cycle compare with the denominator in each case in Exercise 17? Which of these cycles represents a "cyclic number?" The cycle of $\frac{1}{13}$ is called "partially cyclic." Why?

**19.** Will any of the following terminate in base 7 or base 9? If so expand them; if not, find the cycle. $\frac{1}{6}$; $\frac{3}{5}$; $\frac{2}{3}$.

**20.** Write the following as base ten common fractions:
(a) $.111_{(two)}$ (b) $1.10101_{(two)}$ (c) $.666_{(seven)}$ (d) $32.13_{(five)}$

**21.** Prove that $.45 = .449\bar{9}\ldots$.

## 7.3 Nonrepeating Decimals

If it is possible for a decimal not to be a rational number we know from Section 7.2 that it does not terminate or continue after some point as a repeating cycle. We cannot tell from an examination of any finite number of digits whether such is possible. We might examine a million digits without the appearance of a repeating cycle. Yet this first million digits might be the cycle. For that matter, if we know nothing beyond our million digits we have no way of knowing whether it terminates. On the other hand, even though a decimal consists of a million repetitions of 1, 2, 3, that alone gives us no assurance what the 3-million-and-first digit is. If we write .1763 we have written a terminating decimal whether we meant to or not. If we write .1763 . . . we have indicated that the decimal is endless but we have not indicated what its repeating cycle is, or for that matter whether it has one. If we write $.17\overline{63}\ldots$ we have indicated an endless decimal and further we have shown how to continue it as far as we please, by repeating the last two digits 6, 3 over and over.

If we can describe the manner of extending an endless decimal such that there will be no repeating cycle we will have exhibited an endless decimal which is not a rational number. This can be done in many ways. Consider the following: .10 110 1110 . . . . The rule of formation is obvious—a *one* followed by zero, followed by 2 *ones* followed by zero, followed by 3 *ones* followed by zero, and so on, continuing to increase the number of *ones* by one each time. Another decimal which is not a rational number is

.1 12 123 1234 12345 123456 1234567 12345678 123456789
12345678910 1234567891011 123456789101112

The spacing is employed to indicate the manner of forming the sequence At each interval we repeat the previous one and extend it one more number. Not one more digit after we get past 9, but one more number in the sense that we are adjoining the integers 1, 2, 3 . . . .

What are such sequences? Are they mere freaks of nature or do they have the properties of number? It can be shown that all endless decimals, both those that repeat and those that do not, have all the properties of the rational numbers. We shall, however, approach the question intuitively.

The usual square root algorithm can be continued indefinitely so long as an exact result is not reached. There are other ways to find square roots. For example, we may find $\sqrt{2}$ as follows: $1^2 = 1$, $2^2 = 4$; then $\sqrt{2}$ lies between 1 and 2. By trial we may discover that $1.4^2 = 1.96$, $1.5^2 = 2.25$; then $\sqrt{2}$ lies between 1.4 and 1.5. Continuing, $1.41^2 = 1.9881$, $1.42^2 = 2.0164$; then $\sqrt{2}$ is between 1.41 and 1.42. We can continue this process until we find the exact square root of 2 if it has one or until we get as many digits as we like. If we carry the process one more step we get 1.414. If this suggests the repeating cycle 14 disappointment is the reward for finding the next digit. Assuming the process does not terminate, how are we to know whether the sequence repeats?

It cannot repeat because if it did $\sqrt{2}$ would be a rational number. We can prove $\sqrt{2}$ is not a rational number. Incidentally, in so doing we shall not be concerned with any of the digits of the sequence. Let us assume $\sqrt{2}$ is the ratio of two integers. If the ratio exists we can further stipulate that it has been reduced to lowest terms. Symbolically we are asserting

$$\sqrt{2} = \frac{a}{b} \text{ (} a, b \text{ have no common factors)}$$

From this assumption it follows by squaring on both sides

$$2 = \frac{a^2}{b^2} \qquad \text{or} \qquad 2b^2 = a^2$$

The fundamental theorem of arithmetic requires that $2b^2$ and $a^2$ have the same prime factors. Furthermore, each $b$ in $b^2$ must have the same prime factors, and each $a$ in $a^2$ must also have the same prime factors. Specifically, the factor 2 must appear an even number of times on the right side of the equation because each $a$ in $a^2$ must have the factor 2 the same number of times. Similarly, $b^2$ must have 2 as a factor an even number of times. Hence the left side of the equation, $2b^2$, must have the factor 2 an odd number of times. Since 2 is a prime number the two sides of the equation cannot have exactly the same prime factors. But the fundamental theorem of arithmetic requires that the two sides have exactly the same prime factors if the two sides are equal. We must conclude that $2b^2$ cannot equal $a^2$. This contradiction forces us to conclude that there are no two integers whose ratio is $\sqrt{2}$. There is no rational number whose square is 2.

We have seen that on a directed line there is a point corresponding to every rational number. If we take the distance from 0 to 1 as our unit of

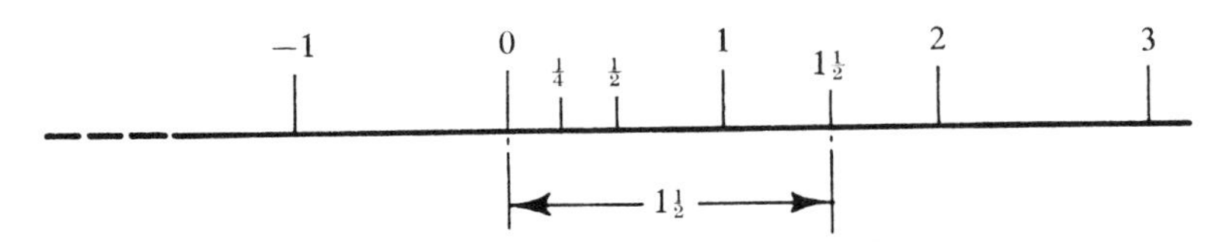


measure the distance from 0 to any other point has the numerical value of that point.

There is a line whose distance is $\sqrt{2}$. According to the Theorem of Pythagoras the square of the hypotenuse of a right triangle is equal to the sum of the squares of its legs. If we construct a square whose side is 1, application of this theorem establishes the diagonal as a line whose square is 2. That is, the diagonal is $\sqrt{2}$ times as long as the side. Then if we lay off this distance from the origin of a directed line it will not terminate on a rational point. Although there is a point to correspond to each

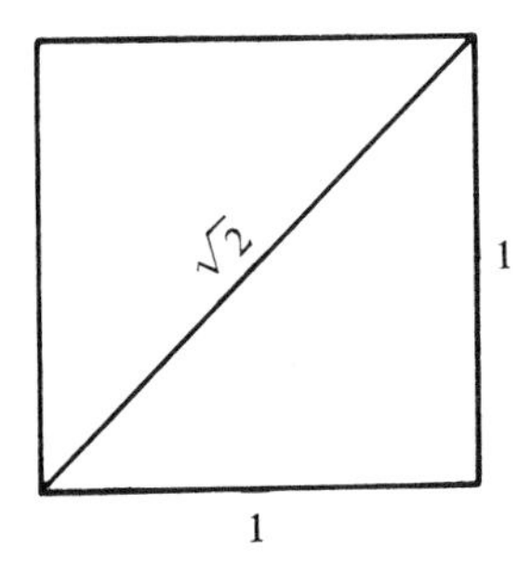


rational number there is not a rational number to correspond to each point. There are other points on the line and therefore there are distances which cannot be expressed as rational numbers.

If we wish these distances or, what is the same thing, endless non-repeating decimals to be numbers we are in the same predicament as when we attempt to subtract the natural number 7 from the natural number 4 or when we attempt to divide the integer 5 by the integer 2; we must create a new kind of number. We *define* an endless decimal (remember that a terminating decimal is followed by an endless succession of zeros) as a *real number*.

## THE REAL NUMBERS

A real number is a number represented by an endless decimal.

If an endless decimal repeats, it is a rational number. Otherwise, it is an *irrational* number.

An irrational number is a real number that is not rational.

We have, beginning with the idea of an equivalence class of sets, developed successively the cardinal numbers, the integers, the rational numbers, and now the real numbers. Let us change our viewpoint for a moment. We define the set of real numbers as the set of all infinite decimals. A subset of the reals, all *repeating* endless decimals, we identify as the set of rational numbers. A subset of the rationals, all rationals whose digits in position value less than $10^{\circ}$ are all zero, or all nine, we identify as the set of integers. The integers can be partitioned into three disjoint and exhaustive subsets, {0}, {positive integers}, {negative integers}. Finally, we recognize the original set of finite cardinal numbers as $\{0\} \cup$ {positive integers}, that is, the set whose elements are zero and all positive integers.

One final question concerning the set of real numbers—do the real numbers satisfy the closure, associative, cummutative, and distributive principles? Are there real addition and multiplication identity elements and inverses? A satisfactory logically complete answer is considerably beyond the scope of this book. However, an affirmative answer to all these points can be reached in an intuitive way.

In earlier times addition was done

$$\begin{array}{r} 7358 \\ 4267 \\ \hline 11{,}\not{5}\not{1}5 \\ 62\phantom{5} \end{array}$$

from left to right. We first add $7 + 4 = 11$, $3 + 2 = 5$, then when we come to $5 + 6 = 11$ the right-hand 1 is placed under the 6 and the left-hand 1 is combined with the digit to the right, 5, by cancelling the 5 and replacing it with 6. Finally, $8 + 7 = 15$ and the 5 is placed under the 7 with the 1 combined with the 1 immediately to the right. Using this left to right form for addition, it should be evident that the sum of two infinite decimals is an infinite decimal. That is, the set of real numbers is closed with respect to addition.

$$\begin{array}{r} .938762\ldots \\ .483669\ldots \\ \hline 1.311321\ldots \\ 42243\phantom{\ldots} \end{array}$$

It is also possible to multiply in a left to right fashion. We shall illustrate by finding 137 × 265.

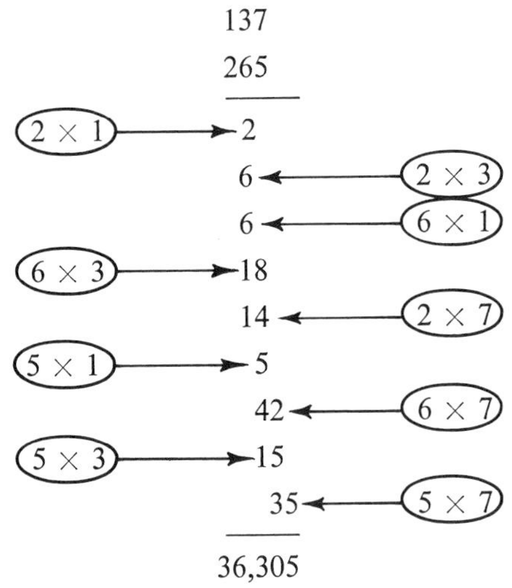


The sequence of steps is

$$2 \times 1,\ 2 \times 3,\ 6 \times 1,\ 6 \times 3,\ 2 \times 7,\ 5 \times 1,\ 6 \times 7,\ 5 \times 3,\ 5 \times 7$$

The circled numbers in the array indicate the sequence of steps. By working through

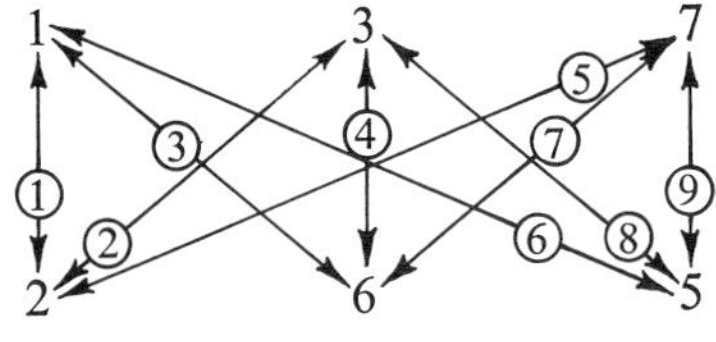


the steps, you can discover a definite pattern. The first product is the product of the extreme left digits. We then find all cross products (2 × 7 and 6 × 1) up to the next pair of similarly placed digits (3 and 6). We then find the product of these similarly placed digits (6 × 3) and proceed as before. We must find all cross products not previously found, up to the next pair of similarly placed digits (2 × 7, 5 × 1, 6 × 7, 5 × 3). Then find the product of the similarly placed digits (5 × 7). This pattern can be extended in as many digits as desired. For example, suppose we find 1374 × 2658. All products of the previous example are found as before; then we continue

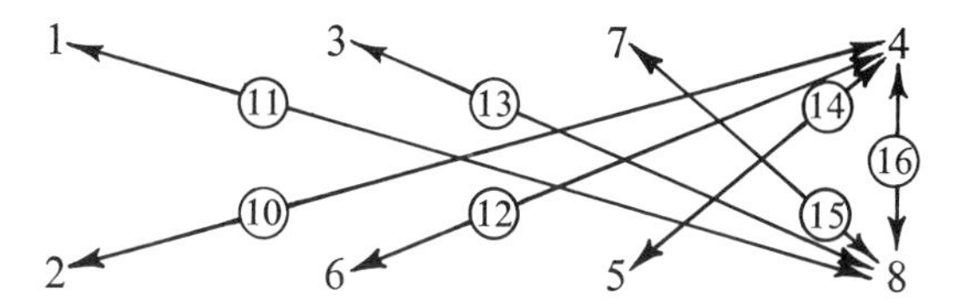


as indicated by the numbered arrows. All that remains is a scheme for preserving place value. This can be done quite easily if the first product is aligned on the left, as in the example 2 × 1 is recorded at the extreme left. Each succeeding product is shifted a number of places to the right equal to the sum of the number of places to the right each factor is found.

If the above algorithm is employed it should be evident that the product of two infinite decimals is an infinite decimal. That is, the set of real numbers is closed with respect to multiplication.

```
  .4631 . . .
  .2512 . . .
  ----------
   8                (2 × 4)
   12               (2 × 6)
   20               (5 × 4)
    30              (5 × 6)
     6              (2 × 3)
     4              (1 × 4)
     15             (5 × 3)
      6             (1 × 6)
       3            (1 × 3)
      2             (2 × 1)
      8             (2 × 4)
       5            (5 × 1)
      12            (2 × 6)
        1           (1 × 1)
        6           (2 × 3)
         2          (2 × 1)
  ----------
 1.1633072
```

## NONREPEATING DECIMALS

This is hardly recommended as an efficient multiplication algorithm. The point is that we *can* multiply from left to right, and can complete the process for as many digits as we wish. It will be worth your time to multiply .4631 × .2512 in the usual way and compare the result with the above multiplication.

The first $n$ digits of an infinite decimal is a rational approximation to the real number. For example .33 differs from $\frac{1}{3} = .3\bar{3}\ldots$ by $\frac{1}{300}$; .333 differs from $\frac{1}{3} = .33\bar{3}\ldots$ by $\frac{1}{3000}$. As the number of digits in the rational approximation is increased the difference between it and the infinite decimal decreases. In fact, a sufficiently large number of digits can make the difference less than any specified amount. Since this is true, we know that arbitrarily close rational approximations to real numbers obey the commutative, associative, and distributive principles. Hence, it seems reasonable to accept these properties as properties governing the set of real numbers.

## EXERCISES

1. Devise a rule for writing an endless nonrepeating decimal other than the examples in the text.
2. Explain the difference between 17.3, 17.3 . . . , and $17.\bar{3}\ldots$.
3. Use the argument of Section 7.3 to show that $\sqrt{3}$ is irrational.
4. Follow the argument of Section 7.3, using $\sqrt{4}$. Show where the argument breaks down.
5. Adapt the argument of Section 7.3 to show $\sqrt[3]{2}$ irrational. Indicate where the arguments differ.
6. Show $\sqrt[3]{4}$ irrational.
7. Describe a method for constructing a line $\sqrt{3}$ units long.
8. If we use $\sqrt{2} = 1.4$, is the error an excess or a deficiency?
9. Which is the closer approximation to $\frac{2}{3}$, .66 or .67?
10. Using the fact that every rational number either repeats or terminates when expressed decimally, prove that there is a rational number between any two rational numbers.
11. Prove that there is an irrational number between any two rational numbers.
12. Prove there is a rational number between any two irrational numbers.
13. Prove there is an irrational number between any two irrational numbers.

14. Do Exercises 10 through 13 justify the contention that there are the same number of rational numbers and irrational numbers? If not, why not?

15. Use the left-to-right algorithm illustrated in this section to perform the following addition:

$$\begin{array}{r} .35426170 \\ .08372542 \\ \hline \end{array}$$

16. Illustrate that addition is commutative by performing the following addition as in Exercise 15:

$$\begin{array}{r} .08372542 \\ .35426170 \\ \hline \end{array}$$

17. Use the left-to-right algorithm illustrated in this section to perform the following multiplication:

$$\begin{array}{r} .4372 \\ .7613 \\ \hline \end{array}$$

18. Illustrate that multiplication is commutative by performing the following multiplication as in Exercise 17:

$$\begin{array}{r} .7613 \\ .4372 \\ \hline \end{array}$$

19. What endless decimal is the multiplication identity?

20. What endless decimal is the addition identity?

21. Does each endless decimal have an additive inverse? Discuss.

22. Does each nonzero endless decimal have a multiplicative inverse? Discuss.

23. Each nonzero integer can be expressed as an endless decimal in two ways. Is this true of zero? Discuss.

## 7.4 Approximation

As we saw in the last section, numbers are sometimes used as approximations of other numbers. When we refer to approximate numbers this is not a reference to the kind of number, it is a reference to the use to which the number is put. Just as .67 may be used as an approximation of $\frac{2}{3}$ we may also on occasion use $\frac{2}{3}$ as the approximate value of .67 or possibly .7. It is quite possible to use irrational numbers as approximate values of rationals or other irrationals. A very good approximation to $\pi$ is $\sqrt{10}$. Verify this by finding decimal approximations for each of them.

We use rational approximations of irrational numbers as an aid to computation. It is possible to express the area of a circle exactly, assuming we know the exact radius, but the result will have to be in terms of $\pi$. A circle whose radius is exactly 2 inches has an exact area of $4\pi$ square inches. But the result is usually more useful if it is expressed as $\frac{88}{7}$ square inches. Although many uses of approximate numbers are a matter of convenience, many others are unavoidable.

Every measurement is an approximation. A measurement is a comparison with a standard. We measure a room as 12 ft wide. This means that it is 12 times as wide as the length of a foot rule. The room may be exactly 12 ft wide but we can never establish the fact by measurement. We must place the rule end to end and count the number of one-foot intervals. We may get exactly 12 intervals but we cannot be certain that each interval starts exactly where the preceding one ended. We cannot be certain whether the last interval exactly completes the width of the room. Nor can we be certain the rule is exactly one foot long. If a random collection of half-a-dozen yardsticks (the give-away variety) are compared, the results may be surprising. Our measuring instruments are copies of the legal standard and we can never be certain that they are perfect. We are limited both by the extent to which the measuring instrument agrees with the standard and by its precision. A yardstick is usually subdivided into eighths of an inch. This means that we can obtain a measurement which is correct to the nearest eighth of an inch. We can usually go a step further. We can usually determine the measurement to the nearest sixteenth of an inch. If we attempt to go beyond this point we are in the realm of guessing. Limitations of the instrument itself and human limitations make it impossible for a measurement to be exact.

Most enumerations are exact. We can count the number of people in a room and know exactly how many there are but we could never determine exactly what they weigh. Sometimes even enumerations are not exact. The taking of the census is an enumeration, but births and deaths which occur while the count is in progress, as well as people who are missed, make the final result only approximately correct.

If it is impossible to make an exact measurement we must have some means of evaluating the appropriateness of our approximation. How far from the true value is the measurement? How much variation from the true value is permissible?

Let us assume that the measuring instrument is perfect in the sense that it is an exact duplicate of the standard and that it is perfectly subdivided. For example, assume we have a yardstick that is exactly a yard long and is perfectly subdivided into eighths of an inch. Let us further assume that we make no mistakes in using it. We align the zero end perfectly with one end of the distance to be measured. We read correctly the marking on the rule which corresponds to the other end. These assumptions are impossible to obtain in practice; deviations from the ideal are unavoidable *errors*. Suppose the end of the measured distance coincides with a point on the yardstick which lies between $23\frac{5}{8}$ in. and $23\frac{3}{4}$ in. The user of the instrument must exercise judgment at this point in deciding whether the point is nearer $23\frac{5}{8}$ or $23\frac{3}{4}$. If the point is very near the center of the interval it is quite possible for an error of judgment to enter. The same measurement might appear nearer $23\frac{5}{8}$ to some observers and nearer $23\frac{3}{4}$ to others. In a case of this sort we could with assurance report the distance as $23\frac{11}{16}$ in., but not exactly. Is it closer to $23\frac{21}{32}$, $23\frac{22}{32}$, or $23\frac{23}{32}$? The process could go on endlessly.

Let us suppose the end of the distance measured is definitely nearer $23\frac{5}{8}$ in. and we make no attempt to read sixteenths. We then record the distance as $23\frac{5}{8}$ in. If another distance is measured and found to be between $23\frac{1}{2}$ and $23\frac{5}{8}$ in., but nearer the latter, it too is recorded $23\frac{5}{8}$ in. All measurements which are recorded as $23\frac{5}{8}$ in. are presumed to be measures of distances which are nearer $23\frac{5}{8}$ in. than $23\frac{1}{2}$ or $23\frac{3}{4}$. Then they are measurements which lie between $23\frac{9}{16}$ and $23\frac{11}{16}$ in. If the distance is so near an end of the interval, say $23\frac{9}{16}$, that we cannot determine whether it is less than, or greater than, or for that matter exactly, $23\frac{9}{16}$ we have equal justification for recording the measurement as $23\frac{4}{8}$ or $23\frac{5}{8}$. The arbitrary rule which is usually followed includes the lower end of the interval but not the upper. Then all distances $23\frac{9}{16}$ and above but less than $23\frac{11}{16}$ are recorded as $23\frac{5}{8}$. We would, of course, record $23\frac{11}{16}$ as $23\frac{6}{8}$ under this rule.

In the foregoing situation the instrument used, the yardstick, imposes a limitation on the closeness with which we can approximate. We can make a measurement *to the nearest eighth of an inch*, the smallest unit of length with which we can deal. We could, of course, use the instrument to make measurements to the nearest inch or nearest foot but not to the nearest thousandth of an inch.

The smallest unit of measure used in a measurement determines its *precision*. The smaller the unit the greater the precision. The manner in which an approximate number is written should indicate its precision. For example, $23\frac{1}{2}$ in. is to be interpreted as precise to the nearest $\frac{1}{2}$ in. It is the measure of a distance which is $23\frac{1}{4}$ in. or more but less than $23\frac{3}{4}$ in. Note that in the foregoing statement both $23\frac{1}{4}$ and $23\frac{3}{4}$ are exact numbers. If our measurement is $23\frac{1}{2}$ in. to the nearest eighth of an inch it should be written as $23\frac{4}{8}$ in.

When decimal notation is employed we may indicate precision in any one of three ways:

(1) The last significant digit of the number (see Section 7.5) indicates the smallest unit of measure and thus the precision. For example, the approximate number 12.7 lb is precise to the nearest tenth of a pound, but 12.70 lb is precise to the nearest hundredth of a pound.

(2) We may indicate precision by indicating the possible correction. If we write $12.7 \pm .05$ we indicate that the true value approximated may be as low as 12.65 and as high as 12.75. This is the same degree of precision as was implied in (1). But the second method has broader application. For example, $12.7 \pm .3$ means the true value may deviate from 12.7 by not more than .3; it lies between 12.4 and 13.

(3) We may indicate precision by explicitly stating the degree of refinement of the measure; for example, 12.7 lb to the nearest tenth pound.

The degree of precision of two measurements cannot be compared unless they are of the same kind. One cannot say $15\frac{1}{2}$ hr is more or less precise than $6\frac{1}{8}$ in. since we cannot compare the sizes of $\frac{1}{2}$ of an hour and $\frac{1}{8}$ of an inch. The measurements need not be made in the same units, however, if they are the same kinds of unit. We know that 105 in. is more precise than 5.16 miles because, both being units of length, we know one inch is less than $\frac{1}{100}$ of a mile.

Precision is not the sole criterion upon which we may evaluate a measurement. A measurement of 3 in., precise to the nearest inch, is far more precise than one of 516 miles precise to the nearest mile. But in another sense 516 miles is a closer approximation than 3 in. The possible divergence from the true value, $\frac{1}{2}$ mile, is much smaller *compared to the total* measurement of 516 miles than is $\frac{1}{2}$ in. compared to 3 in. The ratio of maximum variation to the total measure determines the *accuracy* of the measurement. The smaller the ratio the more accurate the measurement. The accuracy of 516 miles is

$$\frac{\frac{1}{2}}{516} = \frac{1}{1032}$$

The accuracy of 3 in. is

$$\frac{\frac{1}{2}}{3} = \frac{1}{6}$$

which is far less accurate than 516 miles.

Since accuracy is a ratio, a pure number, and not feet or pounds or seconds, the accuracy of any two measurements can be compared. We see that $15\frac{1}{2}$ hr is less accurate than $6\frac{1}{8}$ in. because

$$\frac{\frac{1}{4}}{15\frac{1}{2}} = \frac{1}{62} \quad \text{is larger than} \quad \frac{\frac{1}{16}}{6\frac{1}{8}} = \frac{1}{98}$$

Which of the two properties, precision and accuracy, is the more important? In making measurements should we strive for precision or accuracy? That depends on the situation. There are times when precision is of overriding importance. The situation may call for a high degree of precision but not much accuracy. At other times a high degree of accuracy is desired but precision is important only to the extent that it gives the requisite accuracy. For example, if a carburetor requires a jet opening .005 in. in diameter, this is a high degree of precision. But if the tolerance is .0005 in. the opening may vary from .0045 to .0055 in. Here the accuracy is low, the relative error being $\frac{1}{10}$. On the other hand, the accepted distance to the sun, 93,000,000 miles, is precise only to the nearest million miles. Yet the per cent of error is only slightly more than $\frac{1}{2}$ of 1 per cent.

Measurements must be approximate because of the presence of unavoidable errors. A mistake usually results in error but an error is not necessarily due to a mistake. Our concern here is with those errors which do not result from mistakes. Errors may be *constant*. For example, a 100-ft steel tape may have been made 0.2 in. too short. If we are aware of constant errors which cannot be eliminated we can compensate for them. Errors may also be *random*. Such factors as imperfect alignment, temperature changes (which will cause a steel tape to expand and contract), and the estimating essential to reading the instrument are possible sources of random errors in making linear measurements. Random errors may be positive or negative; they tend to cancel each other out.

The error introduced by virtue of the fact that there must be a smallest unit in any measurement is called its *absolute error*. It is one half the smallest unit of measure. It is the maximum amount the true value can vary from the measurement. The measure $6\frac{1}{8}$ in. has for its smallest unit $\frac{1}{8}$ in.; its absolute error is $\frac{1}{16}$ in. since this is the maximum amount the measurement can be off. *Relative error* is the ratio of the absolute error to the measurement. *Per cent of error* is simply 100 times the relative error.

We state precision in terms of the smallest unit rather than absolute error, $6\frac{1}{8}$ in. is precise to the nearest $\frac{1}{8}$ in. Relative error is a direct measure of accuracy. The relative error of $6\frac{1}{8}$ in. is $\frac{1}{98}$. This means that our measurement can differ from the true value not more than one part in 98.

## EXERCISES

**1.** Interpret the meaning of the following approximate numbers:

(a) 12.5 ft
(b) $\frac{2}{3}$
(c) .67
(d) 12.50 ft
(e) $4\frac{0}{8}$ in.

2. Determine which of the following pairs of numbers is the more precise and which is the more accurate:
   (a) 126 in.; 126 miles
   (b) 5 lb; 250 tons
   (c) $\frac{1}{3}$ yd; 1 ft
   (d) 56 gal; .00056 gal.

3. Is it possible for two like measures to have the same precision and accuracy? Can the more precise be the more accurate? Can the less precise be the more accurate? Can they have the same precision and different accuracy? Can they have the same accuracy and different precision? Illustrate each of the above to which your answer is *yes*. Explain why those to which your answer is *no* are impossible.

4. Distinguish between errors of measurement and mistakes.

5. Find the absolute error, the relative error, and the per cent of error in the following measurements:
   (a) 126 $\pm$ .5 miles
   (b) .025 cm
   (c) $\frac{1}{4}$ cm
   (d) 25,000 miles

## 7.5 Approximate Computation

The concept of *significant digits* is an important consideration in connection with both precision and accuracy. The digits of an approximate number are significant if they serve a purpose other than merely helping to place the decimal point. All nonzero digits are significant. A zero may be significant or nonsignificant. A nonsignificant one is not therefore insignificant, unimportant, or useless. It serves solely as a place holder. Zeros situated between significant digits are always significant. In the number 506.3 the zero is a place holder; it gives the 5 its correct position relative to the decimal point. But it does more; it tells us how many sets of ten are present—there are none.

On the other hand, if 5000 is an approximate number precise to the nearest thousand none of the zeros are significant. Their only function is to give the 5 its correct position, or—what amounts to the same thing—they place the decimal point. There is no reason for writing fifteen, correct to the nearest one, as 15.0. If 15.0 is correctly used the zero is used to specify that to the nearest tenth we have no tenths. If we know nothing, or wish to say nothing, about the number of hundredths in the measurement we should not write 15.00.

Terminating zeros in a fraction are used solely to specify that we know there are no units of that particular size. They do not help place the decimal; that has already been done. But they serve a role other than that and therefore are significant. On the other hand, initial zeros in a fraction are never significant. In the number .05 the zero merely places the decimal. But is it not true that it tells us we have no tenths? It is true that we have no tenths but we do not need the zero to tell us. The fact that the 5 is the first nonzero digit tells us that it stands in the position corresponding to the largest unit in the measurement. We do not write 56 as 056. There are no hundreds present but we do not need the zero to tell us.

All digits of a mixed number are significant. Consider 5000.0. The final zero specifies there are no tenths. If we know how many tenths are present we must of necessity know how many ones, tens, and hundreds are present. The zeros in the integral part are between significant digits and are thus significant.

Consider the number 560 out of context. Is this a number correct to the nearest ten or the nearest one? It might be either. If we want to indicate a number correct to the nearest ten the zero is not significant. On the other hand, if we want to indicate that to the nearest one we have 560, we know there are no ones present and the zero is significant. This ambiguity may be cared for from the context in which the number is used. If we have a set of like measures 17, 19, 20, 23 it is reasonable to assume the 20 is a measure to the nearest one just as the others are. We may also eliminate the ambiguity by stating the absolute error or by indicating it as $20 \pm .5$. Finally, we may indicate that a terminating zero in an integer is significant by underscoring it, $2\underline{0}$. In the number $50\underline{0}0$ we indicate a measure of five thousand correct to the nearest ten; the first two zeros are significant and the last one is not. In the absence of any indication that terminal zeros in an integer are significant they should be considered nonsignificant.

In summary we may say all digits are significant except (1) terminal zeros of an integer which are not by one of the above means designated as significant, and (2) initial zeros of a pure fraction.

The last significant digit of a number indicates its precision. Of two numbers the one with the greater number of significant digits is the more accurate. For example, 100.0 is more accurate than 931,000 because the relative error is $\frac{1}{2}$ the smallest unit divided by the measure, and the position of the decimal point is of no consequence. The relative error of 100.0 is $.05/100.0 = 5/10{,}000$ and that of 931,000 is $500/931{,}000 = 5/9310$. In fact, we may say that of two measures that one whose significant digits represent the greater number is the more accurate. For example, .00531 is more accurate than $53\underline{0}$.

## APPROXIMATE COMPUTATION

When we compute with approximate numbers our results frequently contain digits which indicate unjustified precision. If for this or other reasons we wish to reduce the precision of a number the process is known as *rounding off*.

If we round off an integer, each digit discarded must be replaced by a zero. We round off 1523 to the nearest hundred and get 1500 because 1523 is nearer 1500 than 1600. If the number is a fraction the discarded digits must *not* be replaced by zeros. The fraction .03745, when rounded to two significant digits, becomes .037. If the 4 and 5 were replaced by zeros we would still have four significant digits. The two above rules are combined when we round off a mixed number. Discarded digits of the fraction are not replaced with zeros but if digits to the integer are dropped they are.

*Example:* 174.33 = 174.3 to four significant digits.
174.33 = 170 to two significant digits.

If the highest digit dropped is 0, 1, 2, 3, or 4, the lowest digit retained is left intact. If the highest digit dropped is 5, 6, 7, 8, or 9, the lowest digit retained is increased by one.

*Example:* 9342 = 9300 to two significant digits because 9342 is nearer 9300 than 9400. But
9372 = 9400 to two significant digits because 9372 is nearer 9400 than 9300.

There is one exception to the above rule. If the highest digit dropped is a terminal 5, as 165 or .325 to be rounded to two significant digits, or a 5 followed by zeros as 1.7500 to be rounded to two digits, the rule is altered. In these cases we have no evidence to indicate which rounded number we are nearer. For example, 165 is, to the extent of our knowledge, equally close to 160 and 170. Here we must adopt an arbitrary rule of procedure. Our objective is to minimize the error in the final result. The rule most frequently followed requires that the lowest digit retained be kept or increased by one, whichever is necessary to give an *even* digit:

*Example:* 1.650 = 1.6 to two digits
1.750 = 1.8 to two digits
1.850 = 1.8 to two digits

The justification for this process lies in the fact that our result will have a positive error about half the time and a negative error the other half. The two sets of errors will tend to cancel each other out over a large number of cases.

Suppose we attempt to add the following weights: 500 lb, 1.5 lb, and 136 lb. These weights represent values between 450 and 550 lb, 1.45 and 1.55 lb, and 135.5 and 136.5 lb, respectively. The sum of the minimum values is $450 + 1.45 + 135.5 = 586.95$ lb. The sum of the maximum values is $550 + 1.55 + 136.5 = 688.05$ lb. The true value lies somewhere between the two. Then we are not certain of the value even to the nearest hundred pounds. The maximum value is slightly closer to 700 lb than the minimum is to 600 lb.

The maximum error of the 500-lb measure, 50 lb, is several times as great as the 1.5-lb entry. It is of little value to know the 136-lb item to the nearest pound. The limit of precision imposed by the 500-lb measure places the same limitation on the sum.

When we add or subtract, the measurements must be not only the same kind—we cannot add 15 lb and 25 ft—they must be in the same units. If they are the same kind of measures they can be converted to common units which will also be common to the sum. We can compare the addends and the sum in terms of precision. The least precise addend sets the limit as to the precision with which the sum can be obtained. *A sum of approximate numbers should be expressed to the same degree of precision as that of the least precise addend.* The same situation holds for subtraction. In addition or subtraction we are not concerned with accuracy, for the least precise addend may be the most accurate or the least accurate.

One rule for adding approximate numbers requires that we round off each addend to the degree of precision of the least precise one, then add. A variation of this rule requires that we round to within one place of the least precise addend, add, then round off the sum one place. Still another variation permits the addition of the numbers without rounding off. We then round off the sum to the precision of the least precise measure. The first procedure is the easiest, the last minimizes the error. Frequently all three rules will give the same final result but occasionally the results may differ slightly.

*Example:* Add $12.6 + 120.31 + .073 + 2.436$.

BY THE FIRST RULE

$$\begin{array}{r} 12.6 \\ 120.3 \\ .1 \\ 2.4 \\ \hline 135.4 \end{array}$$

BY THE SECOND RULE

$$\begin{array}{r} 12.6 \\ 120.31 \\ .07 \\ 2.44 \\ \hline 135.42 \end{array} \rightarrow 135.4$$

BY THE THIRD RULE

$$\begin{array}{r} 12.6 \\ 120.31 \\ .073 \\ 2.436 \\ \hline 135.419 \end{array} \rightarrow 135.4$$

*Example:* Add 3.49 + 133 + 2.38 + 16.6.

BY THE FIRST RULE

$$\begin{array}{r} 3 \\ 133 \\ 2 \\ 17 \\ \hline 155 \end{array}$$

BY THE SECOND RULE

$$\begin{array}{r} 3.5 \\ 133 \\ 2.4 \\ 16.6 \\ \hline 155.5 \end{array} \rightarrow 156$$

BY THE THIRD RULE

$$\begin{array}{r} 3.49 \\ 133 \\ 2.38 \\ 16.6 \\ \hline 155.47 \end{array} \rightarrow 155$$

When we multiply, one factor must be an abstract number. We cannot multiply 3 ft by 59 gal. We do say that we multiply feet by feet to find area in square feet. But we actually multiply square feet by an abstract number. Consider finding the area of a 3-by-4 rectangle:

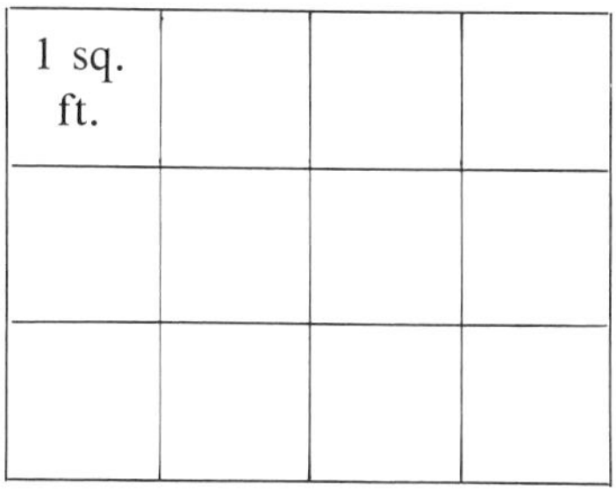

| 1 sq. ft. | | | |
|---|---|---|---|
| | | | |
| | | | |

We may consider this by rows as 3 rows of 4 sq ft each. Then the area is $3 \times 4$ sq ft $= 12$ sq ft. Or by columns, we have 4 columns of 3 sq ft each. And the area is $4 \times 3$ sq ft $= 12$ sq ft. Notwithstanding this fact, the dimensions are linear measure and the product is a measure of area. Consequently the precision of the product is not comparable to the precision of the factors.

Suppose we wish to find the area of a rectangle the dimensions of which are 6.1 ft by 23.4 ft. Should the area be expressed to the nearest tenth of a square foot? Perhaps it should be to the nearest hundredth since a square $\frac{1}{10}$ foot by $\frac{1}{10}$ foot has an area $\frac{1}{100}$ of a square foot.

If we take the minimum value which the measurements may represent we get $6.05 \times 23.35 = 141.2675$ sq ft. But maximum values give $6.15 \times 23.45 = 144.2175$ sq ft. All we know about the exact area is that it lies somewhere within this range. We are certain of the result only to the first two digits. We may say the area is 140 sq ft, a two-significant-digit result. We are certain that the area is between 135 and 145 sq ft. The factors 6.1 and 23.4 had two and three significant digits respectively. A product can be no more accurate than the least accurate factor. *A product of approximate numbers should be expressed with the same number of significant digits as are possessed by the least accurate factor.* Similarly, in the division the quotient should contain the same number of significant digits as possessed by the dividend or divisor, whichever has the least. If one factor is exact the product should contain the same number of significant digits as that of the other factor.

A very satisfactory rule for multiplying approximate numbers is: round off all factors so that they will have one more significant digit than the factor containing the least. Multiply, then round off the product so as to have the same number of significant digits as possessed by the least accurate factor.

## APPROXIMATE COMPUTATION

In summary, a sum or difference should never be more precise than the least precise part of the data used. A product or quotient should never be more accurate than the least accurate part of the data involved. Otherwise we are indicating that we know more about the result than we do.

It should be borne in mind that the above rules are not theorems subject to mathematical proof. They are merely good working rules. In dealing with approximate computation we should always exercise common sense in the interpretation of results.

### EXERCISES

**1.** Determine the number of significant digits in each of the following:
(a) 100.50
(b) 10,050
(c) 100,50$\underline{0}$
(d) .0010050
(e) 9340
(f) 93.40

**2.** Round off the following to two significant digits:
(a) 8463
(b) 92.50
(c) 37,210
(d) .006750

**3.** Use each of the three rules given in the text to add the following approximate numbers:

$$326 + 451.3 + 5\underline{0} + 27.45$$

**4.** Find the maximum and minimum areas enclosed by a rectangle whose sides are measured to be 150.4 ft and 27.3 ft.

**5.** Use the rule for multiplying approximate numbers to find $150.4 \times 27.3$. Compare the result with the result of Exercise 4.

**6.** In finding relative error why do we not use the ratio of the absolute error to the true value instead of absolute error to obtained measurement?

**7.** Find the absolute error and the relative error when we use .67 as an approximation for the exact number $\frac{2}{3}$.

## 7.6 Scientific Notation

This is the age of the astronomically large and the infinitesimally small. Astronomers use as their unit of length the light year, which is the distance traveled by light in one year or approximately 6,000,000,000,000 miles.

Physical scientists use a unit of length, the angstrom unit, which is .0000000001 meter. In spite of such tremendously large and unbelievably small units scientists still have need for a more compact way of writing very large and very small numbers. Scientific notation fills that need.

An approximate number is written in scientific notation if it is written as a number 1 or more but less than 10, multiplied by an integral power of 10. The number between 1 and 10 must indicate the significant digits of the number. Unless the number in ordinary notation has nonsignificant digits nothing is gained by using scientific notation.

We can convert a number to scientific notation by shifting the decimal point to *standard position*, that is, to a position such that one and only one nonzero digit stands to its left, then multiply by the power of ten necessary to shift the decimal point back to its original position.

For example, to express 137,000,000 in scientific notation we first place the decimal point in standard position and drop the nonsignificant terminal zeros. This step yields 1.37. If we were to move the decimal back to its original position it would be equivalent to multiplying by $10^8$. Then $137{,}000{,}000 = 1.37 \times 10^8$. In effect, we have divided by 10,000,000 by shifting the decimal point, then multiplied by $10{,}000{,}000 = 10^8$.

We follow the same procedure with very small numbers. To express .0000016 in scientific notation we first place the decimal point in standard position, giving 1.6. This amounts to multiplying the number by 1,000,000. Then, to divide by 1,000,000 we multiply by $10^{-6}$, giving $1.6 \times 10^{-6}$.

The idea of scientific notation is an obvious extension of the positional character of our base ten notation system. Recall that shifting the decimal point one place to the right increases the value of each digit tenfold. Similarly, shifting one place to the left decreases the position of each digit by one, ones become tenths, tens become ones, and so on. Then shifting the decimal point to the left one place is equivalent to dividing by ten. The integral exponent on ten in scientific notation indicates the number of places and the direction the decimal point must be moved in order to go back to ordinary notation. A negative exponent implies a shift to the left; a positive exponent implies a shift to the right.

The value of scientific notation is more than mere shortening of the symbolism. It is easier to grasp the magnitude of a very large or very small number when it is written in this form. The form also facilitates computation with approximate numbers.

*Example:* Evaluate

$$\frac{179400 \times .00053}{7600 \times .0000226}$$

*Solution:* First, we write in scientific notation, rounding all numbers to two significant digits:

$$\frac{1.8 \times 10^5 \times 5.3 \times 10^{-4}}{7.6 \times 10^3 \times 2.3 \times 10^{-5}}.$$

Combining powers of 10 we get

$$\frac{1.8 \times 5.3}{7.6 \times 2.3} \times 10^3$$

which simplifies to $.55 \times 10^3 = 5.5 \times 10^4$.

## EXERCISES

**1.** Write the following in scientific notation:
(a) 86,300
(b) $150 \times 10^6$
(c) $1.7 \times 10^{-5}$
(d) .000830
(e) $.007 \times 10^3$

**2.** Write the following in ordinary notation:
(a) $5.6 \times 10^8$
(b) $1.1 \times 10^{-5}$
(c) $221 \times 10^4$
(d) $2.34 \times 10^0$
(e) $4.3 \times 10^{-1}$

**3.** Use scientific notation to evaluate the following approximate computations:
(a) $76900000 \times .000063$
(b) $186000 \times 3600 \times 24 \times 365$
(c) $\dfrac{.015 \times 9371}{43.8 \times .0006}$

# 8 The Field of Real Numbers

THE FIRST SEVEN CHAPTERS OF THIS TEXT HAVE BEEN DEVOTED TO A STUDY in depth of the arithmetic of the system of real numbers and its subsystems. For the remainder of the text we shall study algebraic structures as applied to the system of reals and, by extension, the complex numbers.

One of the secrets of the power of mathematics is its abstraction and generality. It is here that we find one of the characteristics which distinguishes algebra from arithmetic. A single abstract mathematical system may have a variety of concrete interpretations. For example, the single algebraic equation

$$x^2 + 4x - 5 = 0$$

will serve as an abstract description of the behavior of an almost limitless number of physical situations. Once the equation is solved, we have the key to all of the physical situations that it describes.

## 8.1 Groups

The concept of a mathematical group illustrates the power and generality of algebra. Mathematicians have discovered that quite diverse mathematical objects sometimes have distinguishing properties in common. Consider for a moment the set of integers. We know this set is closed with respect to addition—the sum of two integers is invariably an integer. The integers obey the associative property: $(3 + 5) + 7 = 3 + (5 + 7)$ or in general, if $a$, $b$, $c$, are integers, distinct or not, $(a + b) + c = a + (b + c)$. There is an integer, zero, that serves as the addition identity: $a + 0 = 0 + a = a$ for any integer $a$. (Note that we are not saying the commutative property holds in general when we say $a + 0 = 0 + a$.) Finally, each integer has an additive inverse: for each integer $a$ there is an integer $-a$ such that $a + (-a) = 0$. The four properties—*closure*, *associativity*, *identity*, and *inverse*—are the required properties for a group. There are many sets of mathematical objects other than the set of integers which satisfy these properties relative to some operation. Any such set and the operation are a mathematical group.

A group is a set, $G$, of elements $a, b, c \ldots$ related to each other through an operation $\odot$ such that

1. The set $G$ is closed: $a \odot b = c$; $a$, $b$, and $c$ elements of $G$.
2. The elements of $G$ obey the associative property

$$(a \odot b) \odot c = a \odot (b \odot c)$$

for any $a$, $b$ and $c$, $\in G$

3. $G$ has an identity element $I$

$$a \odot I = I \odot a = a$$

4. Each element $a$ of $G$ has an inverse $-a$

$$a \odot -a = I$$

In the definition we have said nothing about the nature of either the elements or the operation. We can study the group without any concern for their nature. Any conclusions that are established can then be applied to *any* group.

The definition of a group makes no requirement as to the number of elements it must have. We know the set of integers is infinite. But a group can have just one element. Consider, for example, the integer 1 and ordinary multiplication as the operation. Closure is satisfied because the only possible combination is $1 \times 1$, and since the product is 1 the product is an element of the set. Associativity is surely satisfied since the entire set of integers satisfies the associative property. But specifically $(1 \times 1) \times 1 = 1 \times (1 \times 1)$ since each side of the equation reduces to 1. The identity is 1 because 1 (any member of the set) $\times$ 1 = 1 (the original member of the set). Similarly, 1 is its own inverse because 1 (any member of the set) $\times$ 1 = 1 (the identity). This is admittedly a rather trivial case but nevertheless 1 and multiplication is a group. However, groups, the number of whose elements is a finite number greater than 1, are commonplace.

A word about the operation of a group is in order. We say it is a *binary* operation, meaning that exactly *two* elements, not necessarily different, are combined. We usually think of the operations of arithmetic, addition and multiplication, and their inverses, subtraction and division, in terms of manipulation of physical objects in some way. The definition of the addition of cardinal numbers suggests this kind of interpretation. But in the strict mathematical sense an operation is merely an association of an ordered pair (in the case of *binary* operations) of things onto a single thing. The fact, $3 + 4 = 7$, simply means we associate the ordered pair $(3, 4)$ with 7, $(3, 4) \to 7$. In general, if $a \odot b = c$ we merely are stating that the operation $\odot$ associates the ordered pair of elements $(a, b)$ with the element $c$, $(a, b) \to c$. Why do we stipulate that the pair is *ordered*? We know that $3 + 4 = 4 + 3 = 7$; hence the association $(4, 3) \to 7$ as well as $(3, 4) \to 7$. But this is not true of all operations: $3 - 4$ does not equal $4 - 3$. If the order of the elements in the pair is immaterial we say the group is a *commutative* group. Most of the groups we shall consider are commutative; for example, the set of integers is commutative with respect to addition. However, there are groups that are not commutative.

### EXERCISES

*Determine whether each of the following is a group. In the case of any that are not indicate which property or properties fail.*

**1.** $\{1, -1\}$ and addition.

**2.** $\{1, -1\}$ and multiplication.

**3.** The set of all integers and multiplication.

**4.** The set of all positive integers and addition.

**5.** The set of all odd integers and multiplication.

**6.** The set of all even integers and addition.

**7.** The set of all positive rational numbers and multiplication.

**8.** The set of all rational numbers and addition.

**9.** The set of all integers and subtraction.

**10.** The set of all rational numbers and multiplication.

## 8.2 Fields

Throughout the development of the system of real numbers and its subsystems we have been concerned with not one, but two, primary operations: addition and multiplication, and their inverses. Relative to addition and multiplication, numbers behave in almost parallel fashion. The integers are a commutative addition group. The positive rational numbers are a commutative multiplication group.

The set of rational numbers is a commutative addition group. Except for the fact that zero does not have a multiplicative inverse (there is no rational number $a$ such that $a \cdot 0 = 1$), the rational numbers are a commutative multiplication group. Furthermore, the rational numbers satisfy the distributive property: if $a, b, c$ are rational numbers $a(b + c) = a \times b + a \times c$. The distributive property is the only abstract link connecting the two operations addition and multiplication.

Any set of elements that satisfies the above properties of the rational numbers is called a *field*.

> A field is a set of elements that
> 1. Is a commutative addition group.
> 2. Except that the addition identity, $0 \neq 1$, has no multiplicative inverse, is a commutative multiplication group.
> 3. Satisfies the distributive property—multiplication distributive over addition.

A field can be alternately defined as follows:
A field is a set, $F$, of elements combinable by the binary operations addition ($+$) and multiplication ($\times$) such that the following properties are fulfilled:

1. *Closure for addition:*
   If $a, b \in F$, then $a + b = c$ and $c \in F$

2. *Closure for multiplication:*
   If $a, b \in F$, then $a \times b = c$ and $c \in F$

3. *Addition is associative:*
   $a, b, c \in F$
   $(a + b) + c = a + (b + c)$

4. *Multiplication is associative:*
   $a, b, c \in F$
   $(a \times b) \times c = a \times (b \times c)$

5. *Addition is commutative:*
   $a, b \in F$
   $a + b = b + a$

6. *Multiplication is commutative:*
   $a, b \in F$
   $a \times b = b \times a$

7. *There is an addition identity* $0 \in F$ *such that, for any* $a \in F$*:*
   $a + 0 = a$

8. *There is a multiplication identity* $1 \in F$ $(1 \neq 0)$ *such that, for any* $a \in F$*:*
   $a \times 1 = a$

9. *Each element* $a \in F$, *except* $a = 0$, *has a multiplicative inverse* $\frac{1}{a}$ *such that:*

   $$a \times \frac{1}{a} = 1$$

10. *Each element* $a \in F$ *has an additive inverse* $-a \in F$ *such that:*
    $a + (-a) = 0$

11. *Multiplication is distributive over addition; that is* $a, b, c \in F$:
    $a \times (b + c) = a \times b + a \times c$

We have noted many examples of a mathematical group, the elements being various sets of numbers. We also noted that the number of elements of a group can be either infinite or a finite number $\geq 1$.

There are also many sets of numbers which are the elements of a field. We have developed two such sets of numbers. The set of rational numbers with addition and multiplication is a field; so also is the set of real numbers.

In Section 5.1 we investigated the behavior of even and odd numbers. The discussion was summarized in addition and multiplication tables for even and odd numbers.

| $+$ | $E$ | $O$ |
|---|---|---|
| $E$ | $E$ | $O$ |
| $O$ | $O$ | $E$ |

| $\times$ | $E$ | $O$ |
|---|---|---|
| $E$ | $E$ | $E$ |
| $O$ | $E$ | $O$ |

If we now interpret this as a system of a set of two elements $\{E, O\}$ combined by the binary operations, $+$ and $\times$, which of the 11 field properties are satisfied?

We certainly have closure with respect to both addition and multiplication because each cell in both tables contains either $E$ or $O$. This amounts to the fact that when even and odd numbers are added or multiplied the result is an even number or an odd number. This has to be true since the integers are closed to addition and multiplication and every integer is either even or odd.

Commutativity applies to both operations. This can be seen immediately by observing the symmetry of the table entries relative to the upper left to lower right diagonal. Why does this guarantee commutativity?

The associative and distributive properties can be established by verification of all possible cases. The number of cases can be reduced by using the commutative property. For example if the distributive property holds for $E(O + E)$ we know it must hold for $E(E + O)$ because $EO + EE = EE + EO$ since addition is commutative. The following cases are illustrative of how these properties can be verified:

To show that $(E + O) + E = E + (O + E)$ we substitute from the addition table $E + O = O$ and $O + E = O$, giving

$$O + E = E + O$$

But from the addition table we find

$$O + E = E + O = O$$

Hence $(E + O) + E = E + (O + E)$ because both sides are equal to $O$. To show that $E(O + E) = EO + EE$ we find $O + E = O$ and then $EO = E$ to simplify the left side. On the right we have $EO = E$ and $EE = E$, then finally $E + E = E$ to simplify the right side. Since $E(O + E) = E$ and $EO + EE = E$ we conclude

$$E(O + E) = EO + EE$$

There remain the identity and inverse properties to investigate. Is there an addition identity? Since $E + O = O$ and $E + E = E$ we conclude that $E$ is the addition identity. This merely means that if we add an even number to an integer the sum is even or odd according to whether the original integer was even or odd.

If each element is to have an additive inverse this means that there is an element which we can add to each element for the sum $E$. Since $E + E = E$ this means $E$ is its own inverse. Since $O + O = E$, $O$ is its own inverse.

Is there a multiplication identity? Since $O \times E = E$ and $O \times O = O$, the multiplication identity is $O$. Multiply an integer by an odd integer and the product is even or odd according to whether the original integer is even or odd.

The field properties do not require the addition identity $E$ to have a multiplicative inverse. Since $O \times O = O$, $O$ is its own multiplicative inverse.

Granting that we have completed the verification of the associative and distributive principles, we have now shown the system is a field.

## THE FIELD OF REAL NUMBERS

We can certainly conclude that a field does not have to have an infinite number of elements. In fact, the only two elements necessary are the addition identity and the multiplication identity.

## EXERCISES

**1.** List all properties of a field that the set of all integers under addition and multiplication fail to satisfy.

**2.** What properties of an addition group does the set of all natural numbers fail to satisfy?

**3.** What properties of a multiplication group does the set of all natural numbers fail to satisfy?

**4.** What properties of a field does the set of non-negative rational numbers fail to satisfy?

**5.** Prove that any three element group must be commutative.

**6.** Given the set $\{a, b, c, d\}$ and the operation table

| | $a$ | $b$ | $c$ | $d$ |
|---|---|---|---|---|
| $a$ | $a$ | $b$ | $c$ | $d$ |
| $b$ | $b$ | $a$ | $d$ | $c$ |
| $c$ | $c$ | $d$ | $a$ | $b$ |
| $d$ | $d$ | $c$ | $b$ | $a$ |

Prove that this is a group.

**7.** Consider the operation in Exercise 6 "addition" and let the following table define "multiplication." Is the system exhibited here and in Exercise 6 a field? Justify your answer.

| | $a$ | $b$ | $c$ | $d$ |
|---|---|---|---|---|
| $a$ | $a$ | $a$ | $a$ | $a$ |
| $b$ | $a$ | $b$ | $c$ | $d$ |
| $c$ | $a$ | $c$ | $d$ | $b$ |
| $d$ | $a$ | $d$ | $b$ | $c$ |

8. In Exercise 6 interpret $a = 1, b = 5, c = 7, d = 11$. Interpret the operation as follows: $a \odot b$ equals the remainder when the product $a \times b$ is divided by 12. For example $7 \odot 11$ means the remainder when $7 \times 11 = 77$ is divided by 12. Since this remainder is 5 we have $7 \odot 11 = 5$. In the table we have $c \odot d = b$ which is consistent with the above interpretation. Verify that the entire table is consistent with this interpretation.

9. The *proper factors* of the positive integer $n$ are the positive integral factors of $n$ except 1 and $n$. Consider all integers, 1 through 12. What property can you discover relative to the numbers used in the interpretation in Exercise 8?

10. A *unit fraction* is a fraction with 1 as numerator and a nonzero integer as denominator. Using the usual rules for addition and multiplication of fractions, what field properties does the set of all unit fractions fail to satisfy?

## 8.3 Further Properties of a Field

Any property that can be derived from the 11 field properties is a true statement applicable to the elements of any field. For example, we know that if $a$ is any rational number then $a \cdot 0 = 0$. Is this a property peculiar to the set of rational numbers, or is it a property of the elements of any field? We know it is the latter provided the conclusion $a \cdot 0 = 0$ can be derived from the 11 field properties. In establishing this and other results we of course have the usual properties of equality at our disposal, as well as the 11 field properties.

**Theorem 1:**

TO PROVE: If $a \in F$ then $a \times 0 = 0$

| PROOF: | |
|---|---|
| $a + 0 = a$ | Field property 7 |
| $a(a + 0) = a \times a$ | multiplication property of equality |
| $a \times a + a \times 0 = a \times a$ | Field property 11 |
| $(-a \times a) + a \times a + a \times 0 = (-a \times a) + a \times a$ | addition property of equality |
| $0 + a \times 0 = 0$ | Field property 9 |
| $a \times 0 = 0$ | Field property 7 |

We may conclude that $a \times 0 = 0$ in the field of rational numbers, or the field of real numbers, or any field whatever.

The above theorem shows that if a factor is zero then the product must also be zero. What of the converse of this? If the product is zero does it follow that at least one factor must be zero?

This happens to be a true property of a field. However, the two propositions: "If a factor is zero then the product is zero" and "if the product is zero then a factor is zero" are not equivalent. There are many mathematical systems which satisfy the first proposition but not the second. That is, there are systems, not fields, wherein $a \cdot b = 0$ is possible and neither $a$ nor $b$ is zero.

**Theorem 2:**

TO PROVE: If $a, b \in F$, $b \neq 0$, and $ab = 0$ then $a = 0$

PROOF:

| | |
|---|---|
| $ab = 0$ | Given |
| $ab \times \frac{1}{b} = 0 \times \frac{1}{b}$ | Multiplication property of equality |
| $ab \times \frac{1}{b} = 0$ | Theorem 1 |
| $a\left(b \times \frac{1}{b}\right) = 0$ | Field property 5 |
| $a \times 1 = 0$ | Field property 9 |
| $a = 0$ | Field property 8 |

It is of interest to note that the inverse operations of subtraction and division are not mentioned in the postulational description of a field. If these operations are defined in the usual way it can be shown that they are superfluous in the sense that the same result can be obtained by using the corresponding direct operation and the inverse element. For example: to subtract 5 we get the same result if we add $-5$; to divide by $\frac{3}{5}$ we get the same result if we multiply by $\frac{5}{3}$.

The property: if $a + c = b + c$ then $a = b$ follows immediately by subtracting $c$ from both members of the equation. However, this can be shown to be a property of a field without even defining subtraction.

**Theorem 3:**

TO PROVE: If $a, b, c \in F$ and $a + c = b + c$ then $a = b$

PROOF:

| | |
|---|---|
| $a + c = b + c$ | Given |
| $a + c + (-c) = b + c + (-c)$ | Addition property of equality |
| $a + (c + -c) = b + (c + -c)$ | Field property 3 |
| $a + 0 = b + 0$ | Field property 9 |
| $a = b$ | Field property 7 |

The property stated in Theorem 3 is known as the cancellation property. A corresponding property applies to multiplication.

## FURTHER PROPERTIES OF A FIELD

**Theorem 4:**

TO PROVE: If $a, b, c \in F$, $c \neq 0$, and $ac = bc$ then $a = b$

PROOF:

| | |
|---|---|
| $ac = bc$ | Given |
| $\frac{1}{c}$ is in $F$ | Given that $c \neq 0$ |
| $ac \cdot \frac{1}{c} = bc \cdot \frac{1}{c}$ | Multiplication property of equality |
| $a\left(c \cdot \frac{1}{c}\right) = b\left(c \cdot \frac{1}{c}\right)$ | Field property 4 |
| $a \cdot 1 = b \cdot 1$ | Field property 10 |
| $a = b$ | Field property 8 |

Regardless of the nature of the elements of a field, field property 9 assures the existence of "negative" elements, in the sense that $-a$ is the "negative" of $a$. The rules of signs developed in Chapters 2 and 3 apply to positive and negative numbers. The same rules apply to the elements of a field in the sense that $-a$ merely means the additive inverse of the element $a$. The element $a$ might well be a negative number; it is any element of a field.

**Theorem 5:**

TO PROVE: $a(-b) = -ab$

PROOF:

| | |
|---|---|
| $b + (-b) = 0$ | Field property 9 |
| $a[b + (-b)] = a \cdot 0$ | Multiplication property of zero |
| $a[b + (-b)] = 0$ | Theorem 1 |
| $ab + a(-b) = 0$ | Field property 11 |
| $0 = ab + (-ab)$ | Field property 9 |
| $ab + a(-b) = ab + -ab$ | Substitution |
| $a(-b) = -ab$ | Theorem 4 |

If Theorem 5 is applied to the field of real numbers, with $a$ and $b$ positive real numbers, we see an application of the rule of signs: "the product of a positive number and a negative number is a negative number." If $a = 3$ and $b = 5$, by Theorem 5 we have

$$3 \times (-5) = -15$$

However, the theorem is consistent with all rules of signs. For example, if $a = -4$ and $b = -3$, $(-b = 3)$ and

$$a \times -b = -4 \times 3 = -(-4 \times -3) = -12$$

Or, illustrating the rule: "the product of two negative numbers is positive," if $a = -3$ and $b = 6$ we have

$$(-3) \times (-6) = -(-3 \times 6) = -(-18) = 18$$

If both $a$ and $b$ are positive the last illustration would indicate that $-a \times -b = ab$, $a$ and $b$ elements of any field.

**Theorem 6:**

TO PROVE: $-a \times -b = ab$

| PROOF: | |
|---|---|
| $b + (-b) = 0$ | Field property 9 |
| $-a[b + (-b)] = -a \cdot 0$ | Multiplication property of equality |
| $-a[b + (-b)] = 0$ | Theorem 1 |
| $-a(b) + (-a) \times (-b) = 0$ | Field property 11 |
| $b(-a) + (-a) \times (-b) = 0$ | Field property 6 |
| $-ba + (-a) \times (-b) = 0$ | Theorem 5 |
| $ba + (-ba) + (-a) \times (-b) = ba + 0$ | Addition property of equality |
| $ba + (-ba) + (-a) \times (-b) = ab + 0$ | Field property 6 |
| $ba + (-ba) + (-a) \times (-b) = ab$ | Field property 7 |
| $0 + (-a) \times (-b) = ab$ | Field property 9 |
| $(-a) \times (-b) + 0 = ab$ | Field property 5 |
| $(-a) \times (-b) = ab$ | Field property 7 |

Theorems 5 and 6 are sufficient to establish the laws of signs for multiplication. The laws for addition require, in addition to field properties, the definitions of subtraction, absolute value, and order. However, the next two theorems are indicative of the rules.

**Theorem 7:**

TO PROVE: $-a + -b = -(a + b)$

| PROOF: | |
|---|---|
| $0 + 0 = 0$ | Field property 7 |
| $a + (-a) + b + (-b) = (a + b) + -(a + b)$ | Field property 9 |
| $(a + b) + [(-a + (-b)] = (a + b) + -(a + b)$ | Field properties 3 and 5 |
| $[(-a) + (-b)] + (a + b) = -(a + b) + (a + b)$ | Field property 5 |
| $(-a) + (-b) = -(a + b)$ | Theorem 3 |

If $a$ and $b$ are positive real numbers Theorem 7 justifies the rule: "the sum of two negative numbers is the negative of the sum of their additive inverses." For example, if $a = 3$ and $b = 5$ we have

$$-3 + -5 = -(3 + 5) = -8$$

The theorem is also consistent with the rule for adding oppositely signed numbers.

If $a = 4$ and $b = -7$ we have, substituting $a = -4$ and $-b = 7$,

$$-4 + 7 = -[4 + (-7)]$$

which is a correct result even though it does not indicate how to obtain the sum.

**Theorem 8:**

TO PROVE: $a + (-b) = -[b + (-a)]$

PROOF: $0 + 0 = 0$ — Field property 7

$[a + (-a)] + [b + (-b)] = -[b + (-a)] + [b + (-a)]$ — Field property 9

$[a + (-b)] + [b + (-a)] = -[b + (-a)] + [b + (-a]$ — Field properties 3 and 5

$a + (-b) = -[b + (-a)]$ — Theorem 3

By Theorem 8, if $a = -4$ and $b = -7$ we have,

$$-4 + 7 = -[(-7) + 4]$$

which is consistent with the results obtained using Theorem 7. If $a = -3$ and $b = 5$ then by Theorem 8

$$(-3) + (-5) = -(5 + 3) = -8,$$

a result which is again consistent with the rule for addition of two negative numbers.

## EXERCISES

*Unless otherwise stated, consider all terms $a, b, \ldots,$ as elements of a field.*

1. Prove: If $ab \neq 0$ then $a \neq 0$ and $b \neq 0$.
2. Given the definition of subtraction $a - b = x$ if and only if $x + b = a$. Prove $a - b = a + (-b)$.
3. Prove: If $a = b$ and $c = d$ then $a + c = b + d$.

4. Prove: If $a = b$ and $c = d$ then $ac = bd$.

5. Use Theorem 5 to evaluate $a \cdot (-b)$ if
   (a) $a = 5$ and $b = 3$
   (b) $a = -4$ and $b = -3$
   (c) $a = 3$ and $b = -7$
   (d) $a = -2$ and $b = 5$

6. Use Theorem 6 to evaluate $(-a) \cdot (-b)$ if
   (a) $a = -5$ and $b = 3$
   (b) $a = 4$ and $b = -3$
   (c) $a = -3$ and $b = -7$
   (d) $a = 2$ and $b = 5$

7. Use Theorem 7 to find $(-a) + (-b)$ if
   (a) $a = 5$ and $b = 3$
   (b) $a = -4$ and $b = -3$
   (c) $a = 3$ and $b = -7$
   (d) $a = -2$ and $b = 5$

8. Use Theorem 8 to find $a + (-b)$ if
   (a) $a = -5$ and $b = 3$
   (b) $a = 4$ and $b = -3$
   (c) $a = -3$ and $b = -7$
   (d) $a = 2$ and $b = 5$

## 8.4 Subsets of the Real Numbers

In Chapters 1 through 7 many number systems were developed and studied. This was a *definitional* development. Starting with only simple set concepts, we have constructed by definition successively the finite cardinal numbers, the integers, the rational numbers, and the real numbers.

The field properties do not completely characterize the real numbers because the rational numbers also satisfy the requirements of a field. For that matter the possibility of a field with only a finite number of elements has been suggested.

There is an alternative to the definitional approach to the real numbers. If in addition to the field properties, other properties which are required to completely characterize the real numbers are assumed to be true, we may consider the real numbers as any set of objects that satisfies the complete set of properties. When this approach is used we can identify as subsets of the reals the rational numbers, the integers, the whole numbers, and the natural numbers. In fact, the integers can be shown as a subset of the rationals, the whole numbers as a subset of the integers, and the natural numbers a subset of the whole numbers.

The rational numbers satisfy all properties of a field. Which field properties do the integers not satisfy? We know the integers and addition are a group. Furthermore, the integers satisfy the distributive property. The multiplication identity, 1, is an integer. In fact, the only field property not satisfied by the integers is property 10, the existence of multiplicative inverses. There is no integer by which we can multiply $-3$ for the product 1. Only two integers have multiplicative inverses: one of them is the identity, 1. What is the other?

The system variously called the whole numbers, the positive integers and zero, or the finite cardinal numbers satisfies which field properties? Here again, property 10 is not satisfied. In this system the only element that has a multiplicative inverse is the multiplication identity, 1. But neither is property 9 satisfied; no element has an additive inverse except the addition identity, 0. However, all other field properties are satisfied.

The set of natural numbers differs from the set of whole numbers only in that it does not have 0 as an element. The natural numbers fail to satisfy field property 7, as well as 9 and 10. But all other properties are satisfied.

It would be a mistake to assume that any of these subsets of the real numbers is completely characterized by that subset of the set of properties of a field which it does satisfy. For example, all of these systems have an infinite number of elements, but nothing in the field properties requires this. As we have seen (Section 8.3) a field can have as few as two elements.

## EXERCISES

**1.** Prove: In any group the identity element is its own inverse.

**2.** Prove: In any field the additive inverse of the multiplication identity is its own multiplicative inverse.

**3.** Is there a natural number between 5 and 6? Is there a rational number between $\frac{1}{5}$ and $\frac{1}{6}$? What difference between the nature of the two sets does this suggest?

**4.** Is there a largest natural number less than 10? If so, what is it? Is there a largest rational number less than 1? If so, what is it?

**5.** Is the difference between two natural numbers always a natural number? Illustrate. Is the difference between two integers always an integer? Which field property accounts for this difference?

**6.** Is the quotient of two nonzero integers always an integer? Illustrate. Is the quotient of two nonzero rational numbers always a rational number? Which field property accounts for this difference?

7. List the properties of a field that the natural numbers satisfy.

8. List the properties of a field that the integers satisfy.

9. Theorem 4, Section 8.3, specifies that $a$, $b$, and $c$ are elements of a field. If $a$, $b$, and $c$ are integers and $ac = bc$, $c \neq 0$, does it follow that $a = b$? Justify your answer. Why is it necessary that $c \neq 0$?

10. Theorem 3, Section 8.3, specifies that $a$, $b$, and $c$ are elements of a field. If $a$, $b$, and $c$ are natural numbers and $a + c = b + c$ does it follow that $a = b$?

## 8.5 Order Relations

The field of rational numbers and the field of real numbers are *ordered fields*. Each of the eleven properties of a field listed in Section 8.2 is concerned with the relationship *equality*. *Order* is another relationship between numbers. However, it is not an equivalence relation. In Chapter 7 the relationship "greater than" was defined: $a > b$ ($a$ is greater than $b$) if and only if $a - b$ is a positive number. Which of the three properties of an equivalence relation—reflexive, symmetric, and transitive—does this relation have? We can answer the question on an intuitive basis rather easily. The relation $>$ is not reflexive. We know that $7 > 7$ is false because $7 - 7$ is not a positive number. We also know that $>$ is not symmetric because if $10 > 7$ then $10 - 7$ is positive; but the symmetric property would require $7 > 10$ also. This is false because $7 - 10$ is not a positive number. The transitive property does apply; $10 > 7$ and $7 > 5$; hence, $10 > 5$.

An ordered field is a field whose elements satisfy two properties in addition to the eleven properties of fields in general.

12. *Trichotomy:* There is a subset of the elements of $F$ called positive elements. Any element $a \in F$ is one and only one of the following: (1) $a$ is positive, (2) $a$ is the addition identity zero, or (3) the additive inverse of $a$ is positive.
13. *Closure for positive elements:* If $a$ and $b$ are positive elements then $a + b$ is a positive element and $a \times b$ is a positive element.

The trichotomy principle is sometimes stated differently. If $a, b \in F$ then one and only one of the following is true: (1) $a > b$, (2) $a = b$, (3) $b > a$. The equivalence of the two statements of the principle can be seen from the definition of "greater than." By definition $a > b$ if and only if $a - b$ is a positive number; if $a = b$ then $a - b = 0$; since $(a - b) + (b - a) = 0$, $b - a$ is the additive inverse of $a - b$. Hence we see the three choices $a > b$, $a = b$, or $b > a$ are the same as the three choices $a - b$ is positive, $a - b$ is zero, or the additive inverse of $a - b$ is positive.

Both order properties, 12 and 13, presuppose a subset of elements, designated as positive. The integers, as well as the rational and real fields, satisfy both properties. Do the natural numbers satisfy these properties? In the sense that a natural number is the same thing as a positive integer the answer is "yes." Property 12 does not require that the subset of positive elements be a proper subset. Any set is a subset of itself. In the set of natural numbers every element is positive; hence every element is one of the three choices. It is apparent that each element is only one of the three when we realize that there is no additive identity and no element has an additive inverse.

Is it possible for a field not to be ordered? Consider the "evens" and "odds" field. Does it satisfy the trichotomy principle? Since $E$ is the addition identity and is its own additive inverse, we know that one and *only one* of the following must be true of the remaining element $O$; $O$ is positive or the additive inverse of $O$ is positive. Since $O$ is its own inverse this is impossible. If it is not possible to designate a subset of elements as positive then property 13 is meaningless.

### EXERCISES

**1.** Prove: If $a$ is a positive number then $a > 0$.

**2.** Prove: If $a > 0$ then $a$ is a positive number.

**3.** Prove: If $a > 0$ and $b < 0$ then $a > b$.

**4.** Show that $15 > 10$. Does it follow that $-15 > -10$? Discuss.

**5.** Show that $1 > -7$. Does it follow that $-1 > 7$? Discuss.

**6.** Prove: If $a > b$ then $-b > -a$.

**7.** Illustrate on a number line. If $a > b$ then the point corresponding to $a$ is farther to the right than the point corresponding to $b$. Use $a > 0$, $b > 0$, and $a < 0$, $b < 0$ as well as $a > 0$, $b < 0$.

## 8.6 Consequences of the Order Properties

We have seen that the order relation is quite different from the equality relation. However, since it is a relation between numbers it is natural to inquire what effect the number operations have on order. Specifically, we accept the addition and multiplication properties of equality:

If $a = b$ then $a + c = b + c$

$$a, b, c \in \text{R (the field of real numbers)}$$

If $a = b$ then $ac = bc$

$$a, b, c \in \mathrm{R}$$

If $=$ is replaced with $>$ are the above statements true?

We know that $7 > 3$ and if we add $-4$ to each side the relation is preserved: $7 + (-4) > 3 + (-4)$ because $3 > -1$. How do we know $3 > -1$? Apply the definition and we have $3 - (-1) = 4$, a positive number.

We wish to establish the general case: if $a, b, c \in \mathrm{R}$ and $a > b$ then $a + c > b + c$.

Since it is given that $a > b$ it follows from the definition of $>$ that $a - b = p$, a positive number. If the conclusion, $a + c > b + c$, is true then $(a + c) - (b + c) = p_2$, a positive number. Then we wish to show that if $a - b$ is a positive number then $(a + c) - (b + c)$ is also a positive number. But

$$\begin{aligned}(a + c) - (b + c) &= a + c - b - c \\ &= (a - b) + (c - c) \\ &= (a - b) + 0 \\ &= a - b\end{aligned}$$

Therefore $(a + c) - (b + c)$ is a positive number and $a + c > b + c$.

We should take special note of the fact that $a, b, c$, are *any* real numbers in the above argument.

*Example:* $4 > 2$ because $4 - 2$ is positive $4 + (-10) > 2 + (-10)$ or $-6 > -8$ because $(-6) - (-8) = 2$, a positive number.

*Example:* $-2 > -6$ because $-2 - (-6) = +4$ and $-2 + (-10) > -6 + (-10)$ or $-12 > -16$ because $-12 - (-16) = +4$

When we examine the corresponding statement for multiplication we find a different situation.

It is true that $7 > 5$ and $3 \cdot 7 > 3 \cdot 5$. But consider $7 > 5$ and $(-3)7 > (-3)5$. The latter relation is false because $(-3)7 = -21$ is not greater than $(-3)5 = -15$. In fact, $(-3)5 > (-3)7$ since $-15 - (-21) = +6$. These numerical examples suggest the possibility that we should restrict the multiplier to positive numbers. A positive number and a number greater than zero are synonymous, that is, $a$ is positive if and only if $a > 0$. This is consistent with our definition because $a > 0$ means $a - 0$ is positive, but $a - 0 = a$.

We wish to show that if $a > b$ and $c > 0$ then $ac > bc$. If $a > b$ then $a - b$ is positive. But $c(a - b) = ac - bc$ is positive if and only if $c$ is positive. Finally, if $ac - bc$ is positive then $ac > bc$. We conclude that we can multiply the numbers in an inequality by the same *positive* number without changing the sense of the inequality.

## CONSEQUENCES OF THE ORDER PROPERTIES

### EXERCISES

*Solve the following inequalities:*

1. $x + 5 > 0$
2. $2x - 3 > x + 6$
3. $\frac{2}{3}x > 14$
4. $-2x > x + 6$
5. $x - 6 > x - 15$
6. $x + 12 > x - 3$
7. $x - 5 > x + 7$
8. $(x + 1)(x - 2) > 0$
9. $(x - 3)(x - 4) < 0$
10. $(x + 2)(x + 1) > 0$

## 8.7 Completeness of the Field of Reals

Although properties 12 and 13 are common to the integers, the rational numbers, and the real numbers, none of the three have identical order properties. The expression "$b$ is between $a$ and $c$" simply means one of the following statements is true: $a > b > c$ or $c > b > a$. Thus, 7 is between 3 and 12 because it is true that $12 > 7 > 3$. But there is no integer between 8 and 9. In general, there is no integer between the integers $a$ and $a + 1$.

In regard to "betweenness" the rational numbers behave quite differently from the integers. We know that between any two specified rational numbers there is always a rational number. We can find a number between $\frac{1}{4}$ and $\frac{1}{5}$ by taking half of their sum $\dfrac{\frac{1}{4} + \frac{1}{5}}{2} = \frac{9}{40}$. Verify that $\frac{1}{4} > \frac{9}{40} > \frac{1}{5}$. We can use the same scheme to find a rational number between $\frac{1}{4}$ and $\frac{9}{40}$ and one between $\frac{1}{5}$ and $\frac{9}{40}$. Since this process can be continued without end we must conclude that between every two rational numbers there are infinitely many rational numbers. This property is called the *denseness* of the rational numbers. We say the points on the number line corresponding to the rational numbers are dense on the line.

It is natural to inquire what order property distinguishes the real numbers from the rational numbers. We have seen, page 200, that, surprising though it may seem, the rational numbers do not exhaust the points on the line.

To see the distinction between the rationals and the reals we need the concept of boundedness. The set of integers $\{1, 2, 3, 4\}$ is bounded from above by any integer greater than 4. Ten is an upper bound, so also are 6 and 5. We wish also to consider 4 an upper bound since there is no element of the set greater than 4. In order for the concept of an upper bound to apply to a set, the elements of the set must conform to properties 12 and 13. Otherwise, there would be no significance to the statement $a > b$. In our example, 4 is an upper bound but there is no number less than 4 which is an upper bound. We call 4 the *least upper bound.*

An *upper bound* of the set

$$\{x_1, x_2, \ldots, x_n, \ldots\}$$

is a number $a$ such that $a$ is equal to or greater than any element of the set. If $a$ is less than any other upper bound then $a$ is the *least upper bound.*

The set $N = \{n \mid n \text{ is an integer less than } 10\}$ has 10 as an upper bound. But it is not the least upper bound. There are many rational numbers, such as $9\frac{1}{2}$, $9\frac{1}{4}$, $9\frac{1}{100}$, which are also upper bounds. In fact, 9 is an upper bound. It is the greatest member of the set. Consequently, no number less than 9 is an upper bound; 9 is the least upper bound.

Consider the set of *rational* numbers equal to or less than 2. Here, 2 is the least upper bound; it is the greatest member of the set. Now consider the set of rational numbers less than 2. There is no greatest member of the set; there is always a rational number between 2 and any rational number less than 2. Is 2 the least upper bound? It is certainly the least rational number that is an upper bound. In fact, it is the least upper bound because there is always a rational number between 2 and any irrational number less than 2.

However, there are sets of rational numbers that do not have any rational numbers as upper bound. We know there is no rational number whose square is 2 (see page 199). Consider two sets: $A$, the set of all positive rational numbers whose square is less than 2; and $B$, the set of all positive rational numbers whose square is greater than 2. The union of $A$ and $B$ is the set of all positive rational numbers. If set $A$ has a least upper bound that is a rational number it must be either the greatest member of $A$ or the least member of $B$. But $A$ has no greatest member and $B$ has no least member. Assume that $A$ has a greatest member $a$. Then $a^2 < 2$. But we know there is a rational number $x$ such that $a^2 < x < 2$ because the set of rational numbers is dense. If $\sqrt{x}$ is rational we have a contradiction; $a$ is not the greatest member of $A$. If $\sqrt{x}$ is not rational we again have a contradiction, because there is a rational number $y$ such that $a < y < \sqrt{x}$ and $y^2 < x < 2$. We can use the same type of argument to show that $B$ has no least member. Then set $A$ is a set of rational numbers that has no rational number as least upper bound. Its upper bound is $\sqrt{2}$, a real, but irrational, number.

Every nonempty subset of the set of real numbers that has an upper bound must have a least upper bound. This is the characteristic of the real number that distinguishes it from the rational number. It is called the *completeness* property of the real numbers. When we assign to a line points corresponding to the real numbers we say the line is complete; no further points can be assigned to it without altering its geometric properties.

When we defined every endless decimal as a real number we were really describing the decimal representation of a real number. However, corresponding to every endless decimal there is a set of rational numbers obtained by using the first, the first two, the first $n$, and so on, digits of the decimal. For example from the decimal expansion of $\frac{1}{3}$ we have

$$\{.3, .33, .333, \ldots .\}$$

The least upper bound of this set of rational numbers is $\frac{1}{3}$. The real numbers can be defined as the least upper bounds of all such sets.

## EXERCISES

*Determine whether each of the following sets has a least upper bound. Determine the least upper bound of those that do have one.*

**1.** $\{x \mid x \text{ is an integer } 0 \leq x < 25\}$

**2.** $\{x \mid x \text{ is a rational number } 0 < x < 1\}$

**3.** $\{x \mid x \text{ is a real number } 0 < x < 1\}$

**4.** $\{x \mid x \text{ is a real number } \geq 10\}$

**5.** $\{x \mid x \text{ is a real number, } x^2 < 5\}$

**6.** $\{x \mid x \text{ is a rational number, } x^2 < 5\}$

**7.** $\{x \mid x \text{ is an integer, } x^2 > 100\}$

**8.** $\{x \mid x \text{ is an integer, } -10 < x < 10\}$

**9.** $\{x \mid x \text{ is a real number, } x^2 > 2\}$

**10.** Since there is a rational number between any two irrational numbers and an irrational number between any two rational numbers, is it true that the rationals and irrational alternate on the number line? Discuss.

# 9 Linear Relations in Two Variables

THROUGHOUT MOST OF THIS TEXT WE HAVE BEEN CONCERNED WITH TWO relations, equality and order. Any property of equality can be derived from the five assumed properties:

1. *Reflexive:* $a = a$
2. *Symmetric:* If $a = b$ then $b = a$
3. *Transitive:* If $a = b$ and $b = c$ then $a = c$
4. *Addition:* If $a = b$ then $a + c = b + c$
5. *Multiplication:* If $a = b$ then $ac = bc$

On the other hand, the order relation does not possess all five of these properties. It is neither reflexive nor symmetric. It is transitive: if $a > b$ and $b > c$ then $a > c$. It does satisfy the addition property: if $a > b$ then $a + c > b + c$. It also satisfies the multiplication property with the proper restriction placed on $c$: if $a > b$ and $c > 0$ then $ac > bc$.

Another symbol is also used to express the order relation. The expression $a > b$ ($a$ is greater than $b$) can be written $b < a$ ($b$ is less than $a$). The two expressions mean exactly the same thing.

## 9.1 Linear Relations in One Variable

A mathematical statement involving the equality relation is an *equation*. For example

$$3x + 4 = 13$$

is an equation. It is frequently called an open sentence. It is called an *open* sentence because it is neither true nor false that the equality relation exists between $3x + 4$ and 13. You will recall that the variable $x$ is a symbol replaceable by any element of its replacement set. The replacement set is understood to be the set of real numbers unless it is otherwise specified. There are many replacements for $x$ which would make the sentence $3x + 4 = 13$ false. For example, if $x$ is replaced by 5 we have $3 \cdot 5 + 4 = 13$ is a false statement. On the other hand if $x$ is replaced with 3 the statement is true, $3 \cdot 3 + 4 = 13$ is a true statement because the equality is reflexive and we have $9 + 4 = 13$, or $13 = 13$.

The set of replacements of the variable which make a mathematical sentence true is called its *truth set* or *solution set*. The elements of the solution set of an equation are the *solutions* or the *roots* of the equation. The solution set of the equation $3x + 4 = 13$ is the unit set $\{3\}$.

Mathematical sentences may also involve the order relation. Consider the sentence $3x + 4 > 13$. For simplicity we shall take as replacement set for $x$ the set of integers $\{0, 1, 2, 3, 4, 5, 6\}$. If $x$ is replaced with 4 we have $12 + 4 > 13$, a true statement because $16 - 13 = 3$, a positive number. Similarly, if $x$ is replaced by 5 we have the true statement $15 + 4 > 13$, and if $x$ is replaced with 6 we have $18 + 4 > 13$. Thus, 4, 5, and 6 are elements of the solution set of the statement $3x + 4 > 13$. But are there other elements? If $x = 3$, as we have seen above, we have the equality $13 = 13$. Hence $13 > 13$ is false. If $x = 2$, we have $6 + 4 > 13$, which is also false because $10 - 13$ does not equal a positive number. Similarly, for $x = 1$ we have the false statement $7 > 13$, and for $x = 0$ we have the false statement $4 > 13$. Hence, the solution set is $\{4, 5, 6\}$.

The solution set of a sentence in one variable can be plotted on the number line since there is a one-to-one correspondence between the real numbers and the points of a line.

The graph of the solution set for $3x + 4 = 13$ is the single point 3. This is indicated by the enlarged dot at the point $+3$.

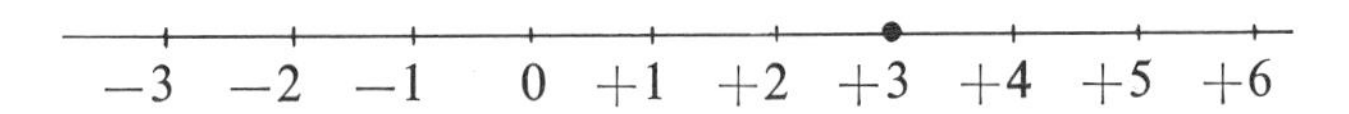


The graph of $3x + 4 > 13$ with replacement set $\{0, 1, 2, 3, 4, 5, 6\}$ consists of three points $+4$, $+5$, and $+6$.

−4 −3 −2 −1 0 +1 +2 +3 +4 +5 +6 +7

On the other hand, if the replacement set for $x$ is the set of all real numbers greater than $+3$, we indicate this with the heavy line to the right of $+3$. The point $+3$ is circled to indicate that 3 is not a member of the solution set. The arrow pointing to the right indicates that the graph

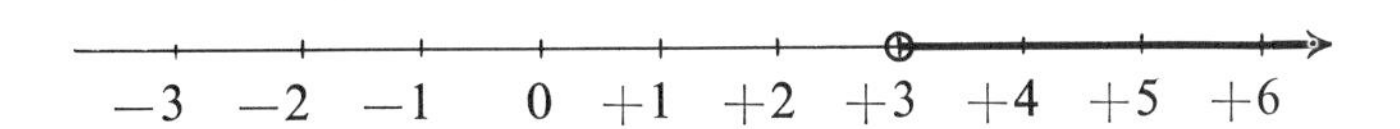

includes the entire half line to the right of $+3$. Does this graph have a first point on the left? Does it have a last point on the right?

Mathematical sentences sometimes include both the equality and order relation. For example

$$3x + 4 \geq 13$$

means $3x + 4$ is equal to *or* greater than 13. This is a compound sentence. Its solution set is the union of the solution sets of $3x + 4 > 13$ and

$-5 \quad -4 \quad -3 \quad -2 \quad -1 \quad 0 \quad +1 \quad +2 \quad +3 \quad +4 \quad +5 \quad +6$

$3x + 4 = 13$. Here, the point $+3$ is shown as an enlarged dot, indicating 3 is included in the solution set. In this case the solution set does have a smallest number, $+3$, but it does not have a largest number.

## EXERCISES

*Graph the solution set of each of the following sentences. Unless otherwise stated the replacement set for the variable is the set of real numbers.*

**1.** $3x + 5 = 20$

**2.** $3x + 5 = 20$, $x$ a real number $> 10$

**3.** $5x - 6 > 14$, $x$ an integer $0 < x < 10$

**4.** $5x - 6 \leq 14$, $x$ an integer $0 < x < 10$

**5.** $5x - 6 \lessgtr 14$

**6.** $2x - 7 < x + 5$

**7.** $2x + 6 \geq 3x - 1$

**8.** $3x - 5 = 9$, $x$ an integer

**9.** $3x - 5 > 9$, $x$ an integer $\leq 10$

**10.** $3x - 5 \leq 9$

## 9.2 The Equation $ax + by = c$

The open sentence $ax + by = c$ is an open sentence concerning the equality relation, but involving *two* variables. The variables $x$ and $y$ need not have the same replacement set, but they usually do. In fact, unless otherwise stated, we shall assume the replacement set of each is the set of real numbers.

The sentence $3x + 4y = 18$ is true or false, depending on the replacements for $x$ and $y$. It should be noted carefully that the truth or falsity of the statement is still indeterminate if we make a replacement for only one variable. If we replace $x$ with 2 we have $6 + 4y = 18$ or $4y = 12$, which is still an open sentence in $y$. The statement becomes true or false as we make a simultaneous replacement for both $x$ and $y$. Consequently, the solution set for the statement is not a set of numbers. It is a set of *ordered pairs of numbers.* Order is important because we must know which number is the $x$ replacement and which is the $y$ replacement. It is an accepted convention that the first number be the $x$ replacement and the second be the $y$ replacement. For example the ordered pair (2, 3) is an element of the solution set because if $x$ is replaced by 2 and $y$ is replaced by 3 the sentence becomes

$$3 \times 2 + 4 \times 3 = 18,$$

a true statement. But the ordered pair (3, 2) is not an element of the solution set because

$$3 \times 3 + 4 \times 2 = 18$$

is a false statement.

Although the solution set of a linear equation in one variable has one element, it should be evident that a linear equation in two variables has infinitely many elements. For example, no matter what replacement we use for $x$ in the equation $3x + 4y = 18$ the resulting equation is a linear equation in the one variable $y$ and has one solution. Consequently, we can arbitrarily select one of the numbers of the $(x, y)$ pairs of the solution set and determine the other.

*Example:* Find the missing number in each of the order pairs (0, _), (_, −4), (−1, _), (_, 0) which will make it an element of the solution set of

$$2x - 3y = 6$$

*Solution:* If $x = 0$

$2x - 3y = 6$ becomes

$0 - 3y = 6$ or $y = -2$

Hence, $(0, -2)$ is a solution.

If $y = -4$
$2x - 3y = 6$ becomes
$2x + 12 = 6$ or $x = -3$
Hence, $(-3, -4)$ is a solution.

If $x = -1$
$2x - 3y = 6$ becomes
$-2 - 3y = 6$ or $y = -\frac{8}{3}$
Hence, $(-1, -\frac{8}{3})$ is a solution.

If $y = 0$
$2x - 3y = 6$ becomes
$2x - 0 = 6$ or $x = 3$
Hence $(3, 0)$ is a solution.

## EXERCISES

**1.** Determine which of the following ordered pairs are elements of the solution set of

$$3x - 5y = 7$$

$(0, 0)$, $(1, 1)$, $(2, 2)$, $(3, 0)$, $(0, 1)$, $(4, 1)$, $(7, 2)$, $(9, 4)$

**2.** Find three ordered pairs of integers that are elements of the solution set of

$$7x - 3y = 8$$

**3.** Find a linear equation in $x$ and $y$ that has $(3, 2)$ as an element of its solution set.

**4.** Find a linear equation in $x$ and $y$ that has $(1, 1)$ and $(3, 4)$ as elements of its solution set.

**5.** Can more than one linear equation in $x$ and $y$ have $(2, 2)$ as an element of their solution sets? Discuss.

**6.** Can more than one linear equation in $x$ and $y$ have $(0, 1)$ and $(1, 0)$ as elements of their solution sets? Discuss.

**7.** Is it possible to have a linear equation in $x$ and $y$ that has $(0, 0)$ $(0, 1)$, and $(1, 0)$ as elements of its solution set?

**8.** Complete the following ordered pairs so as to make them elements of the solution set of $2x + 3y = 9$.

$(0, \_)$, $(\_, 0)$, $(1, \_)$, $(-3, \_)$, $(\_, -5)$

**9.** Find the constant $c$ such that $(3, 4)$ is an element of the solution set of

$$2x - y = c$$

**10.** Find $a$ if $(4, -2)$ is an element of the solution set of

$$ax + 2y = 8$$

## THE EQUATION $ax + by = c$

## 9.3 A Coordinate Frame of Reference

If we wish to show the graph of a relation in two variables we need more than a number line since the elements of the solution set are ordered pairs of numbers. We need a means for picturing a number pair. This can be accomplished by using two number lines. Take two number lines, perpendicular to each other, and select their point of intersection as the zero point on each. One line is conventionally placed horizontal and

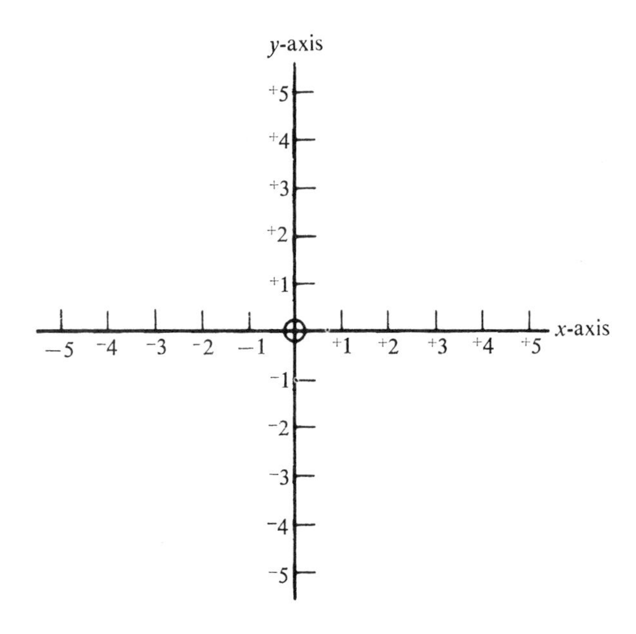


designated as the *x-axis*, and the other placed vertical and designated as the *y-axis*. We further agree that the positive side of the *x-axis* is to the right and the positive side of the *y-axis* is up. The two axes together are called coordinate axes or a coordinate frame of reference. With the aid of the coordinate frame of reference we can place the points in the plane in one-to-one correspondence with all ordered pairs of real numbers. If the first number of the ordered pair is located on the $x$-axis, the second located on the $y$-axis, and perpendiculars drawn to the axes at these points, the intersection of the perpendiculars is the point corresponding to the ordered pair of numbers. Every point on the $x$-axis represents a number pair whose second part is zero. Every point on the $y$-axis represents a number pair whose first part is zero. Hence the intersection of the axes, called the origin, corresponds to the ordered pair $(0, 0)$.

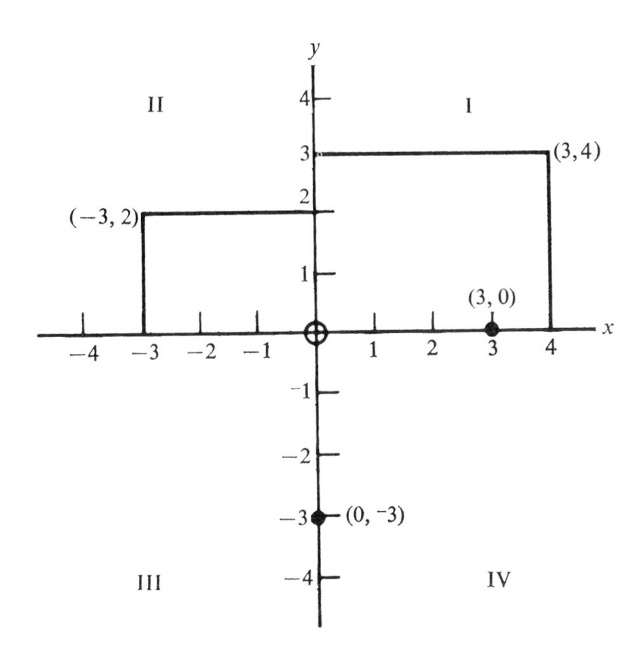


The coordinate axes divide the plane into four *quadrants*. In the illustration the quadrants are numbered I, II, III, IV. In the first quadrant both $x$ and $y$ are positive. In quadrant II $x$ is negative and $y$ is positive. Both $x$ and $y$ are negative in quadrant III, and in the fourth quadrant $x$ is positive but $y$ is negative.

## EXERCISES

1. Determine the quadrant in which each of the following points lies. If a point does not lie in a quadrant indicate between which two quadrants it lies.
   (a) $(3, -5)$ (b) $(-1, -4)$ (c) $(0, -5)$ (d) $(5, 0)$ (e) $(4, 7)$ (f) $(-6, 3)$ (g) $(1, -4)$
2. Plot in the same coordinate axes the points in Exercise 1.
3. Construct on one set of axes the following points:
   $(5, 0), (3, 4), (4, 3), (0, 5), (-5, 0), (-3, 4), (-4, 3), (0, -5), (3, -4), (4, -3), (-3, -4), (-4, -3)$
4. On the same axes as used in Exercise 3 construct a circle with center at the origin and radius 5.
5. In Exercise 3 decrease the first component of each ordered pair by 3 and increase the second component by 2. Plot the resulting points.

**6.** On the axes used in Exercise 5 construct a circle with center $(-3, +2)$ and radius 5.

**7.** Plot on one set of axes the following points:
(3, 1) (4, 3) (6, 7) (2, $-1$)
Draw a straight line between any two of the points.

**8.** Decrease the first coordinate of each pair in Exercise 7 by 1 and increase the second coordinate by 2. Plot the resulting points. Draw a straight line through any two of the points.

## 9.4 The Graph of $ax + by = c$

The equation $ax + by = c$ is called a linear equation because its graph is a straight line. Consider first the case where $c = 0$; for example, $3x - 4y = 0$. If this is expressed as $y = \frac{3}{4}x$ it is evident that the ratio of the coordinates of each point of the graph is constant, $\dfrac{y}{x} = \dfrac{3}{4}$. Since

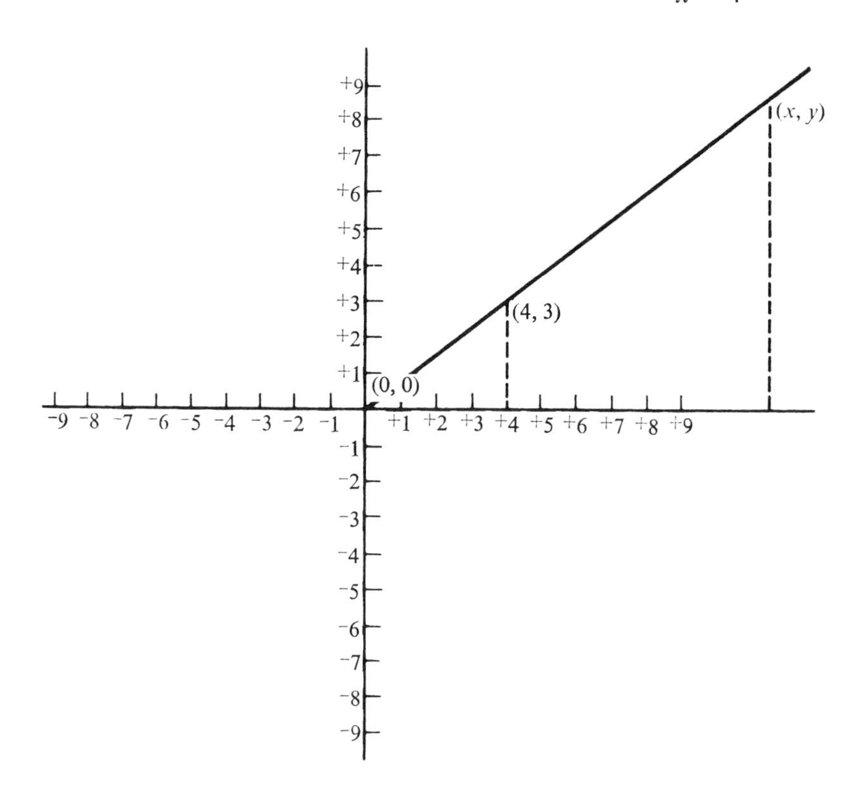

(0, 0) is an element of the solution set, the origin and any point whose coordinates are in the ratio $\frac{y}{x} = \frac{3}{4}$ will determine the line.

For example, any of the points (4, 3), (8, 6), or (1, $\frac{3}{4}$) have coordinates in the required ratio.

The assertion that any two of the above points will determine the graph of the equation contains a double implication. *One*, any point with $y$-ordinate $\frac{3}{4}$ of its $x$-ordinate will lie on the line. *Two*, any point on the line will have as its $y$-ordinate a value $\frac{3}{4}$ of its $x$-ordinate.

Since this constant relationship exists between the coordinates we can predict the difference between the $y$-ordinates of any two points, given the difference between their $x$-ordinates. For example, suppose two points $P_1$ and $P_2$ on the curve have $x$-ordinates that differ by 12, the corresponding $y$-ordinates will differ by 9. Suppose $P_1 = (x_1, y_1)$. Let us indicate $P_2$ as $(x_1 + 12, y_2)$. We know the ratio of the coordinates $y:x$ is always 3:4. Since $y_1/x_1 = \frac{3}{4}$ and $y_2/(x_1 + 12) = \frac{3}{4}$ we have

$$\frac{y_1}{x_1} = \frac{y_2}{x_1 + 12}, \quad \text{or} \quad y_1x_1 + 12y_1 = y_2x_1$$

and dividing by $x_1$

$$y_1 + 12\frac{y_1}{x_1} = y_2$$

Substituting

$$\frac{y_1}{x_1} = \frac{3}{4}$$

we have

$$y_1 + 12 \cdot \tfrac{3}{4} = y_2$$

$$y_1 + 9 = y_2$$

The constant ratio,

$$\frac{y_1 - y_2}{x_1 - x_2}$$

is called the *slope* of the line.

> If the points, $P_1 = (x_1, y_1)$ and $P_2 = (x_2, y_2)$ are any two points of a line, the ratio, $\frac{y_1 - y_2}{x_1 - x_2}$, is the slope of the line.

### THE GRAPH OF $ax + by = c$

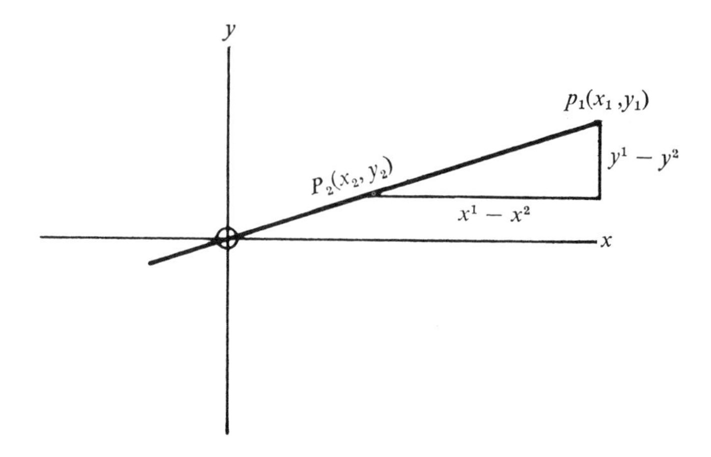


The slope of a line is often referred to as the "rise" to the "run." In the figure the line rises $(y_1 - y_2)$ between $P_1$ and $P_2$; the corresponding "run" or horizontal change is $(x_1 - x_2)$.

If the equation $Ax + By = C$ is solved for $y$ we have

$$y = -\left(\frac{A}{B}\right)x + \frac{C}{B}$$

Thus, any linear equation $Ax + By = C$ can be expressed in the form

$$y = mx + b$$

where $m = -\dfrac{A}{B}$, and $b = \dfrac{C}{B}$. The number $m$, the coefficient of $x$, is the slope of the line. If $x = 1$, we have

$$y = m(1) + b = m + b$$

If $x = 4$, we have

$$y = m(4) + b = 4m + b$$

As $x$ increases from 1 to 4, that is, increases 3, $y$ changes from $m + b$ to $4m + b$, a change of $3m$. Thus, the ratio of the change in $y$ to the change in $x$ is $3m/3 = m$.

More generally,

$$\text{if } x = a_1, \quad \text{then} \quad y = ma_1 + b$$
$$\text{if } x = a_2 \quad \text{then} \quad y = ma_2 + b$$

The change in $y$ is $ma_2 + b - ma_1 - b$ and the corresponding change in $x$ is $a_2 - a_1$. The ratio of the two changes is

$$\frac{ma_2 + b - ma_1 - b}{a_2 - a_1} = \frac{m(a_2 - a_1)}{a_2 - a_1} = m$$

What is the role of $b$ in the equation $y = mx + b$? If $x = 0$ we have

$$y = m(0) + b$$
$$y = b$$

Thus, $(0, b)$ is an element of the solution set. The number $b$ is the *y-intercept* of the line. The intercepts of a line are the distances from the origin at which the line cuts the axes.

*Example:* Find the graph of the equation $2x - 3y = 6$.

*Solution:* If we solve the equation for $y$ we have

$$y = \tfrac{2}{3}x - 2$$

The slope, $m = \frac{2}{3}$, the $y$-intercept, $b = -2$

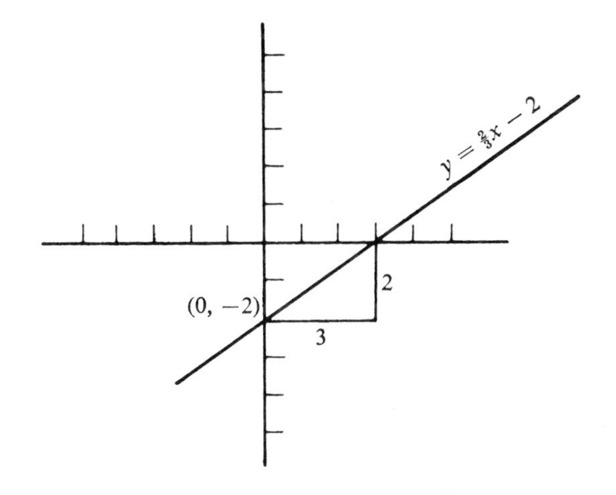


The graph cuts the $y$-axis at $(0, -2)$. As $y$ increases 2, $x$ increases 3.

*Example:* Find the equation for the line that crosses the $y$-axis at $(0, 5)$ and has slope 4.

*Solution:* Since the line crosses the $y$-axis at $(0, 5)$ the $y$-intercept, $b = 5$. Since the slope, $m = 4$ the equation

$$y = mx + b \qquad \text{becomes} \qquad y = 4x + 5$$

### THE GRAPH OF $ax + by = c$

*Example:* Find the slope of the line whose $x$-intercept is $-3$ and $y$-intercept is 2.

*Solution:* The line passes through the points $(-3, 0)$ and $(0, 2)$. Hence its slope is $m = \dfrac{0 - 2}{-3 - 0} = \dfrac{2}{3}$. Since the $y$-intercept, $b = 2$, the equation is

$$y = \tfrac{2}{3}x + 2$$

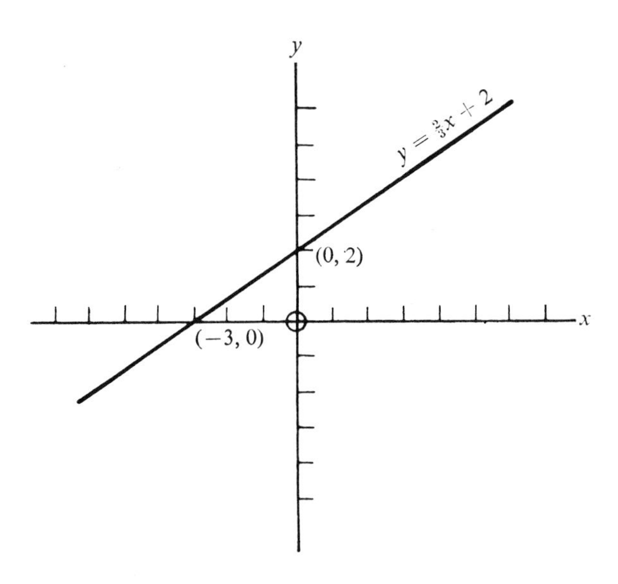


## EXERCISES

*Find the slope and the y-intercept of each of the following. Construct the graph.*

**1.** $2x - 5y = 7$

**2.** $x = 6y - 12$

**3.** $3x - 4y = 12$

**4.** $4x + 3y = 12$

**5.** $2x + 3y + 5 = 0$

**6.** Find the equation for the line through $(0, 2)$ and with slope 3.

**7.** Find the equation for the line through the origin and with slope 3.

**8.** Find the equation for the line through $(3, 4)$ and $(7, 5)$.

## LINEAR RELATIONS IN TWO VARIABLES

**9.** Find the equation for the line whose $x$-intercept is (3, 0) and $y$-intercept is (0, $-2$).

**10.** Find the equation for the line with slope 0 and passing through (7, 1).

## 9.5 Families of Equations

We have seen that when a linear equation is expressed in the form

$$y = mx + b$$

the slope is $m$ and the $y$ intercept is $b$. What effect does a change in the value of $m$ have upon the graph of the equation? Consider the equation

$$y = mx + 3$$

Each value assigned to the constant $m$ yields the equation for a line through the point (0, 3). We may think of the equation as the equation of the family of lines through the point (0, 3). When used in this way, $m$ is called the *parameter* of the family of lines. If $m = 0$ we have

$$y = 0 \cdot x + 3$$
$$y = 3$$

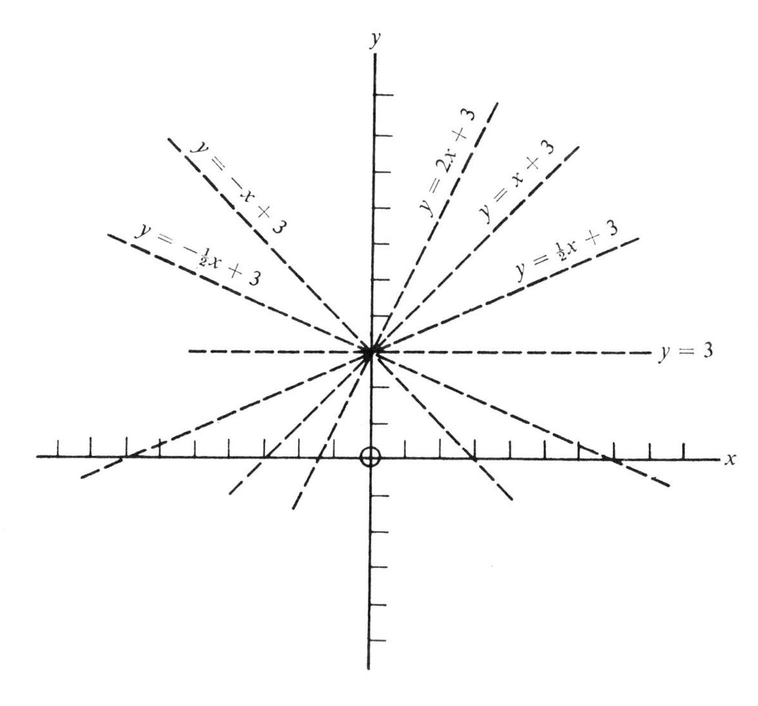


FAMILIES OF EQUATIONS

The graph of this equation is a line parallel to the $x$-axis. This is true since the $y$-ordinate of any point on the line is 3, and the equation places no restriction on the $x$-ordinate of points on the line.

If $m = \frac{1}{2}$ we have

$$y = \tfrac{1}{2}x + 3$$

a line with slope $\frac{1}{2}$ and passing through (0, 3).

As $m$ increases the line rises more and more steeply, and approaches coincidence with the $y$-axis. The equation for the $y$-axis is $x = 0$. This equation has no slope. We cannot find the ratio of "rise" to "run" if there is no "run." If $x$ is constant there is no change in $x$ to compare to change in $y$. Consider the general equation

$$Ax + By = C$$

If $B = 0$ we have an equation in the form

$$x = k \text{ ($k$ being a constant)}$$

But if we solve the general equation for $y$ we have

$$y = -\left(\frac{A}{B}\right)x + \frac{C}{B}$$

When $B = 0$ this result is meaningless because division by 0 is undefined.

Imagine the line $y = 3$ being rotated about the point (0, 3) in a counter-clockwise direction. In the initial position $m = 0$. As the line rotates, $m$ increases continually until we reach coincidence with the $y$-axis, where there is no $m$. If we continue to rotate the line, $m$ becomes negative because, for increasing values of $x$, $y$ is decreasing. The negative values of $m$ approach zero as the line approaches its original position.

We may summarize the above considerations as follows:

1. If a line is parallel to the $x$-axis its slope is zero.
2. If a line is parallel to the $y$-axis it has no slope.
3. If $y$ decreases as $x$ increases the slope of the line is negative.
4. The slope of a line may be any real number, positive, zero, or negative.

Suppose we change the constant $b$ but do not change $m$ in the equation

$$y = mx + b$$

What is the nature of this family of lines? Since $m$ is fixed, all lines are parallel. The value of $b$ determines the $y$ intercept. Hence the family with $m$ fixed and parameter $b$ is a family of parallel lines.

## LINEAR RELATIONS IN TWO VARIABLES

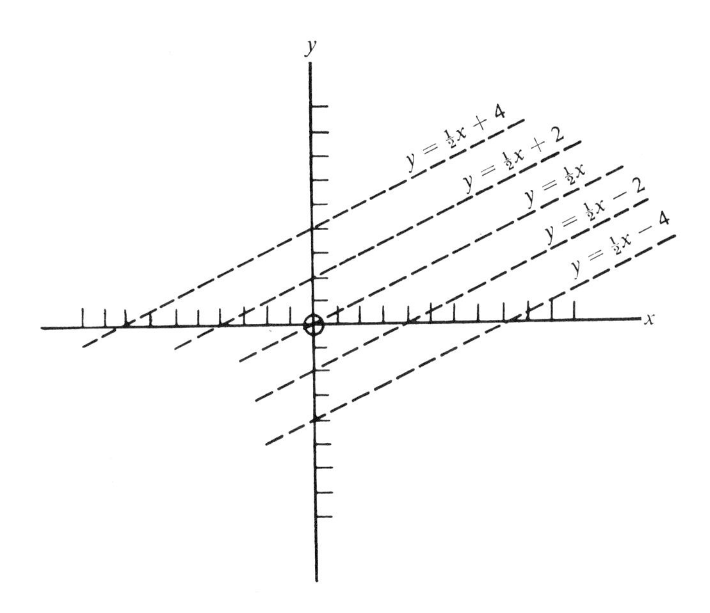


*Example:* Find the equation of a line parallel to

$$3x + 4y = 7$$

and passing through the point (8, 6).

*Solution:* If the original equation is solved for $y$ we have

$$y = -\tfrac{3}{4}x + \tfrac{7}{4}$$

The slope of the original line is $-\frac{3}{4}$.
Thus the slope of the required line is also $-\frac{3}{4}$.
Its equation is

$$y = -\tfrac{3}{4}x + b$$

where $b$ is to be determined. Since the line is to pass through (8, 6) the replacements $x = 8$ and $y = 6$ must satisfy the equation.

$$6 = -\tfrac{3}{4} \cdot 8 + b$$

and solving for $b$

$$b = 12$$

Hence the required equation is

$$y = -\tfrac{3}{4}x + 12 \quad \text{or} \quad 3x + 4y = 48$$

## EXERCISES

**1.** Find the equation for the line through (5, 6) with slope 2.

**2.** Find the equation for the line through (5, 6) with slope $-1$.

## FAMILIES OF EQUATIONS

3. In what respect do the equations in Exercises 1 and 2 differ? In what respect are they similar?
4. Find the equation for the line through (3, 1) with slope 2.
5. In what respect do the equations in Exercises 1 and 4 differ? In what respect are they similar?
6. With a given slope, what determines whether $y = mx + c$ passes through a given point?
7. Determine the constant $c$ such that $2x - y = c$ will pass through $(5, -1)$.
8. Find the equation for the line parallel to $2x - 3y = 7$ and passing through $(5, -1)$.
9. Find the equation for the line with slope $-3$ and passing through the origin.
10. What is the maximum number of quadrants through which a line may pass? What is the minimum number?
11. Describe all possible positions of a line that passes through exactly two quadrants.
12. What is the slope of a line that cuts the second and fourth quadrants?
13. What is the slope of a line that cuts the first and third quadrants?
14. What is the slope of a line that lies wholly in the first and second quadrants?
15. What is the slope of a line that lies wholly in the first and fourth quadrants?

## 9.6 Graphs of Linear Inequalities

A linear inequality may be either of two kinds, a *strict inequality*, or a *mixed inequality*.

The sentences

$$y < 2x + 3 \qquad (y \text{ less than } 2x + 3)$$

and

$$y > 2x + 3 \qquad (y \text{ greater than } 2x + 3)$$

are examples of a strict inequality. If $y$ is not equal to $2x + 3$ one of the above relations must be true.

If we wish to express the idea that $y$ is not less than $2x + 3$ we may have $y = 2x + 3$ or $y > 2x + 3$. This may be expressed as one sentence:

$$y \geq 2x + 3 \quad (y \text{ greater than or equal to } 2x + 3)$$

This is a mixed inequality. Under this relation, if $x = 1$ then $y$ can equal 5 or any real number greater than 5. On the other hand, in the strict inequality $y > 2x + 3$, if $x = 1$ then $y$ cannot equal 5, it can equal any real number greater than 5.

Any linear inequality can be solved for $y$ in very much the same way that an equation can. There is one caution that should be remembered however. If each member of an inequality is multiplied by the same *positive* number the inequality is preserved.

$$5 > 3$$

and $$2 \times 5 > 2 \times 3$$

But if each member is multiplied by a negative number the sense of the inequality is changed.

$$5 > 3$$

but $$(-3) \times 5 < (-3) \times 3$$

If a linear inequality is solved for $y$ its graph can be obtained from the graph of the corresponding equation.

We illustrate by constructing the graph of the inequality

$$2x - 3y < 5$$

First, solve for $y$

$$-3y < 5 - 2x \qquad \text{(add } -2x\text{)}$$

$$y > \tfrac{2}{3}x - \tfrac{5}{3} \qquad \text{(multiply by } -\tfrac{1}{3}\text{)}$$

The corresponding equality is

$$y = \tfrac{2}{3}x - \tfrac{5}{3}$$

Construct the graph of this equation.

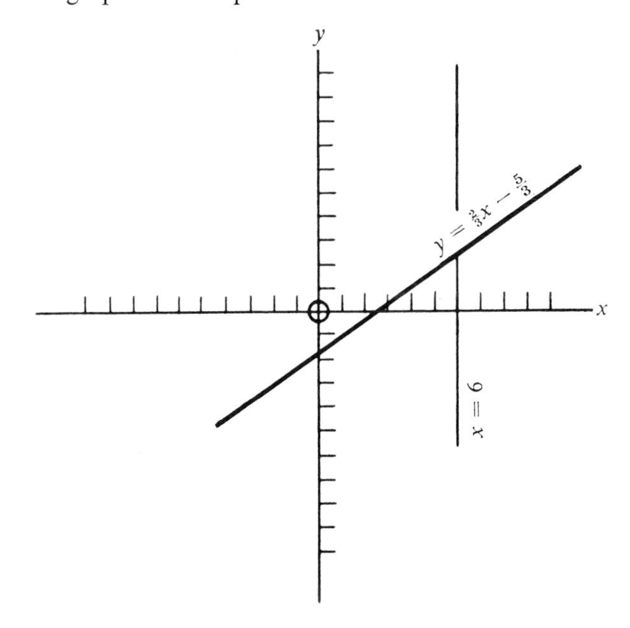

The coordinates of the points on the line are such that the $y$-ordinate is equal to $\frac{2}{3}$ of the $x$-ordinate minus $\frac{5}{3}$. The inequality $y > \frac{2}{3}x - \frac{5}{3}$ requires that corresponding to any replacement for $x$, $y$ be greater than the $y$-ordinate of that point on the line. For example, the point $(6, \frac{7}{3})$ is a point on the graph of the equation. The ordered pair $(6, \frac{7}{3})$ is not an element of the solution set of the inequality $y > \frac{2}{3}x - \frac{5}{3}$. Every point on the vertical line through $(6, 0)$ has 6 for $x$-ordinate. Every point above the line $y = \frac{2}{3}x - \frac{5}{3}$ has a $y$-ordinate greater than that of the point on the line. Thus, we see that the solution set of the inequality $y > \frac{2}{3}x - \frac{5}{3}$ is the set of all points above the graph of the equation $y = \frac{2}{3}x - \frac{5}{3}$.

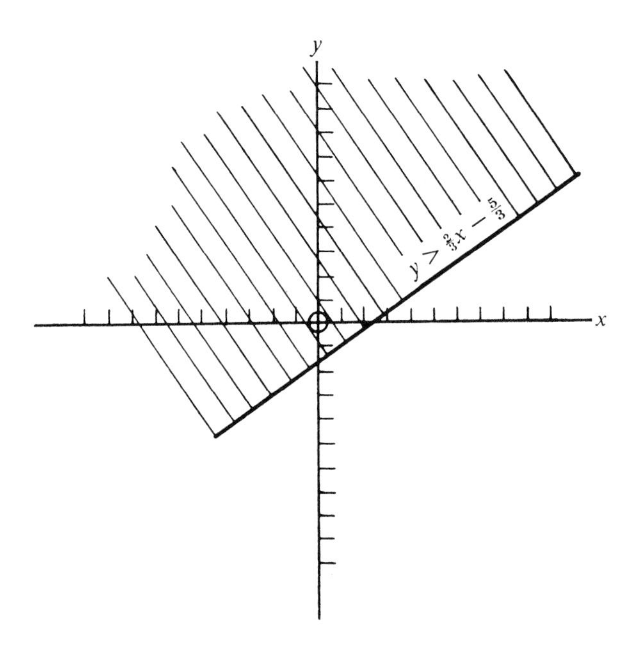


A line divides a plane into two regions called *half planes.* Two points are in opposite half planes if the segment joining them contains a point of the line, and in the same half plane if a segment joining them does not contain a point of the line. What about the points of the line itself, in which region do they lie? The line actually assigns the points of the plane to three sets: the set of points on the line, the set of points on one side of the line, and the set of points on the other side of the line. Two points are on the same side of a line if the segment joining the points does not contain a point of the line. The term *half plane* is used to designate the set of points on one side of a line. If we wish not to include the points on the line in the region it is called an *open half plane.* If we wish to include the points of the line the region is called a *closed half plane*. The solution set of $y > \frac{2}{3}x - \frac{5}{3}$ is an open half plane. The compound statement $y \geq \frac{2}{3}x - \frac{5}{3}$ means $y > \frac{2}{3}x - \frac{5}{3}$ *or* $y = \frac{2}{3}x - \frac{5}{3}$. Hence the solution set of the mixed inequality is the union of the solution sets of the component statements $y > \frac{2}{3}x - \frac{5}{3}$ (the open half plane) and $y = \frac{2}{3}x - \frac{5}{3}$ (the line).

### EXERCISES

**1.** Solve the inequality $2x - 3y > 6$ for $y$.

**2.** Construct the graph of $2x - 3y > 6$.

**3.** How does the graph of $2x - 3y \geq 6$ differ from the graph in Exercise 2?

**4.** Without constructing the graph determine whether the points (4, 3) and (−2, −5) are on the same side or opposite sides of $2x - 3y = 12$.

**5.** Without constructing the graph determine which of the following points belong to the graph of $3x \leq 2y + 5$:
(a) (1, 1) (b) (5, 0) (c) (1, −2) (d) (3, 3) (e) (−2, −10)

**6.** Describe the graph of $x - 3y \gtrless 7$.

**7.** Construct the graph of $y \geq 5$.

**8.** Construct the graph of $x \leq 4$.

**9.** Construct the graph of $y > x$.

## 9.7 Physical Applications of Linear Relations

There are numerous examples of the linear relation in our physical environment. The essential characteristic of a linear relationship is that the ratio of the changes in the two variables be constant.

A familiar example of a linear relation is the relationship between Fahrenheit and centigrade temperature readings. Any linear scale requires two things, a zero point and a unit. In the illustration we have placed the thermometer scale in horizontal position for convenience. The freezing temperature of water is the zero point on the centigrade scale,

CENTIGRADE SCALE

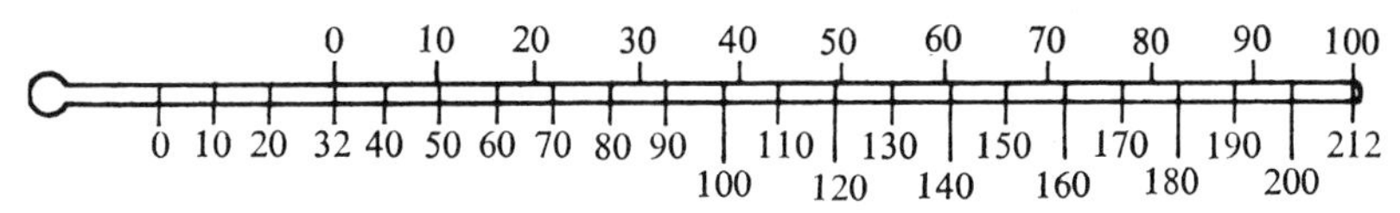


FAHRENHEIT SCALE

and it is 32° on the Fahrenheit scale. The boiling point of water is 100° on the centigrade scale and 212° on the Fahrenheit scale. These two points of reference enable us to determine the relative size of the units on each scale.

$$100 \text{ centigrade units} = 180 \text{ Fahrenheit units}$$

If we wish to express the Fahrenheit temperature as a function of the centigrade temperature, from the above relationship we have 1 centigrade degree $= \frac{9}{5}$ Fahrenheit degrees. This would give the equation

$$F = \tfrac{9}{5}C$$

if the two scales had the same zero point. If we correct for the difference in zero points we must add 32 Fahrenheit degrees to $\frac{9}{5}C$. This is because $\frac{9}{5}C$ expresses the centigrade reading (degrees above zero centigrade) in Fahrenheit degrees. Since zero Fahrenheit is 32 Fahrenheit degrees below zero centigrade we must add 32.

$$F = \tfrac{9}{5}C + 32$$

Here we have a linear equation, slope $\frac{9}{5}$, F intercept 32. The slope $\frac{9}{5}$ means the difference between two temperatures on the Fahrenheit scale is $\frac{9}{5}$ of the same difference measured on the centigrade scale. The F intercept 32 indicates that when $C = 0$, $F = 32$.

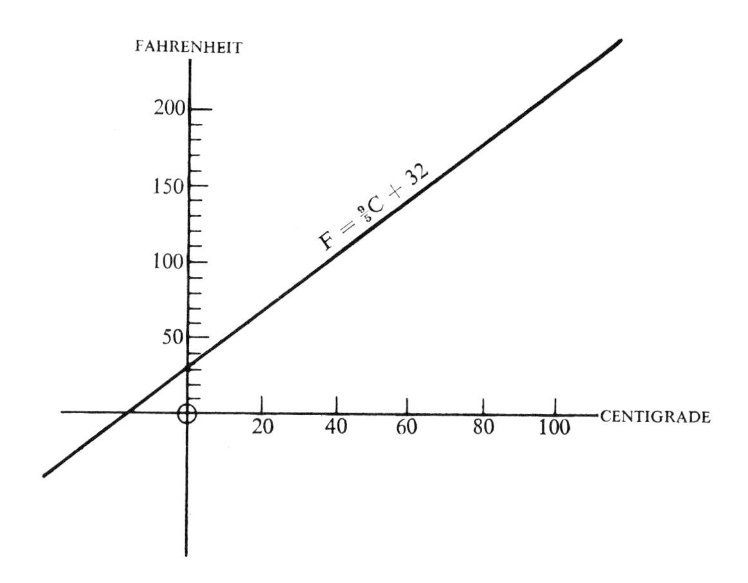

The equation

$$F = \tfrac{9}{5}C + 32$$

can be solved for C.

$$5F = 9C + 160$$
$$9C = 5F - 160$$
$$C = \tfrac{5}{9}(F - 32)$$

Thus, we can change Fahrenheit reading to centigrade by subtracting 32° from the Fahrenheit reading then multiplying the result by $\frac{5}{9}$. When the 32° is subtracted we have found the number of Fahrenheit degrees above zero centigrade. Multiplication by $\frac{5}{9}$ converts the Fahrenheit degrees to centigrade degrees.

## EXERCISES

**1.** The theoretical low limit of temperature is −273° centigrade. Temperatures within 1° of this have been obtained. Assume the lowest temperature which has been obtained is −270° centigrade. What would this temperature be on the Fahrenheit scale?

**2.** Normal body temperature is 98.6° Fahrenheit. What is normal body temperature on the centigrade scale?

**3.** It has been estimated that the temperature at the center of the sun is on the order of 40,000,000° centigrade. What is this on the Fahrenheit scale?

**4.** A manufacturer has a daily "overhead" of \$150 and a cost of \$25 per unit of his product. Express his daily cost as a function of the number of units made.

**5.** The manufacturer in Exercise 4 can sell his product at \$35 per unit. What is the minimum number of units per day necessary for him to break even?

**6.** If taxi fare is 35¢ plus 10¢ for each $\frac{1}{4}$ mile express the fare in terms of the number of miles traveled.

**7.** On the basis of the rate in Exercise 6 what is the fare for a $3\frac{1}{2}$ mile trip?

**8.** If the first ten words of a telegram costs 45¢ and each additional word costs 3¢ express the cost of a telegram in terms of the total number of words.

**9.** What are the replacement sets for the variables in the relationship obtained in Exercise 8?

**10.** On the basis of the rates in Exercise 8 find the cost of a 24-word message.

# 10 Quadratic Equations and Inequalities

IN CHAPTER 9 WE EXAMINED THE PROPERTIES OF LINEAR EQUATIONS AND inequalities in one and two variables. The solution set of a linear equation in one variable consists of a single number. When the equation involves two variables the solution set is an infinite set of ordered pairs, the components of each ordered pair being replacements for the variables which make the sentence true. That is, we cannot find values for each variable independently. If a value is arbitrarily assigned to one variable it becomes the independent variable, and the corresponding value of the other, the dependent variable, depends on what value is assigned to the first variable.

The algebraic ideas developed in Chapter 9 can be extended in two ways. We can consider a system of more than one equation, and we can consider an equation with the variables not restricted to the first power. In this chapter we shall consider equations and inequalities in which the variable may appear to the second power ($x^2 = x \cdot x$ is the second power of $x$).

## 10.1 The Equation $(x - a)(x - b) = 0$

The equation $(x - a)(x - b) = 0$ is a quadratic equation in $x$. Although it appears that the highest power of $x$ in the equation is $x^1 = x$, this is not the case. If the two factors $(x - a)$ and $(x - b)$ are multiplied we have $x^2 - ax - bx + ab = 0$. This can be verified by applying the distributive principle to $(x - a)(x - b)$

$$(x - a)(x - b) = (x - a)x + (x - a)(-b)$$

then applying the commutative principle

$$(x - a)x + (x - a)(-b) = x(x - a) + (-b)(x - a)$$

and finally the distributive principle again, as well as the law of signs for multiplication

$$x(x - a) + (-b)(x - a) = x^2 - ax - bx + ab$$

The final expression can be written

$$x^2 - (a + b)x + ab$$

Then the original equation is identically the same as the equation

$$x^2 - (a + b)x + ab = 0$$

This is in keeping with the general form of the quadratic equation in $x$.

$$ax^2 + bx + c = 0$$

If the quadratic equation is given in factored form its solution set is immediately apparent. Recall the properties of zero in multiplication. If a product is zero, $a \cdot b = 0$, at least one of its factors must be zero, $a = 0$, or $b = 0$. And, if at least one factor is zero, $a = 0$, then the product must be zero, $a \cdot b = 0$.

From this we know that in the equation

$$(x - a)(x - b) = 0$$

the statement is true if one of the statements $x - a = 0$ or $x - b = 0$ is true. Otherwise it is false. Of course both $x - a = 0$ and $x - b = 0$ will make $(x - a)(x - b) = 0$ a true statement, but the only way for both $(x - a) = 0$ and $(x - b) = 0$ to be true is for $a$ and $b$ to be equal.

*Example:* Find the solution set for $(x - 3)(x + 2) = 0$

*Solution:* If $x - 3 = 0$, the statement is true.
But if $x - 3 = 0$ then $x = 3$.
If $x + 2 = 0$ the statement is true. But if $x + 2 = 0$ then $x = -2$.
The solution set is $\{3, -2\}$.

To generalize the results of the example, we see the solution set of $(x - a)(x - b) = 0$ is $\{a, b\}$. Hence, the graph of a quadratic equation in $x$ is a pair of points. The graph of $(x - a)(x - b) = 0$ is the two points $a$ and $b$ on the number line.

*Example:* Draw the graph of $(x - 3)(x + 2) = 0$

*Solution:* Since the solution set is $\{3, -2\}$ the graph consists of the two points 3 and $-2$ on the number line

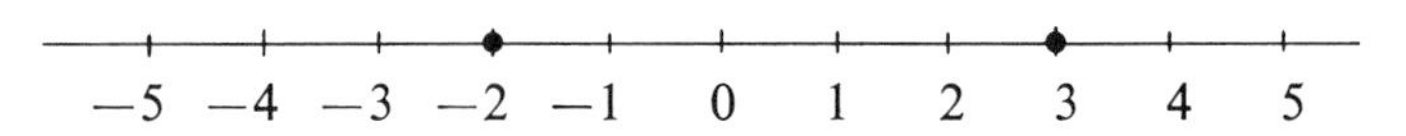


The graph of a quadratic inequality can also be shown on the number line. Here the rule of signs for multiplication must be taken into account. If we wish to graph $(x - 3)(x + 2) > 0$ we know the two factors must both be positive ($x - 3 > 0$ and $x + 2 > 0$) or both negative ($x - 3 < 0$ and $x + 2 < 0$), since the product is to be positive.

If $x - 3 > 0$, then $x > 3$. This is shown on the number line as

–3 –2 –1 0 1 2 3

The point corresponding to 3 is circled to indicate that it is not included. The heavy line to the right indicates all numbers greater than 3. The arrow shows the line continues infinitely.

If $x + 2 > 0$, then $x > -2$. This is shown on the number line as

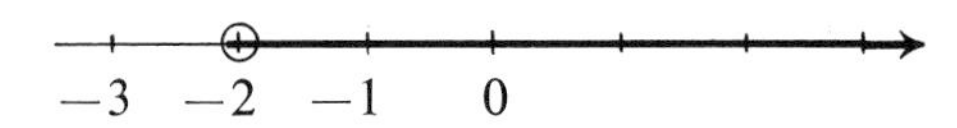


We wish to find the intersection of the solution sets of $x - 3 > 0$ and $x + 2 > 0$. This is the set of points belonging to both graphs. But the graph of $x + 2 > 0$ includes the graph of $x - 3 > 0$. That is, the solution set of $x - 3 > 0$ is a subset of the solution set of $x + 2 > 0$. Hence the intersection of the two sets is the solution set of $x - 3 > 0$. Then, in set notation, we wish the graph of the set of points

$$\{x \mid x + 2 > 0\} \cap \{x \mid x - 3 > 0\} \tag{I}$$

–3 –2 –1 0 1 2 3

The original inequality is also satisfied if $x - 3 < 0$ and $x + 2 < 0$. If $x - 3 < 0$, then $x < 3$, and its graph is

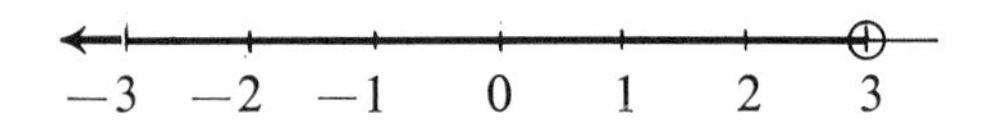

If $x + 2 < 0$, then $x < -2$, and its graph is

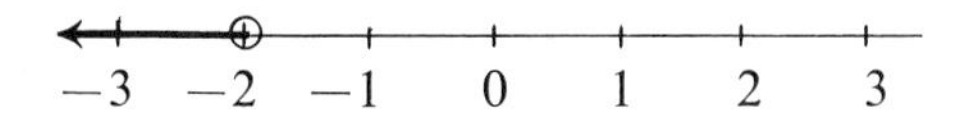

The intersection of these two sets

$$\{x \mid x - 3 < 0\} \cap \{x \mid x + 2 < 0\} \qquad \text{(II)}$$

is

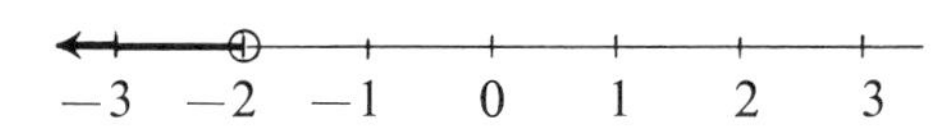

The graph of the inequality

$$(x - 3)(x + 2) > 0$$

is the union of (I) and (II)

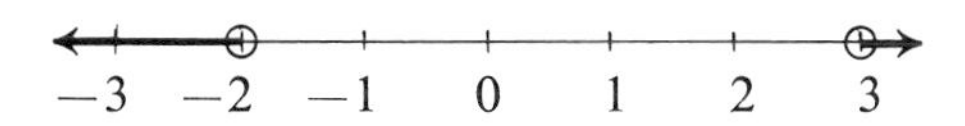

The solution set is the set of all numbers greater than 3 or less than $-2$.

*Example:* If $x = 5$
$(x - 3)(x + 2) = 2 \cdot 7 > 0$
If $x = -4$
$(x - 3)(x + 2) = -7 \cdot -2 = 14 > 0$
If $x = 1$
$(x - 3)(x + 2) = -2 \cdot 3 = -6 < 0$
Then 5 and $-4$ are members of the solution set, but 1 is not a member.

*Example:* Find the solution set of $(x + 2)(x - 1) < 0$.

*Solution:* Here the product of the two factors $(x + 2)$ and $(x - 1)$ is to be negative. Hence, one factor must be positive and the other negative.

The set satisfying both $x + 2 > 0$ and $x - 1 < 0$ will belong to the solution set of $(x + 2)(x - 1) < 0$. If $x + 2 > 0$ then $x > -2$. If $x - 1 < 0$ then $x < 1$. The intersection of these two sets is $\{x \mid -2 < x < 1\}$, that is, the set of all $x$ between $-2$ and 1.

**THE EQUATION** $(x - a)(x - b) = 0$

The set satisfying both $x + 2 < 0$ and $x - 1 > 0$ will also belong to the solution set of $(x + 2)(x - 1) < 0$. If $x + 2 < 0$ then $x < -2$. If $x - 1 > 0$ then $x > 1$. But there is no $x$ both less than $-2$ and greater than 1. The intersection of these two sets is the null set.

−3 −2 −1 0 1 2 3

The union of $\{x \mid -2 < x < 1\}$ and the null set is the set $\{x \mid -2 < x < 1\}$.
Hence the solution set of the inequality

$$(x + 2)(x - 1) < 0$$

is the set of all numbers greater than $-2$ and less than 1.
For example, if $x = 0$

$$(x + 2)(x - 1) = 2 \cdot -1 = -2 < 0$$

If $x = 4$

$$(x + 2)(x - 1) = 6 \cdot 3 = 18 > 0$$

If $x = -5$

$$(x + 2)(x - 1) = -3 \cdot -6 = 18 > 0$$

Hence, 0 is a member of the solution set, but 4 and $-5$ are not members.

## EXERCISES

**1.** Solve and check the following by substitution:
(a) $(x - 3)(x + 5) = 0$
(b) $(x + 1)(x - 1)(x - 3) = 0$
(c) $(x - 2)^2 = 0$

**2.** Solve the following by first factoring the quadratic into two linear factors:
(a) $x^2 + x - 6 = 0$
(b) $x^3 + 6x^2 + 8x = 0$
(c) $x^2 - 2x - 15 = 0$

**3.** Draw the graphs of each of the following on separate number lines:
(a) $(x + 5)(x - 4) = 0$
(b) $(x - 1)(x + 5) = 0$
(c) $x^2 - x - 12 = 0$
(d) $x^3 - 5x^2 - 14x = 0$

**4.** Graph the following inequalities:
(a) $(x - 3)(x - 2) < 0$
(b) $(x + 5)(x - 1) > 0$
(c) $(x + 4)(x - 2) \leq 0$
(d) $x^2 - x - 20 \geq 0$

## 10.2 Solving the Equation $ax^2 + bx + c = 0$ by Graphing

In Section 10.1 we saw that the graph of the equation $(x - a)(x - b) = 0$ is the set of two points on the number line $\{a, b\}$. If the equation $ax^2 + bx + c = 0$ can be factored into a product of two linear factors equal to zero we can obtain its graph readily. But here we have the solution set before we obtain the graph.

Is it possible to find the solution set by graphical methods?

The elements of the solution set of an equation of the form

$$y = ax^2 + bx + c$$

are not numbers, they are ordered pairs of numbers. For example,

$$y = 5x^2 + 9x - 2$$

has as an element of its solution set (1, 12) because if $x$ is replaced with 1 and $y$ replaced with 12 we have the true statement

$$12 = 5 \cdot (1)^2 + 9(1) - 2$$

If we replace $x$ with $-(\frac{14}{5})$ and $y$ with 12 we see that $(-\frac{14}{5}, 12)$ is also an element of the solution set.

$$\begin{aligned} 12 &= 5(\tfrac{14}{5})^2 + 9(\tfrac{14}{5}) - 2 \\ 12 &= \tfrac{196}{5} - \tfrac{126}{5} - \tfrac{10}{5} \\ 12 &= \tfrac{60}{5} \\ 12 &= 12 \end{aligned}$$

Thus we have two replacements for $x$ which can be paired with the $y$ replacement 12. This is one of the characteristic properties of this type of equation. This is not true of the linear equation

$$y = mx + b$$

Here there is exactly one $x$ for each $y$ replacement. On the other hand, any real number can be used as a replacement for either $x$ or $y$ in the linear equation, but not in the quadratic equation. In the quadratic equation, any real number can be used as an $x$ replacement but only a subset of the real numbers can be used for $y$ replacements. The significance of this can best be shown through an example.

*Example:* Construct the graph of

$$y = x^2 - x - 6$$

*Solution:* Begin by substituting small convenient values for $x$ and obtain the following table of $(x, y)$ pairs that are members of the solution set:

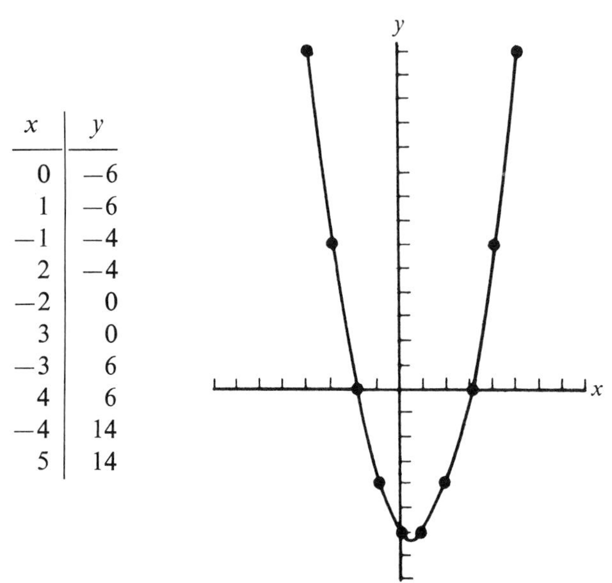


| $x$ | $y$ |
|---|---|
| 0 | −6 |
| 1 | −6 |
| −1 | −4 |
| 2 | −4 |
| −2 | 0 |
| 3 | 0 |
| −3 | 6 |
| 4 | 6 |
| −4 | 14 |
| 5 | 14 |

If we locate these points on the coordinate plane and draw a smooth curve connecting them, going from smallest to largest $x$ value, we have an approximation of the graph of the equation. The points are symmetric to the line $x = \frac{1}{2}$. In drawing that portion of the graph between the points $(0, -6)$ and $(1, -6)$ it is helpful to know the $y$ value corresponding to $x = \frac{1}{2}$. By substitution this can be found to be $y = -(\frac{25}{4})$. This is the minimum value of $y$. Corresponding to this specific value of $y$ there is only one value of $x$. For each value of $y > -(\frac{25}{4})$ there correspond two possible values of $x$. For each value of $y < -(\frac{25}{4})$ there is no $x$.

The line $x = \frac{1}{2}$ is called the *axis of symmetry* of the graph. In constructing the graph it is quite useful to find the axis of symmetry. It can be shown that the axis of symmetry of the graph of

$$y = ax^2 + bx + c$$

is $x = -\left(\frac{b}{2a}\right)$. The minimum (or maximum if $a < 0$) value of $y$ is the value corresponding to $x = -\left(\frac{b}{2a}\right)$. The maximum, or minimum, point is called the *vertex* of the graph.

The graph of the equation $y = ax^2 + bx + c$ is called a *parabola.* The parabola is defined geometrically as the set of points which are equidistant from a fixed point, called the *focus*, and a fixed line, called the *directrix*. In the foregoing example, $y = x^2 - x - 6$, the axis of symmetry is $x = \frac{1}{2}$; the vertex is the point $(\frac{1}{2}, -(\frac{25}{4}))$; the focus is $(\frac{1}{2}, -6)$; and the directrix is $y = -(\frac{26}{4})$.

A reasonably good graph can be obtained by finding the vertex of the curve and a few values on each side of the axis.

*Example:* Find the graph of

$$y = x^2 - 4x + 3$$

*Solution:* The axis of symmetry is $x = -\left(\frac{-4}{2}\right) = 2$. Substituting $x = 2$ in the equation, we have

$$y = 4 - 8 + 3 = -1$$

Then the vertex is $(2, -1)$

Find a table of values of points symmetric to $x = 2$,

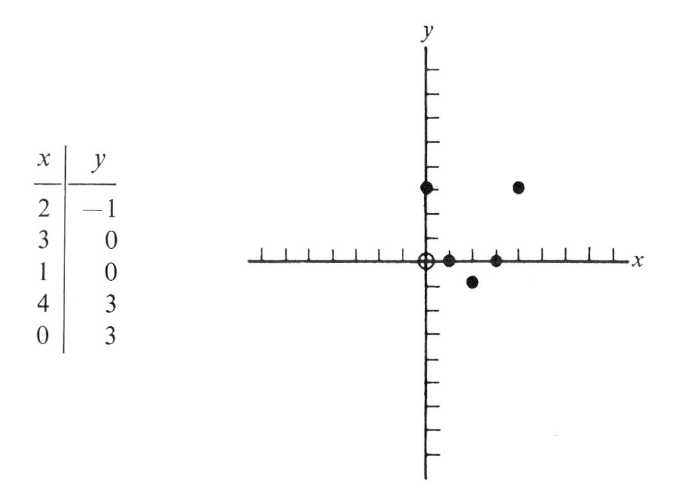


| $x$ | $y$ |
|---|---|
| 2 | $-1$ |
| 3 | 0 |
| 1 | 0 |
| 4 | 3 |
| 0 | 3 |

and connect the points with a smooth curve, going from smallest to largest values of $x$.

## SOLVING THE EQUATION $ax^2 + bx + c = 0$ BY GRAPHING

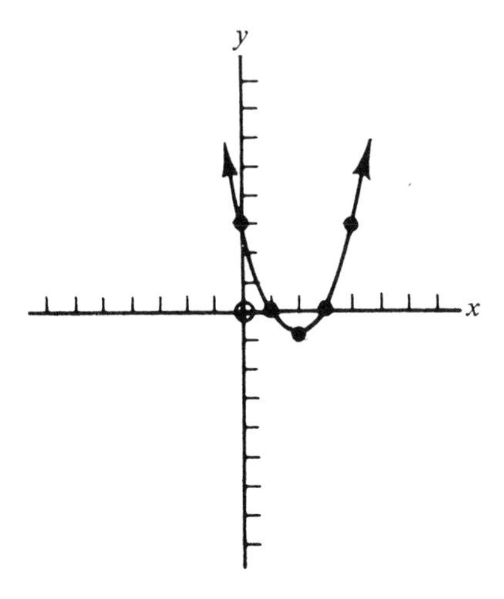


One can now solve the equation $ax^2 + bx + c = 0$ graphically by drawing the graph of $y = ax^2 + bx + c$. Those points where the graph cuts the $x$-axis are those points where $y = 0$ and hence $ax^2 + bx + c = 0$. The $x$-ordinates of those points give the solution set of $ax^2 + bx + c = 0$.

*Example:* Solve $2x^2 + 2x - 5 = 0$ graphically.

*Solution:* Find the graph of $y = 2x^2 + 2x - 5$
The axis of symmetry is $x = -(\frac{2}{4}) = -(\frac{1}{2})$
The $y$-ordinate of the vertex is

$$y = 2(-\tfrac{1}{2})^2 + 2(-\tfrac{1}{2}) - 5 = -(\tfrac{11}{2})$$

Construct a table of values and plot the points. Connect the points with a smooth curve. Estimate the $x$-ordinates of the points where the graph cuts the $x$-axis. The curve crosses the $x$-axis between $+1$ and $+2$ and between $-2$ and $-3$. A fairly close estimate of the points is $+(\frac{5}{4})$ and $-(\frac{9}{4})$. Substitution in the equation will show both $+(\frac{5}{4})$ and $-(\frac{9}{4})$ are slightly too large:

$$2(\tfrac{5}{4})^2 + 2(\tfrac{5}{4}) - 5 = \tfrac{5}{8}$$
$$2(-\tfrac{9}{4})^2 + 2(-\tfrac{9}{4}) - 5 = \tfrac{5}{8}$$

and $\frac{9}{8}$ and $-(\frac{17}{8})$ are slightly too small:

$$2(\tfrac{9}{8})^2 + 2(\tfrac{9}{8}) - 5 = -(\tfrac{7}{32})$$
$$2(-\tfrac{17}{8})^2 + 2(-\tfrac{17}{8}) - 5 = -(\tfrac{7}{32})$$

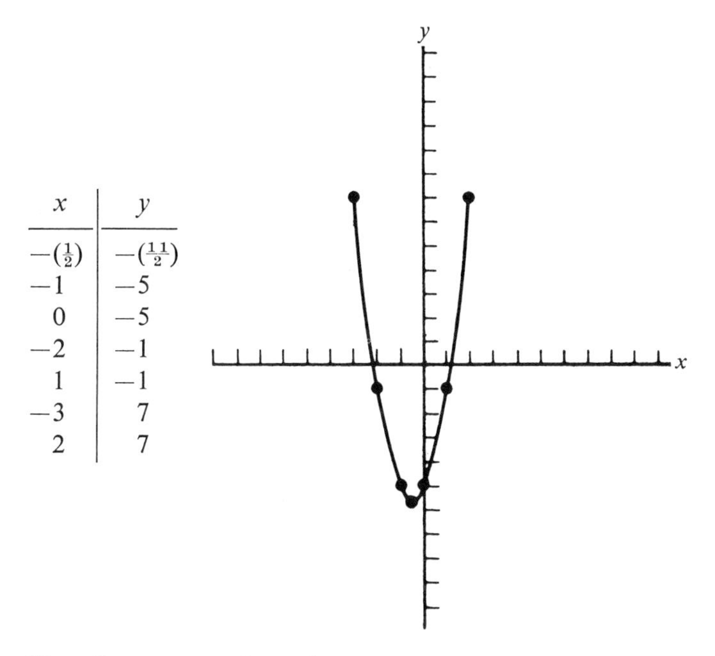


| $x$ | $y$ |
|---|---|
| $-(\frac{1}{2})$ | $-(\frac{11}{2})$ |
| $-1$ | $-5$ |
| $0$ | $-5$ |
| $-2$ | $-1$ |
| $1$ | $-1$ |
| $-3$ | $7$ |
| $2$ | $7$ |

Then the correct values of $x$ are

$$\tfrac{5}{4} > x > \tfrac{9}{8} \qquad \text{and} \qquad -(\tfrac{9}{4}) < x < -(\tfrac{17}{8})$$

If the graph of $y = ax^2 + bx + c$ does not cut the $x$-axis, this implies that the corresponding equation $ax^2 + bx + c = 0$ has the null set for solution set.

If the vertex of the graph of $y = ax^2 + bx + c$ is on the $x$-axis, this implies that the solution set of the corresponding equation $ax^2 + bx + c = 0$ consists of a single number.

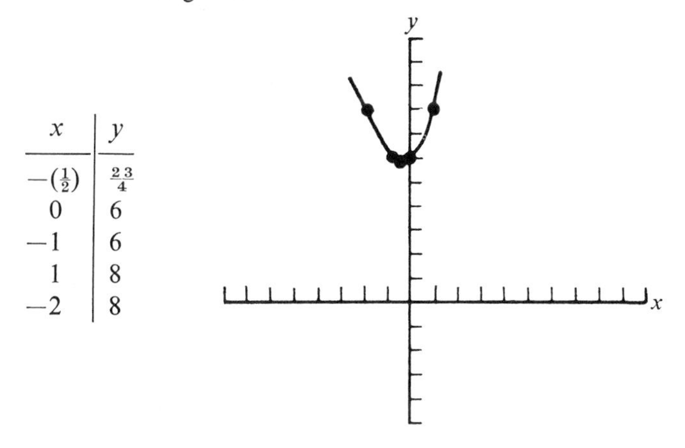


| $x$ | $y$ |
|---|---|
| $-(\frac{1}{2})$ | $\frac{23}{4}$ |
| $0$ | $6$ |
| $-1$ | $6$ |
| $1$ | $8$ |
| $-2$ | $8$ |

## SOLVING THE EQUATION $ax^2 + bx + c = 0$ BY GRAPHING

*Example:* Determine the solution set of $x^2 + x + 6 = 0$.

*Solution:* Construct the graph of $y = x^2 + x + 6$
axis of symmetry $x = -(\frac{1}{2})$
Vertex $(-\frac{1}{2}, \frac{23}{4})$
Since the graph does not cut the $x$-axis there is no value of $x$ for which $y = 0$. Hence, the solution set of $x^2 + x + 6 = 0$ is the null set.

*Example:* Determine the solution set of

$$x^2 + 4x + 4 = 0$$

*Solution:* Construct the graph of

$$y = x^2 + 4x + 4$$

axis of symmetry $x = -2$
Vertex $(-2, 0)$

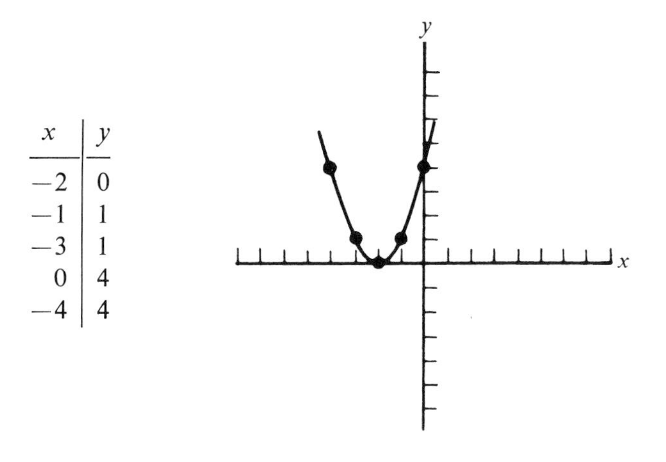


| $x$ | $y$ |
|---|---|
| $-2$ | 0 |
| $-1$ | 1 |
| $-3$ | 1 |
| 0 | 4 |
| $-4$ | 4 |

The graph touches the $x$-axis at the one point $(-2, 0)$. Hence the solution set of $x^2 + 4x + 4 = 0$ is $\{-2\}$.

## EXERCISES

**1.** Find the axis of symmetry and vertex of the graph of each of the following:
(a) $y = 2x^2 - x + 6$
(b) $y = x^2 + 3x - 5$
(c) $y = 2x^2 + 3x + 4$

2. Find the real roots of the following equations by constructing the graph of the quadratic function:
   (a) $x^2 - x - 6 = 0$
   (b) $2x^2 + 5x - 3 = 0$
   (c) $2x^2 - x - 3 = 0$

3. On the same axes construct the graphs of the following:
   (a) $y = x^2 + 2x + 1$
   (b) $y = x + 1$
   (c) $y = 1$

4. On the same axes construct the graphs of the following:
   (a) $y = x^2$
   (b) $y = 4x^2$
   (c) $y = 16x^2$

5. On the same axes construct the graphs of the following:
   (a) $y = x^2$
   (b) $y = x^2 + 4$
   (c) $y = x^2 - 4$

6. On the same axes construct the graphs of the following:
   (a) $y = x^2 + 4$
   (b) $y = x^2 + 2x + 4$
   (c) $y = x^2 - 2x + 4$

7. On the same axes construct the graphs of the following:
   (a) $y = x^2$
   (b) $y = -x^2$
   (c) $y = 4x^2$
   (d) $y = -4x^2$

8. In the equation $y = ax^2 + bx + c$ if $a > 0$ what does this tell us about the graph? If $a < 0$ what does this tell us about the graph?

9. In the equation $y = ax^2 + c$ what effect does a change in $c$ have on the graph?

## 10.3 Solution by Completing the Square

The next-to-last example in Section 10.2 illustrates the fact that the graphic solution of a quadratic equation may lead to approximate results, owing to the impossibility of reading exactly the coordinates of the points of intersection of the graph with the $x$-axis.

If the equation has real roots exact results can be obtained by the method known as *completing the square*. As a preliminary to this let us examine the form of the square of any binomial $(a + b)$. We can evaluate

$(a + b)^2 = (a + b)(a + b)$ by first applying the distributive property

$$(a + b)(a + b) = (a + b)a + (a + b)b$$

then the commutative property

$$(a + b)a + (a + b)b = a(a + b) + b(a + b)$$

and then the distributive property

$$a(a + b) + b(a + b) = a^2 + ab + ba + b^2$$

Then, applying the commutative property to $ba$ and collecting the two middle terms by using the distributive property, we have

$$(a + b)^2 = a^2 + 2ab + b^2$$

Notice the form of the expansion. The first term of the binomial, $a$, is squared, $a^2$, for the first term of the expansion. The second term of the binomial, $b$, is squared, $b^2$, for the last term of the expansion. The middle term of the expansion is 2 times the product of the terms of the binomial.

This expansion can be applied to any binomial squared.

*Example:* Expand $(2x + a)^2$

*Solution:* The first term of the expansion is the square of $2x$, that is, $(2x)^2 = 4x^2$. The last term of the expansion is the square of $a$ or $a^2$. The middle term is $2(2x)(a) = 4ax$. Hence,

$$(2x + a)^2 = 4x^2 + 4ax + a^2$$

*Example:* Expand $(\frac{1}{2}m - 3n)^2$

*Solution:* Here the binomial is in the form $(a + b)^2$ with $a = \frac{1}{2}m$ and $b = (-3n)$. That is, $(\frac{1}{2}m - 3n)^2 = [\frac{1}{2}m + (-3n)]^2$. Hence, the expansion is

$$\begin{aligned} [\tfrac{1}{2}m + (-3n)]^2 &= (\tfrac{1}{2}m)^2 + 2(\tfrac{1}{2}m)(-3n) + (-3n)^2 \\ &= \tfrac{1}{4}m^2 - 3mn + 9n^2 \end{aligned}$$

Consider the equation

$$2x^2 - 3x + 1 = 0$$

Since both sides of an equality can be divided by any number different from zero, we simplify matters by dividing by 2 and working with the equivalent equation

$$x^2 - \tfrac{3}{2}x + \tfrac{1}{2} = 0$$

Subtract $\frac{1}{2}$ from both sides, and we have the equivalent equation

$$x^2 - \tfrac{3}{2}x = -\tfrac{1}{2}$$

We now wish to add to both sides whatever constant is necessary to make the left side become the expansion of a binomial squared. The first term of the expansion is $x^2$, hence the first term of the binomial is $x$. The middle term of the expansion, $-(\frac{3}{2})x$, is twice the product of the terms of the binomial. Hence the second term of the binomial is $-(\frac{3}{2})x \div 2x = -(\frac{3}{4})$. We wish to add the square of the second term of the binomial to both sides of the equation

$$x^2 - \tfrac{3}{2}x + (-\tfrac{3}{4})^2 = -(\tfrac{1}{2}) + \tfrac{9}{16}$$

Expressing the left side as a binomial squared, we have

$$(x - \tfrac{3}{4})^2 = \tfrac{1}{16}$$

Taking the positive square root of both sides, we have

$$(x - \tfrac{3}{4}) = \tfrac{1}{4} \qquad \text{(I)}$$

and taking the negative square root

$$(x - \tfrac{3}{4}) = -\tfrac{1}{4} \qquad \text{(II)}$$

The union of the solution sets of (I) and (II) is the solution set of the original equation.

From (I)

$$x - \tfrac{3}{4} = \tfrac{1}{4}$$
$$x = 1$$

From (II)

$$x - \tfrac{3}{4} = -(\tfrac{1}{4})$$
$$x = \tfrac{1}{2}$$

Hence the solution set of the original equation $2x^2 - 3x + 1 = 0$ is $\{1, \frac{1}{2}\}$. The correctness of this can be verified by substitution.

$$2(1)^2 - 3(1) + 1 = 2 - 3 + 1 = 0$$

and

$$2(\tfrac{1}{2})^2 - 3(\tfrac{1}{2}) + 1 = \tfrac{1}{2} - \tfrac{3}{2} + 1 = 0$$

*Example:* Solve by completing the square

$$x^2 + 2x - 6 = 0$$

SOLUTION BY COMPLETING THE SQUARE

*Solution:*

$$x^2 + 2x - 6 = 0$$
$$x^2 + 2x = 6$$
$$x^2 + 2x + 1 = 7$$
$$(x + 1)^2 = 7$$
$$x + 1 = \sqrt{7};\ x = -1 + \sqrt{7}$$

or

$$x + 1 = -\sqrt{7};\ x = -1 - \sqrt{7}$$

The required solution set is $\{-1 + \sqrt{7}, -1 - \sqrt{7}\}$.

If no real numbers will satisfy the equation this will become evident when using the method just given. The method will require finding the square root of a negative number. Since the product of two positive numbers is positive, and the product of two negative numbers is also positive, no negative number has a real square root.

*Example:* Show that no real number will satisfy the equation

$$x^2 + 2x + 4 = 0$$

*Solution:* Apply the method of completing the square.

$$x^2 + 2x = -4$$
$$x^2 + 2x + 1 = -3$$
$$(x + 1)^2 = -3$$

Then to find $x + 1$ we must find the square root of $-3$. But $-3$ has no square root. Hence, no real number satisfies the equation.

## EXERCISES

**1.** Expand the following binomials by inspection:
(a) $(x - 2y)^2$
(b) $(x + \frac{1}{2})^2$
(c) $(x - \frac{1}{3})^2$
(d) $(2x + \frac{1}{2})^2$
(e) $(\frac{1}{2}x - \frac{1}{3}y)^2$

**2.** Supply the missing term so as to make each of the following a perfect square:
(a) $x^2 -$ ____ $+ 16$
(b) $4x^2 + 12x +$ ____
(c) ____ $+ 50x + 1$
(d) $x^2 - 3x +$ ____
(e) $x^2 + 8x +$ ____

**3.** Use the method of completing the square to find the real roots of the following quadratic equations:
(a) $x^2 + 2x - 3 = 0$
(b) $2x^2 - x - 6 = 0$
(c) $x^2 + 12x - 1 = 0$
(d) $x^2 - 6x + 8 = 0$
(e) $x^2 + 2x - 7 = 0$

## 10.4 Solving Inequalities by Completing the Square

The method of completing the square also can be used to solve quadratic inequalities. One caution must be kept in mind. If in the inequality

$$ax^2 + bx + c < 0$$

we divide by $a$, the sense of the inequality is unchanged for $a > 0$, but it is reversed for $a < 0$. (See Section 8.6.) The same situation will, of course, prevail if the inequality is of the form

$$ax^2 + bx + c > 0$$

When one takes the negative square root of an inequality the sense of the inequality must be reversed. Consider the relation $x^2 > 4$. For any positive $x > 2$, $x^2 > 4$. But for any negative $x$, we must have $x < -2$ if $x^2 > 4$. For example, $x = -3$ is less than $-2$, and $(-3)^2 = 9 > 4$. The graph of $x^2 > 4$ is the set of all points to the right of $+2$ *and* to the left of $-2$.

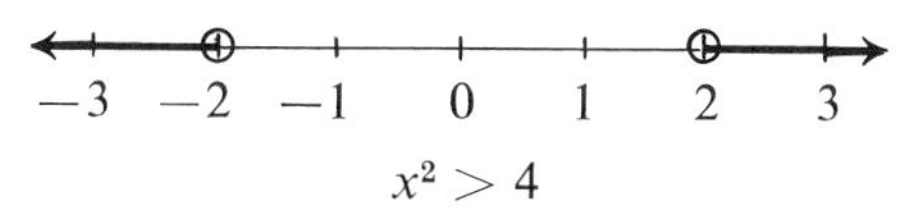


$x^2 > 4$

We illustrate the method with the following examples:

*Example:* Solve the inequality

$$16x^2 - 24x + 5 < 0$$

*Solution:* Divide both sides of the inequality by 16

$$x^2 - \tfrac{3}{2}x + \tfrac{5}{16} < 0$$

Subtract $\tfrac{5}{16}$ from each side

$$x^2 - \tfrac{3}{2}x < -(\tfrac{5}{16})$$

Complete the square on the left side by adding $\tfrac{9}{16}$ to both sides.

$$x^2 - \tfrac{3}{2}x + \tfrac{9}{16} < -(\tfrac{5}{16}) + \tfrac{9}{16}$$
$$(x - \tfrac{3}{4})^2 < \tfrac{1}{4}$$

Taking the positive square root of each side, we have

$$x - \tfrac{3}{4} < \tfrac{1}{2}$$
$$x < \tfrac{5}{4}$$

Taking the negative square root of each side, we have

$$x - \tfrac{3}{4} > -(\tfrac{1}{2})$$
$$x > \tfrac{1}{4}$$

The graph of the inequality is the set of points to the left of $\frac{5}{4}$ and to the right of $\frac{1}{4}$

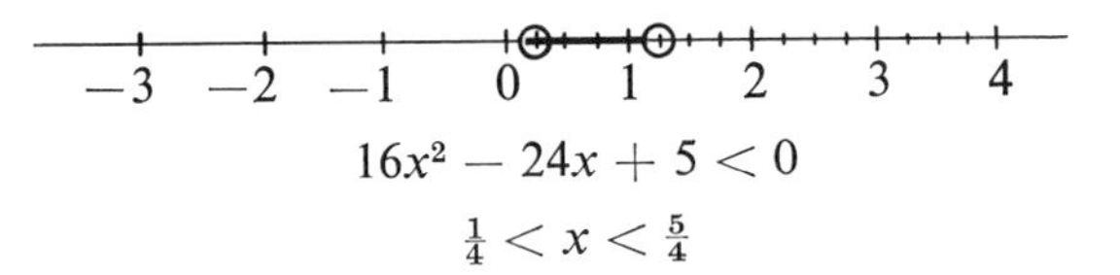


$$16x^2 - 24x + 5 < 0$$
$$\tfrac{1}{4} < x < \tfrac{5}{4}$$

It is instructive to compare the graph of the previous example with that of

$$y < 16x^2 - 24x + 5$$

We construct the graph of the equation

$$y = 16x^2 - 24x + 5$$

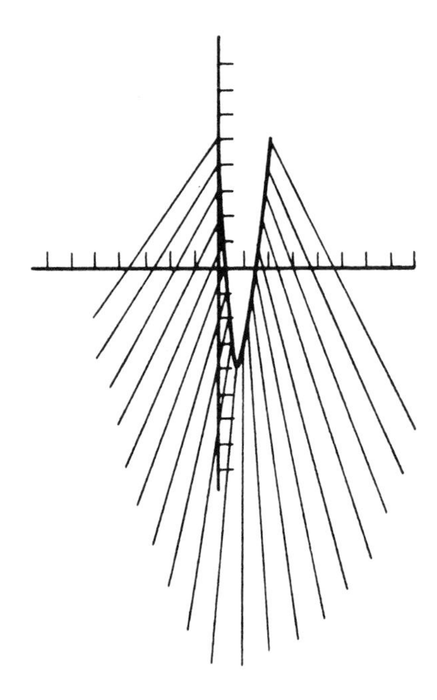

The graph of $y < 16x^2 - 24x + 5$ is the set of all points below the parabola, the shaded portion of the plane. But the graph of $y = 16x^2 - 24x + 5 < 0$ is that portion of the parabola which is below the $x$-axis. We find the parabola below the $x$-axis for precisely those values of $x$ that are members of the solution set of

$$16x^2 - 24x + 5 < 0$$

That is, $\frac{1}{4} < x < \frac{5}{4}$.

### EXERCISES

*Solve each of the following inequalities by completing the square. Graph the solution set of each. Check the solution by substituting two or three members of the solution set.*

**1.** $x^2 - 1 < 8$

**2.** $x^2 + 6x + 3 < 10$

**3.** $4x^2 - 12x + 10 > 26$

**4.** $x^2 + 8x < 0$

**5.** $x^2 + 5 > 0$

**6.** $x^2 + 10 < 0$

**7.** $9x^2 - 6x + 10 \leq 25$

**8.** $x^2 + 6x + 17 < 5$

**9.** $x^2 + 6x + 5 < 5$

**10.** $x^2 + 10x + 24 > 1$

## 10.5 Solution by Factoring

The quadratic expression in an equation or inequality may be such that it can be factored into the product of two linear factors by inspection. When this can be done the solution set can be obtained readily.

Consider the equation

$$2x^2 - x - 6 = 0$$

We have no assurance that the expression $2x^2 - x - 6$ can be factored into two linear factors with integral coefficients, or even rational coefficients. However, if two factors with integral coefficients exist, we know one factor must have the term $x$ and the other factor the term $2x$ because the term $2x^2$ is in the quadratic expression. That is, the factor must be of the form

$$(2x + \_)(x + \_)$$

The constant terms must be such that their product is $-6$. Hence one constant must be positive and the other negative. The possibilities are $(1, -6)$, $(-1, 6)$, $(2, -3)$, $(-2, 3)$, $(-6, 1)$, $(6, -1)$, $(-3, 2)$, and $(3, -2)$. We can determine by trial which, if any, pair will yield the correct first degree term. Since the first degree term must be $-x$ we can verify the correct factors as

$$(2x + 3) \qquad \text{and} \qquad (x - 2)$$

The solution set for $2x^2 - x - 6 = 0$ can now be obtained as the union of the solution sets of $2x + 3 = 0$ and $x - 2 = 0$. The solution set is $[-(\frac{3}{2}), 2]$.

Consider the inequality

$$x^2 - 7x + 12 < 0$$

If the expression $x^2 - 7x + 12$ can be factored into two linear factors, the inequality can be solved by setting each factor greater than zero, then setting each factor less than zero. This is true because the product of the two factors will be greater than zero if and only if the two factors agree, both greater than zero or both less than zero.

To factor the quadratic $x^2 - 7x + 12$ we note that the leading term in each factor must be $x$. The factors are of the form

$$(x \pm \_)(x \pm \_)$$

The product of the constant terms is positive, hence both constants are positive or both are negative. Since the first degree term is negative, at least one, and hence both, constants must be negative. The factors are of the form

$$(x - \_)(x - \_)$$

The product of the constants is 12; hence the possibilities are $(-1, -12)$, $(-2, -6)$, $(-3, -4)$. The middle term has the coefficient $-7$. Therefore the factors are

$$(x - 3)(x - 4)$$

To solve the inequality we have

$$x - 3 > 0 \qquad \text{and} \qquad x - 4 > 0$$

or

$$x - 3 < 0 \qquad \text{and} \qquad x - 4 < 0$$

If $x - 3 > 0$ then $x > 3$; if $x - 4 > 0$ then $x > 4$. The intersection of the sets

$$\{x \mid x > 3\} \cap \{x \mid x > 4\}$$

is the set

$$\{x \mid x > 4\}$$

Hence all real numbers greater than 4 satisfy the original inequality. If

$$x - 3 < 0 \quad \text{then} \quad x < 3$$

If

$$x - 4 < 0 \quad \text{then} \quad x < 4$$

The intersection of the sets

$$\{x \mid x < 3\} \cap \{x \mid x < 4\}$$

is the set $\{x \mid x < 3\}$. Hence all real numbers less than 3 satisfy the original inequality. The solution set of $x^2 - 7x + 12 < 0$ is the set of all real numbers less than 3 or greater than 4.

### EXERCISES

**1.** Factor each of the following into linear factors:
(a) $2x^2 + 7x - 15$
(b) $x^2 - 4x - 5$
(c) $6x^2 - x - 1$
(d) $2x^2 + x - 10$

**2.** Solve each of the following by factoring:
(a) $2x^2 + x - 6 = 0$
(b) $6x^2 + x - 2 = 0$
(c) $x^2 - 8x + 15 = 0$
(d) $x^2 + 8x + 15 = 0$
(e) $x^2 + 2x - 15 = 0$
(f) $x^2 - 4x + 3 > 0$
(g) $x^2 + x - 6 < 0$
(h) $x^2 - 3x + 2 > 0$
(i) $x^2 + x - 2 < 0$
(j) $x^2 - x - 2 > 0$

## 10.6 Applications

Although problems involving linear equations and inequalities occur more frequently, there are also many applications of quadratic equations and inequalities. The following examples are illustrative:

*Example:* We know from physics that the distance, $d$, a body moving under the influence of a constant acceleration, $a$, will travel in

$t$ seconds is

$$d = \tfrac{1}{2}at^2 + v_0t$$

where $V_0$ is the initial velocity of the object.

Find the time required for an object to fall 256 ft if the initial velocity is 64 feet per second.

*Solution:* The acceleration of gravity is 32 ft per second per second. Hence the time required is expressed by the equation

$$256 = 32t^2 + 64t$$

or

$$32t^2 + 64t - 256 = 0$$

which can be solved by factoring the quadratic

$$32t^2 + 64t - 256 = 0$$

$$(32t + 128)(t - 2) = 0$$

$$32t + 128 = 0 \qquad \text{or} \qquad t - 2 = 0$$

$$32t = -128 \qquad\qquad t = 2$$

$$t = -4$$

The conditions of the problem are such that $t = -4$ is meaningless. The object cannot fall $-4$ sec. The object falls 256 ft in 2 sec.

*Example:* A farmer wishes to fence a rectangular field that contains 1 acre (43,560 sq ft). The length of the field is 22 ft greater than the width. Find the number of feet of fence that is required.

*Solution:* If the width of the field is $x$, the length is $x + 22$. The area of the field is 43,560. Hence:

$$x(x + 22) = 43{,}560$$

$$x^2 + 22x - 43{,}560 = 0$$

$$(x - 198)(x + 220) = 0$$

$$x - 198 = 0 \qquad \text{or} \qquad x + 220 = 0$$

$$x = 198 \qquad\qquad x = -220$$

The solution $x = -220$ is meaningless since a field cannot have a negative width. Hence the width of the field is 198 ft and its length is $198 + 22 = 220$ ft. The perimeter is $2 \cdot 198 + 2 \cdot 220 = 836$ ft. The field requires 836 ft of fence.

*Example:* A manufacturer has found that if he produces $x$ units per month his monthly profit is $x^2 - 52x - 480$ dollars. How many units per month must be made if the business is to show a profit?

*Solution:* If there is to be a profit the expression $x^2 - 52x - 480$ must be positive, that is

$$x^2 - 52x - 480 > 0$$

Factoring the quadratic, we have

$$(x + 8)(x - 60) > 0$$

The inequality is satisfied if $x + 8 > 0$ and $x - 60 > 0$; that is, if $x > 60$. It is also satisfied if $x + 8 < 0$ and $x - 60 < 0$; that is, if $x < -8$. Since it is impossible to make less than $-8$ units per month, the manufacturer must make more than 60 units per month to show a profit.

## EXERCISES

**1.** An object falls from a height of 300 ft. If it is given an initial velocity of 40 ft per second how long does it take to fall?

**2.** If an object moves under a constant acceleration of 12 ft per second per second and is given an initial velocity of 4 ft per second how far will the object move in 10 sec?

**3.** Under the conditions described in Exercise 2 how long will it take the object to travel 240 ft?

**4.** Find a positive number whose reciprocal is 1 more than the number. (*Note:* The required number is called the golden ratio.)

**5.** A rectangular plot is 30 ft longer than its width. If it is 13,000 sq ft in area what are its dimensions?

**6.** A circular plot contains 200 sq ft of area. A gardener wishes to plant a circular flower bed in the center of the plot. He wishes the bed and the border to have the same area. To find the radius of the bed, use $A = \frac{22}{7}r^2$ as the formula for the area of a circle of radius $r$.

# 11 Systems of Linear Equations and Inequalities

IN CHAPTER 9 WE FOUND THAT A LINEAR EQUATION IN TWO VARIABLES does not have a unique solution. Each element of the solution set is an ordered pair. The solution set has infinitely many elements. Such an equation is *indeterminate*. In this chapter we wish to investigate *systems* of linear equations and inequalities. The solution set of a system of equations is the intersection of the solution sets of the individual equations.

## 11.1 Graphic Solution of Systems of Two Linear Equations in Two Variables

Quite frequently it is possible to express the conditions of a problem as two independent linear relations between two variables. The solution of the problem is obtained as the common solution of the two linear relations.

*Example:* The length of a rectangular lot is 30 ft more than its width. If the perimeter is 260 ft find its dimensions.

*Solution:* If the width is represented by the variable $w$ and the length is represented by $l$ we have the relation

$$l = w + 30$$

The perimeter, $2l + 2w$, is given as 260 ft. Hence we have the relation

$$2l + 2w = 260$$

Both of the relations must be satisfied; hence, the solution of the problem is obtained by finding the intersection of the solution sets of the two relations.

Since the graph of a linear equation is the set of points whose coordinates satisfy the equation, we can find the solution of a system of two equations by finding the intersection of their graphs. Since two distinct lines have at most one point in common a system of two linear equations will have at most one pair of values of the variables.

*Example:* Solve the system of equations

$$3x - y = 6$$
$$x + 2y = 9$$

by finding the intersection of their graphs.

*Solution:*

$3x - y = 6$

| $x$ | $y$ |
|---|---|
| 2 | 0 |
| 0 | $-6$ |

$x + 2y = 9$

| $x$ | $y$ |
|---|---|
| 9 | 0 |
| 0 | $\frac{9}{2}$ |

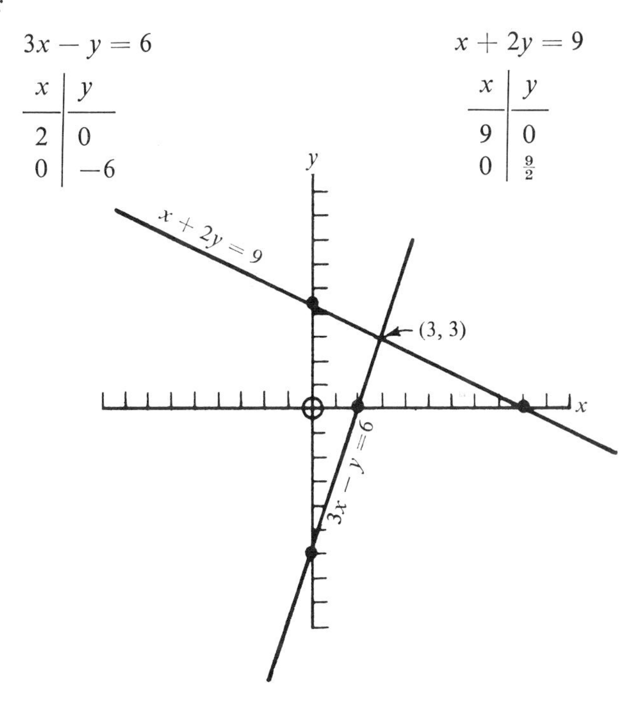


The coordinates of any point on the line through (2, 0) and (0, $-6$) will satisfy the equation $3x - y = 6$. The coordinates of any point on the line through (9, 0) and (0, $\frac{9}{2}$) will satisfy the equation $x + 2y = 9$. Hence, the coordinates of the point common to the lines will satisfy both equations. The point of intersection is the point (3, 3). The solution set of the system is thus $\{(3, 3)\}$. Check this by substituting $x = 3$ and $y = 3$ in each equation.

A problem may require that two conditions be satisfied which are inconsistent with each other. Two statements are inconsistent if it is impossible for both of them to be satisfied. The graphs of two such relations will have no points in common. The solution set of such a system of equations will be the null set. If two lines have no point in common the lines are parallel. We have seen, page 252, parallel lines are lines with the same slope. These ideas are illustrated in the following example:

*Example:* If John had 5 more marbles he would have 3 times as many as Sam. If John had twice as many marbles he would have one less than six times as many as Sam. How many marbles does each have?

*Solution:* Let $y =$ the number of marbles John has, and $x =$ the number of marbles Sam has. From the first condition we have

$$y + 5 = 3x$$

and from the second condition

$$2y = 6x - 1$$

If we draw the graph of these two equations

$y + 5 = 3x$

| $x$ | $y$ |
|---|---|
| 0 | $-5$ |
| 1 | $-2$ |

$2y = 6x - 1$

| $x$ | $y$ |
|---|---|
| 0 | $-(\frac{1}{2})$ |
| 1 | $\frac{5}{2}$ |

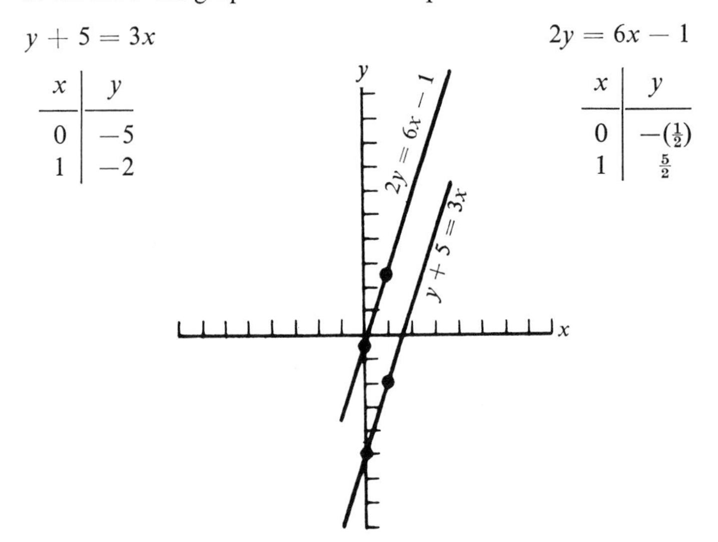


we find the two lines are parallel. The intersection of the solution sets of the two equations is the null set. Hence the problem has no solution; the two conditions are inconsistent.

But how do we know the lines are parallel? Our eyes may deceive us. If the two equations are expressed in slope intercept form we have

$$y = 3x - 5 \qquad \text{and} \qquad y = 3x - \tfrac{1}{2}$$

Each line has the slope 3, but they have different $y$-intercepts Hence, they are parallel.

A system of two linear equations may have a single $(x, y)$ pair as solution set; the two graphs intersect. The system may have a null solution set; the two graphs are parallel. Finally, the solution set may have more than one element. But this will mean the two straight line graphs have two or more points in common. But this is impossible for two distinct lines. The two equations must have the same graph; they have the same solution set. The following example illustrates this situation:

*Example:* Bill has \$4 less than twice the amount Jim has. Jim's money is \$2 more than half of Bill's. How much money does each have?

*Solution:* Let $x$ represent Bill's money and $y$ represent Jim's money. Then $x$ is 4 less than $2y$, hence

$$x + 4 = 2y$$

But

$$y - 2 = \frac{x}{2}$$

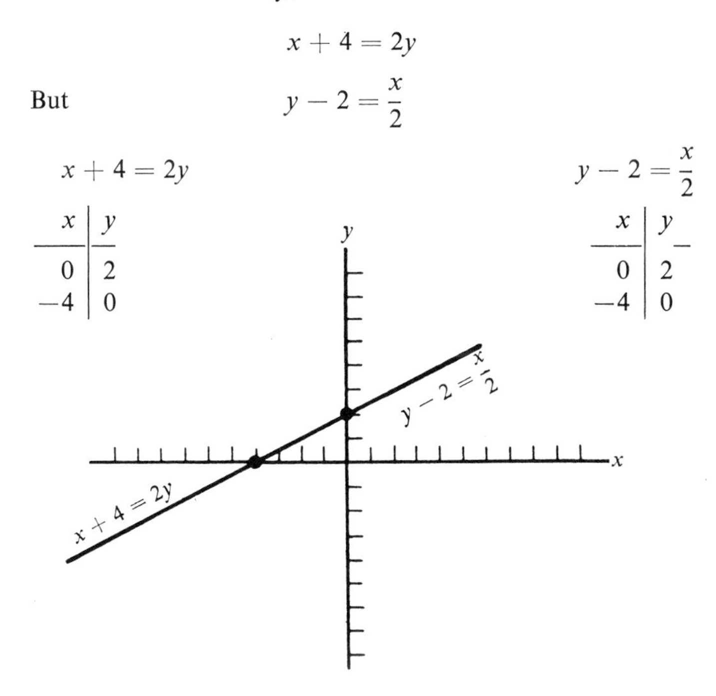


GRAPHIC SOLUTION OF SYSTEMS

If each of these equations is written in slope form we have

$$x + 4 = 2y \qquad \text{and} \qquad y - 2 = \frac{x}{2}$$

$$y = \frac{x}{2} + 2 \qquad\qquad y = \frac{x}{2} + 2$$

The two conditions of the problem are not independent. They are, in fact, two statements of the same relation between the variables.

## EXERCISES

**1.** Find the intersection of the solution sets of $3x - y = 8$ and $x + 2y = 5$ graphically. That is, find graphically

$$\{(x, y) \mid 3x - y = 8\} \cap \{(x, y) \mid x + 2y = 5\}$$

**2.** What is the graph of the union of the two equations in Exercise 1?

*Solve the following systems of equations graphically*:

**3.** $2x + 3y = 1$
$y = 3x - 7$

**4.** $x = 3y - 13$
$y - x = 5$

**5.** $x + y = 2x - 6$
$2y + 6 = 2(x - 9)$

**6.** $3x + y = 7$
$2y = 3(5 - 2x)$

**7.** Supply the value of $A$ for which the solution set of the following system is the null set:

$$3x - 2y = 5$$
$$Ay = 5x + 7$$

**8.** Is there a replacement set for $b$ for which the following system is dependent? If so what is it?

$$2x + y = 7$$
$$3y = b - 6x$$

**9.** If the graphs of two equations have the same slope can the system have a unique (single value) solution? Explain.

**10.** Compare the graphs of the following sets:
(a) $\{(x, y) \mid 2x + 3y = 5\} \cap \{(x, y) \mid x - y = 12\}$
(b) $\{(x, y) \mid 2x + 3y = 5\} \cup \{(x, y) \mid x - y = 12\}$

## 11.2 Graphs of Systems of Linear Inequalities

Linear inequalities occur quite commonly as *restraints* or boundary conditions on practical problems. Consider the following problem situation: A trucking contractor owns eight 2-ton trucks and seven 3-ton trucks. He has 10 drivers available for a hauling job. If we let $x$ represent the number of 2-ton trucks and $y$ the number of 3-ton trucks which the contractor assigns to the job, we know the following inequalities prevail:

$$0 \leq x + y \leq 10$$
$$0 \leq x \leq 8$$
$$0 \leq y \leq 7$$

We wish to construct the graph of these inequalities. Since the domains of the variables are sets of integers the graphs will be discrete points.

The graph of $x + y \leq 10$ is the set of all points the sum of whose coordinates lie in the closed interval from 0 to 10. It is the set of all points with integral coordinates lying on or below the line.

$$x + y = 10$$

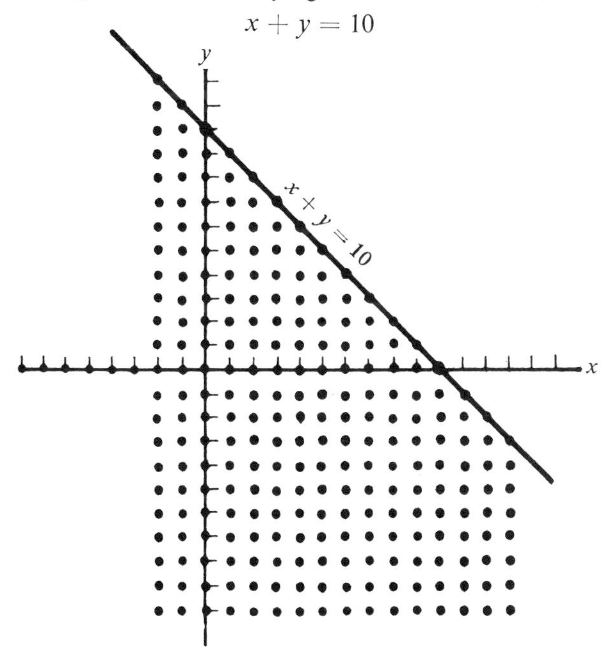


The graph of the relation

$$0 \leq x \leq 8$$

consists of the points with integral coordinates lying on or between the $y$-axis and the line $x = 8$. Then the intersection to the two relations

$$x + y \leq 10 \qquad \text{and} \qquad 0 \leq x \leq 8$$

is found on or between the lines $x = 0$ and $x = 8$ and on or under the line $x + y = 10$.

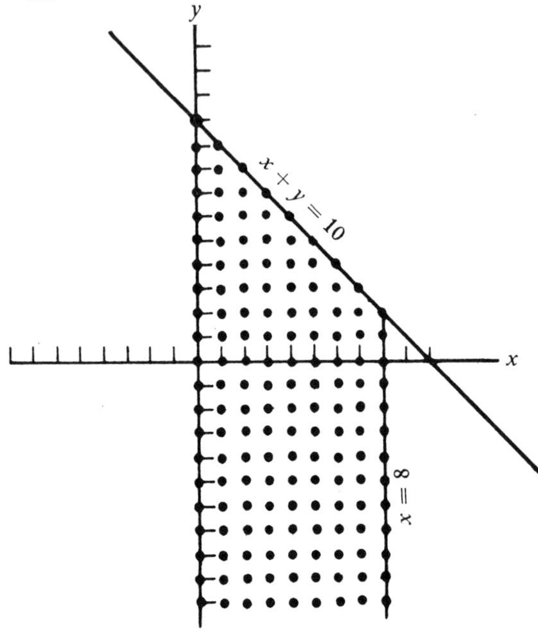


Finally, the graph of $0 \leq y \leq 7$ consists of the points on or between the $x$-axis and the line $y = 7$.

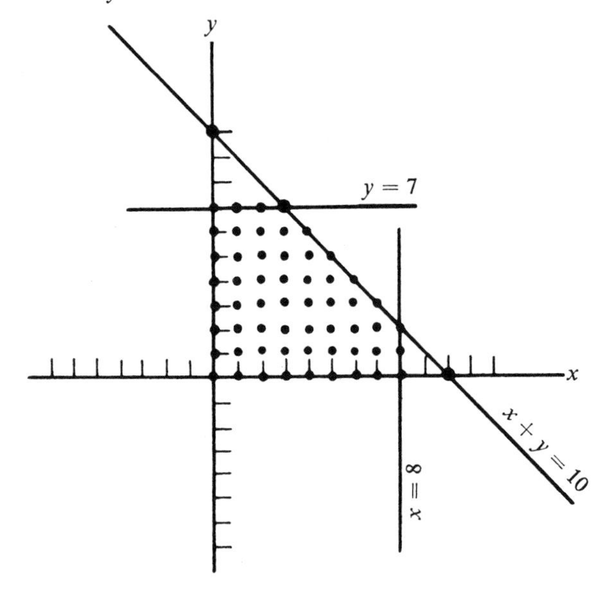

If the domain of the variables were the set of real numbers the graph would then be the set of all points on the boundary or within the polygon determined by the $x$-axis, the $y$-axis, the line $x = 8$, the line $y = 7$, and the line $x + y = 10$.

Inequalities of the form $\leq$ or $\geq$ are called *mixed* inequalities. Without the equality sign, $<$ or $>$, they are called *strict* inequalities. If the inequalities in the above illustration were strict inequalities the graph would consist of the points in the polygon, but not those on the boundary.

A straight line divides the plane into two *half planes*. The graph of any linear inequality is a half plane. If it is a strict inequality the half plane is *open*; the graph does not include the points of the line. If it is a mixed inequality the half plane is *closed*; the graph includes the dividing line.

The question remains, on which side of the line is the graph? Consider the inequality $3x - y < 6$. We construct the graph of $3x - y = 6$. The

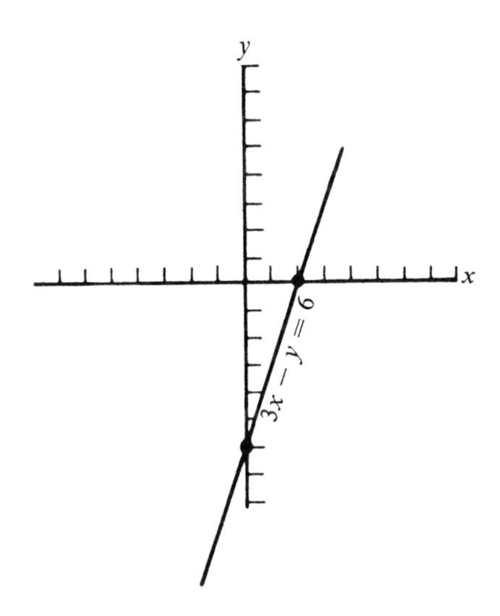


graph of the inequality is either the open half plane above the line or the open half plane below the line. We can substitute the coordinates of a point known to be in one of the half planes and determine whether the inequality is satisfied. For example, the point (4, 0) is obviously below the line. Substituting $x = 4$, $y = 0$ we have

$$3 \cdot 4 - 0 > 6$$

and (4, 0) is not a point of the graph. On the other hand, the point (0, 0) is above the line and

$$3 \cdot 0 - 0 < 6$$

the inequality is satisfied. The graph is the open half plane above the line $3x - y = 6$.

The same result can be obtained by solving the inequality for $y$. Care should be taken to reverse the sense of the inequality if we multiply by a negative number

$$3x - y < 6$$

$$-y < 6 - 3x$$

$$y > 3x - 6$$

Since for any point on the line

$$y = 3x - 6$$

the points satisfying the relation

$$y > 3x - 6$$

are points above the line.

The union of two inequalities is the set of points satisfying either or both relations. The intersection is the points common to the two graphs.

*Example:* Find the union and the intersection of the inequalities

$$x + 2y < 5$$

$$5x - y < 7$$

*Solution:* Solve each inequality for $y$.

$$x + 2y < 5$$

$$2y < 5 - x$$

$$y < \frac{5}{2} - \frac{x}{2}$$

and

$$5x - y < 7$$

$$-y < 7 - 5x$$

$$y > 5x - 7$$

The graph of $x + 2y < 5$ is the open half plane below the line $x + 2y = 5$. The graph of $5x - y < 7$ is the open half

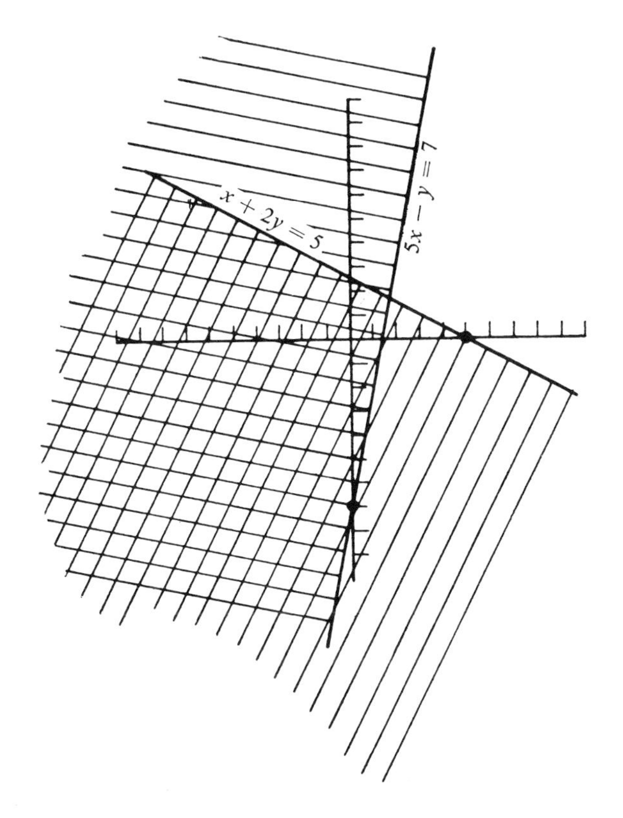


plane above the line $5x - y = 7$. The union of the two relations is the shaded area, the entire plane except that on or above $x + 2y = 5$ and on or below $5x - y = 7$. The intersection of the two relations is the crosshatched region.

## EXERCISES

**1.** Determine whether each of the following is a strict or mixed inequality:
(a) $3x - y < 0$
(b) $x + 5y \geq 12$
(c) $5x - 7 \leq 7$
(d) $x - 3y > 12$

**2.** Describe the graphs of the following:
(a) $3x - y < 7$
(b) $3x - y \leq 7$
(c) The union of the graph of $3x - y < 7$ and $3x - y > 7$.
(d) The intersection of the graphs of $3x - y < 7$ and $3x - y > 7$.

## GRAPHS OF SYSTEMS OF LINEAR INEQUALITIES

3. Construct the graph of the intersection of $2x - y < 5$ and $x + 3y > 6$.

4. Construct the graph of the union of $2x - y < 5$ and $x + 3y > 6$.

5. Any point $(x, y)$ must be an element of the solution set of one and only one of the following: $3x - 4y < 7$, $3x - 4y = 7$, $3x - 4y > 7$. Determine to which of the three each of the following belongs: $(3, 2)$, $(5, 9)$, $(4, -1)$, $(-1, -3)$, $(6, -5)$, $(6, 1)$.

6. Determine whether each of the following points is on, above, or below the line $x - 2y = 7$:

$$(3, -2), (2, 5), (1, -4), (10, 1), (5, -1)$$

*Construct the graphs of the following systems of inequalities:*

7. $x - 3y \leq 6$
   $2x + y \geq 10$
   $x + y \leq 14$

8. $x - 2y \leq 14$
   $2x - y \geq 8$
   $3x + y \geq 9$

9. $2x + 3y \geq 6$
   $x - y \geq 4$
   $3x - y \leq 12$

10. Which of the systems in Exercises 7, 8, and 9 have as graphs a closed polygon and its interior?

## 11.3 Algebraic Solution of Systems of Linear Equations

A system of two linear equations in two variables can be solved by obtaining an equivalent equation in one variable. There are several ways to eliminate one of the variables. The following example illustrates the most general approach:

*Example:* Solve the system

$$3x - 2y = 8$$
$$2x + 3y = 14$$

*Solution:* Multiply each side of the first equation by 3 and each side of the second by 2.

$$9x - 6y = 24$$
$$4x + 6y = 28$$

Since the coefficients of $y$ are additive inverses, the equation obtained by adding the two equations will contain only the variable $x$,

$$13x = 52$$
$$x = 4$$

If we substitute $x = 4$ in either of the original equations we may find $y$,

$$2 \cdot 4 + 3y = 14$$
$$3y = 6$$
$$y = 2$$

The solution set is then $\{(4, 2)\}$.

Let us examine the basis for the solution. The equation $3x - 2y = 8$ is an open sentence; it is neither true nor false until replacements are made for $x$ and $y$. If there are replacements for $x$ and $y$ that will make the statement true, multiplying both members by 3 gives a new statement that is still true. This is the multiplication property of equality. The same thing occurs when the second equation is multiplied by 2. The multipliers, 3 and 2, were selected so as to produce additive inverse coefficients for one of the variables. When we combine the two equations by addition, what do we know about the resulting statement? We can be sure it is a true statement *only* for those $x$, $y$ replacements that make *both* original statements true. If there are replacements for $x$ and $y$ that make both original statements true we are applying the addition property of equality. Then the equation $13x = 52$ is a condition on $x$ that must be met if the first two equations are to be true statements. Hence, the solution, $x = 4$, must be a true statement for any $(x, y)$ pair that satisfies the original equations. It is then a simple matter to replace $x$ with 4 in either equation to find the required $y$.

We could have solved the system by eliminating $x$ first.

*Example:* Solve the system

$$3x - 2y = 8$$
$$2x + 3y = 14$$

by eliminating $x$.

*Solution:* If the first equation is multiplied by $-2$ and the second by 3 the coefficients of $x$ are additive inverses.

$$-6x + 4y = -16$$
$$6x + 9y = 42$$

And adding the two equations

$$13y = 26$$
$$y = 2$$

Substituting $y = 2$ in the first equation

$$3x - 4 = 8$$
$$3x = 12$$
$$x = 4$$

and the solution set is $\{(4, 2)\}$.

We saw in Section 11.1 that a system of two linear equations may be inconsistent or dependent. How is this discovered algebraically?

*Example:* Show the system

$$3x - 2y = 9$$
$$4y = 6 + 6x$$

is inconsistent.

*Solution:* We proceed as though the system had a unique solution. Multiply the first equation by 2.

$$6x - 4y = 18$$

Add $-6x$ to both sides of the second equation

$$-6x + 4y = 6$$

add the two equations

$$0 + 0 = 24$$

The assumption that there is an $(x, y)$ that will satisfy both equations leads to the conclusion that

$$0 = 24$$

Put otherwise, if there is an $(x, y)$ that satisfies both equations then $0 = 24$. Since $0 = 24$ is false we conclude that there is no $(x, y)$ that satisfies both equations. The equations are inconsistent.

If the ratio of the coefficients of $x$ is equal to the ratio of the coefficients of $y$ in two linear equations, when we attempt to eliminate one variable the other is also eliminated. This was the situation in the last example. If the constant terms have this same ratio the equations are dependent.

*Example:* Show the systems

$$2x - 10y = 6$$

$$3x - 15y = 9$$

are dependent.

*Solution:* Multiply the first equation by 3 and the second by $-2$.

$$6x - 30y = +18$$

$$-6x + 30y = -18$$

upon adding the two equations we have

$$0 + 0 = 0$$

a result that is obviously true.

If we had multiplied the first equation by $\frac{3}{2}$ the two equations would be identical. Obviously, any solution for one equation is a solution for the other.

## EXERCISES

*Solve the following systems of equations*:

**1.** $x - 3y = 7$
$2x + y = 21$

**2.** $3x + 4y = 12$
$2x - y = 8$

**3.** $5x - 2y = 13$
$x + 3y = 6$

**4.** $2x - y = 7$
$2y - 4x = 12$

**5.** $3x + 5y = 1$
$6x + 10y = 2$

**6.** $2x + y = 9$
$x - 2y = 9$

**7.** $y = 12 - 3x$
$x + y = 7$

**8.** $2x - 2y = 14$
$x + y = 7$

**9.** $x + y = 5$
$x - y = 5$

**10.** $3x - y = 12$
$2y = 6(x - 2)$

**11.** Find the points at which the graphs of the following equations intersect:

$$x - 2y = 7$$
$$2x + y = 4$$
$$3x - y = 6$$

## 11.4 Linear Programming

One very practical application of systems of linear inequalities is illustrated in a technique known as linear programming.

An expression of the form $ax + by + c$ is called a linear function in $x$ and $y$. The function has a value corresponding to each $(x, y)$ pair. Specifically, as we move along a line the coordinates of each point may be substituted for $x$ and $y$ in the function to determine a value.

*Example:* The function $2x - 3y + 7$ has a value at each point on the line $x + 2y = 6$. Find its value for selected points.

*Solution:* The line has intercepts (6, 0) and (0, 3). The points of the line with integral coordinates that are in the first quadrant are (6, 0), (4, 1), (2, 2), and (0, 3)

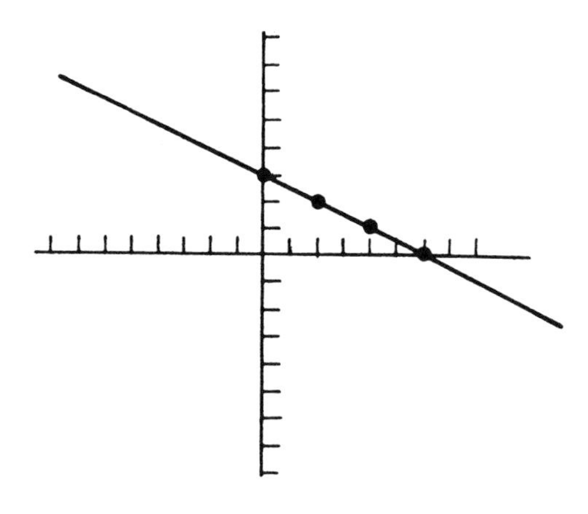

The values of the function at these points are:

| | | |
|---|---|---|
| at | (6, 0) | $2 \cdot 6 - 3 \cdot 0 + 7 = 19$ |
| at | (4, 1) | $2 \cdot 4 - 3 \cdot 1 + 7 = 12$ |
| at | (2, 2) | $2 \cdot 2 - 3 \cdot 2 + 7 = 5$ |
| at | (0, 3) | $2 \cdot 0 - 3 \cdot 3 + 7 = -2$ |

It should be noted that in this example the values of the function decreased as the values of $x$ decreased. It seems apparent that, for any segment of the line, the function has its maximum at one end of the line and its minimum at the other.

Let us consider another function, $x + 4y - 3$, evaluated at the same points as before.

| | | |
|---|---|---|
| at | (6, 0) | $1 \cdot 6 + 4 \cdot 0 - 3 = 3$ |
| at | (4, 1) | $1 \cdot 4 + 4 \cdot 1 - 3 = 5$ |
| at | (2, 2) | $1 \cdot 2 + 4 \cdot 2 - 3 = 7$ |
| at | (0, 3) | $1 \cdot 0 + 4 \cdot 3 - 3 = 9$ |

Here, the function values increase as the values of $x$ decrease. But once again, the maximum value is at one end of the segment and the minimum is at the other.

Consider the general case, the evaluation of the function $ax + by + c$ along a segment of the line $y = mx + d$. The function can be expressed in terms of $x$ only by replacing $y$ with $mx + d$

$$ax + b(mx + d) + c$$

or

$$(a + bm)x + bd + c$$

In this form it should be evident that, since $(bd + c)$ is constant and $(a + bm)$ is constant, different values of $x$ simply give the constant $(a + bm)$ different "stretching factors." In other words, if $(a + bm) > 0$ an increase in $x$ will increase the value of the function. But if $(a + bm) < 0$ an increase in $x$ will decrease the value of the function. This discussion is summarized in a basic theorem underlying linear programming.

> A linear function $ax + by + c$, when evaluated along the points of a segment, will have its minimum value at one end point and its maximum at the other.

A convex polygon is a polygon such that any two interior points may be joined by a segment containing no point of the perimeter.

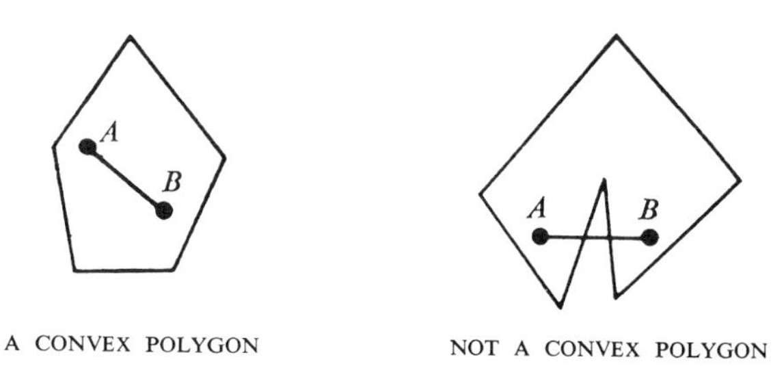


A CONVEX POLYGON NOT A CONVEX POLYGON

Since a mixed linear inequality has as graph a closed half plane, three or more such inequalities may determine a convex polygon.

*Example:* Show the graph of the system of inequalities

$$2x - 3y \leq 6$$
$$x + y \leq 12$$
$$x \geq 0$$

is a convex polygon.

*Solution:* The graph of $2x - 3y \leq 6$ or $y \geq \dfrac{2x-6}{3}$ is the closed half plane above the line $2x - 3y = 6$

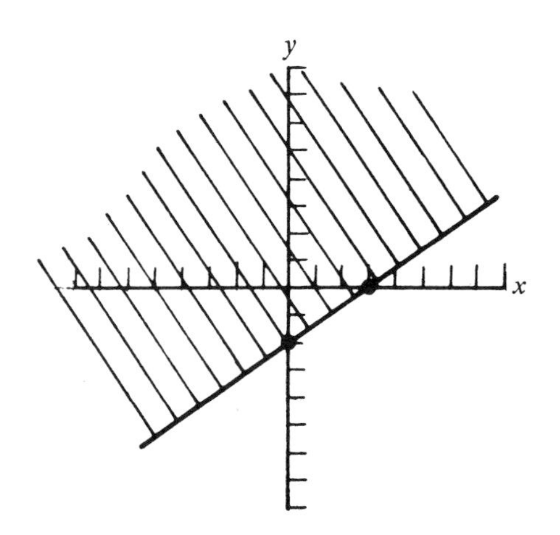


The graph of $x + y \leq 12$ is the half plane below the line $x + y = 12$

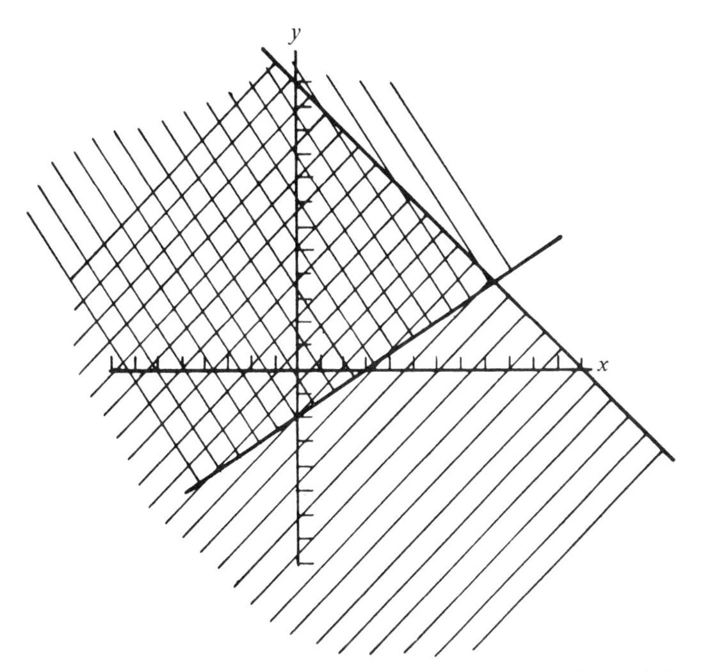


The graph of $x \geq 0$ is the closed half plane to the right of the $y$-axis. Hence the intersection of the three inequalities is the shaded area common to all three half planes.

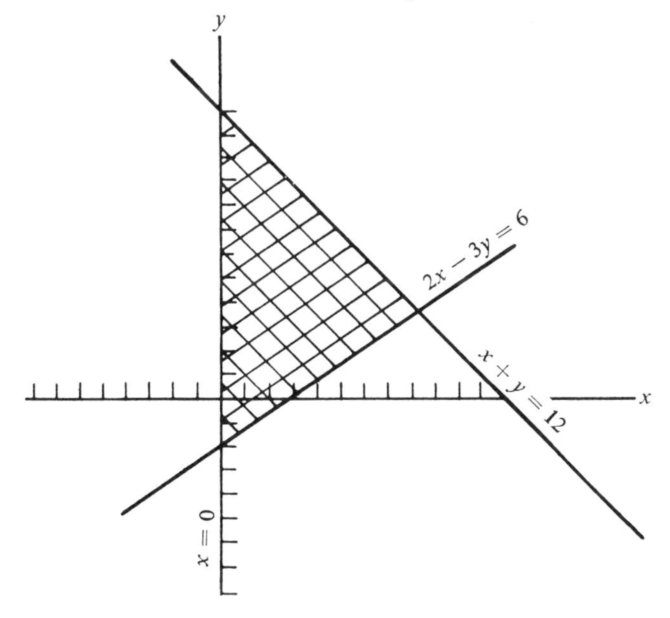

Suppose we wish to find the maximum or minimum value of a linear function evaluated throughout the region determined in the last example. The line joining any two points within the region will intersect the polygon in two points. Our basic theorem assures us that if the function is evaluated along the segment of any line cutting the polygon the maximum will be at one end of the segment and the minimum will be at the other. That is, both maximum and minimum values will be found on the

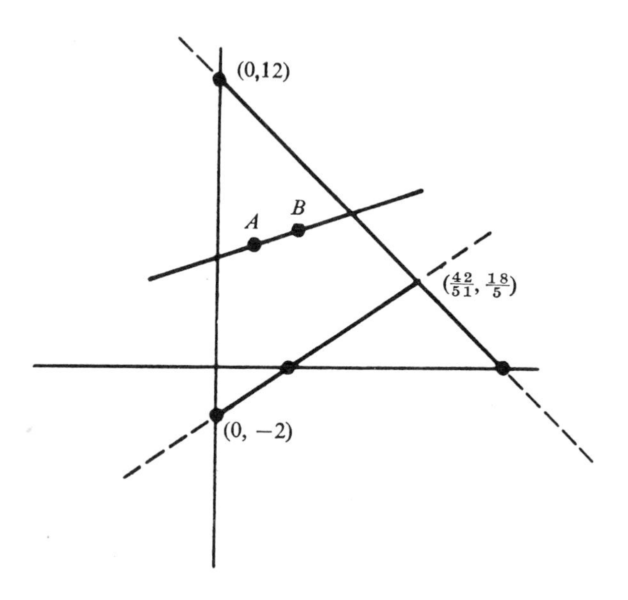


boundary of the polygon. If we now evaluate the function along the sides of the polygon the basic theorem tells us the maximum value is at a vertex and the minimum is at another vertex.

Combining these results, if a linear function is evaluated throughout a convex polygon its maximum value is found at a vertex of the polygon and its minimum value is found at another vertex of the polygon.

*Example:* Find the maximum and minimum values of

$$3x + 4y + 6$$

throughout the polygon determined by the inequalities

$$\begin{aligned} 2x - 3y &\leq 6 \\ x + y &\leq 12 \\ x &\geq 0 \end{aligned}$$

*Solution:* The vertices of the polygon can be found by solving the equations

$$2x - 3y = 6$$
$$x + y = 12$$
$$x = 0$$

in pairs.

The solution of $2x - 3y = 6$ and $x + y = 12$ is $(\frac{42}{5}, \frac{18}{5})$. The solution of $2x - 3y = 6$ and $x = 0$ is $(0, -2)$. The solution of $x + y = 12$ and $x = 0$ is $(0, 12)$.

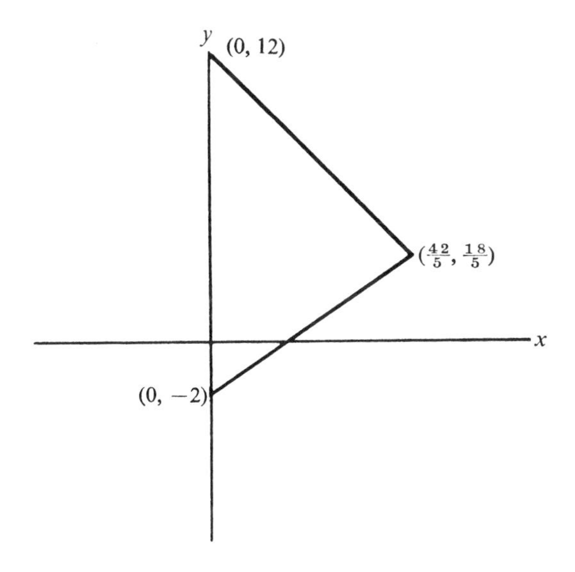


We find the value of the function

$$3x + 4y + 6$$

at these points:

| | | |
|---|---|---|
| at | $(0, 12)$ | $3 \cdot 0 + 4 \cdot 12 + 6 = 54$ |
| at | $(0, -2)$ | $3 \cdot 0 + 4 \cdot (-2) + 6 = -2$ |
| at | $(\frac{42}{5}, \frac{18}{5})$ | $3 \cdot \frac{42}{5} + 4 \cdot \frac{18}{5} + 6 = 45\frac{3}{5}$ |

Hence the minimum value of the function in the region is $-2$ and the maximum value is 54.

To illustrate the utility of the technique of linear programming, let us return to the problem of the contractor at the beginning of Section 11.2. We found the restraints on his operation defined a convex polygon.

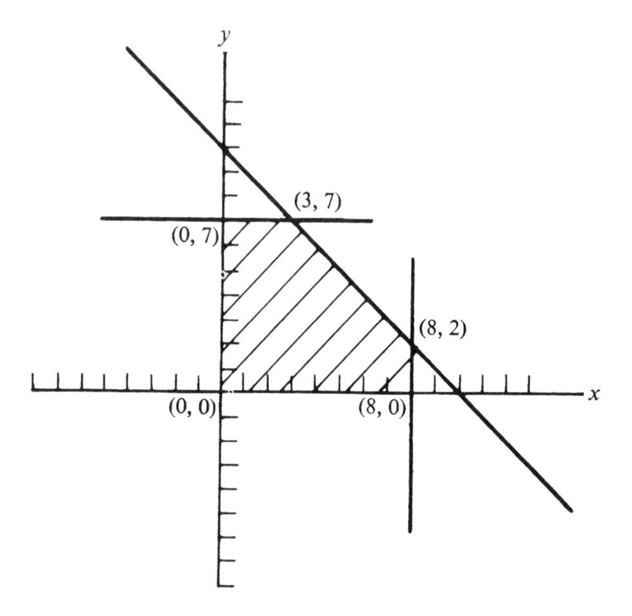


That is, by the nature of his operation his choices are restricted to those represented by the points in or on our polygon. The contractor has found that his daily profit is $15x + 10y - 70$. He wishes to assign the trucks to the job so as to maximize his profit.

We know the profit function $15x + 10y - 70$ is at a maximum at one of the vertices of the polygon. We evaluate the function at the corner points:

| | | |
|---|---|---|
| at | (0, 0) | $15 \cdot 0 + 10 \cdot 0 - 70 = -70$ |
| at | (0, 7) | $15 \cdot 0 + 10 \cdot 7 - 70 = 0$ |
| at | (3, 7) | $15 \cdot 3 + 10 \cdot 7 - 70 = 45$ |
| at | (8, 2) | $15 \cdot 8 + 10 \cdot 2 - 70 = 70$ |

Hence, he assigns eight 2-ton trucks and two 3-ton trucks to the job in order to maximize his profit.

## EXERCISES

1. Find the $y$ values of the following points if they are on the line $3x - y = 7$:
$(-2, \_), (-1, \_), (0, \_), (1, \_), (2, \_), (3, \_)$
2. Evaluate the expression $-2x + y - 7$ at each point found in Exercise 1.
3. At which point in Exercise 1 is the expression in Exercise 2 the greatest? At which point is it the least? Where are these points located on the line $3x - y = 7$?

**4.** Construct the graph of the following system of inequalities:

$$2x + y \geq 7$$
$$x \leq 4$$
$$x + 3y \leq 15$$

**5.** Find the vertices of the polygon determined in Exercise 4. Find the coordinates of six other points that are on or inside the polygon.

**6.** Evaluate the relation $3x - y + 6$ at each of the points found in Exercise 5.

**7.** Evaluate the relation $y - 2x + 8$ at each of the points found in Exercise 5.

**8.** Evaluate the relation $2x + y - 7$ at each of the points found in Exercise 5.

**9.** In Exercises 6, 7, and 8 where are the maximum and minimum values found?

# 12 Modular Systems

IN CHAPTERS 1 AND 2 THE CONCEPT OF NUMBER CONGRUENCE WAS introduced. Through addition and multiplication on a circle, the idea of a modulo system was developed. This concept was utilized to develop tests for divisibility. In this chapter we wish to explore in more detail the properties of modulo systems.

## 12.1 Equivalence Classes of Integers

The term *class* has been used to designate the set of *all* elements satisfying a given criterion. An equivalence class is a class whose elements have some equivalence relation to each other. In Chapter 2 a cardinal number is defined as an equivalence class of equivalent sets. Equivalence of sets is an equivalence relation. This statement may sound redundant, but it actually is not. By definition, two sets are equivalent if and only if they can be placed in one-to-one correspondence. Equivalence of sets is an equivalence relation because the relation is reflexive (a set is equivalent to itself), symmetric (if set $A$ is equivalent to set $B$ then $B$ is equivalent to $A$), and transitive (if set $A$ is equivalent to set $B$ and set $B$ is equivalent to set $C$ then $A$ is equivalent to $C$).

We also used the concept of an equivalence class when we defined a rational number as an equivalence class of ratios of two integers. See page 165.

The definition of congruence of two numbers, $a$ and $b$, with respect to modulus $c$, is

$$a \equiv b, \bmod c$$

if and only if $a$ and $b$ have the same remainder when divided by $c$

Consider the set

$$A = \{1, 5, 9, 13, \ldots, (4n + 1), \ldots\}$$

You will notice that any two elements of the set differ by a multiple of 4. In the general term $4n + 1$, $n$ must be an integer. If $n = x$ we have $4x + 1$; if $n = y$ we have $4y + 1$. The difference,

$$(4x + 1) - (4y + 1) = 4(x - y)$$

is a multiple of 4, since $(x - y)$ is an integer. It is also true that each element has remainder 1 when divided by 4.

$$(4n + 1) \div 4 = n + \tfrac{1}{4}$$

Accordingly, any two elements of the set are congruent, modulo 4.

An alternate definition of congruence is suggested in the preceding paragraph.

> If $a$ and $b$ are any two integers
>
> $$a \equiv b \text{ modulo } c$$
>
> if and only if
>
> $$a - b = ck, \; k \text{ an integer.}$$

Is set $A$ a class? That is, is it true that any number congruent to an element of the set is itself an element of the set? We know that any number of the form $4n + 1$ is an element of the set. Is a number that is congruent, modulo 4, to a number of the form $4n + 1$ also of the form $4n + 1$? Assume

$$x \equiv 4n + 1, \text{ modulo } 4$$

Hence,

$$x - (4n + 1) = 4k, \quad k \text{ an integer}$$

$$x = 4k + 4n + 1$$

$$x = 4(k + n) + 1$$

But $(k + n)$ is an integer and $x$ is of the form $4n + 1$. We may conclude that $A$ is the set of *all* integers congruent to 1, modulo 4. If congruence is an equivalence relation, $A$ is an equivalence class of integers.

But congruence is an equivalence relation.

## EQUIVALENCE CLASSES OF INTEGERS

Congruence is reflexive.

$$a \equiv a, \bmod m \text{ because}$$
$$a - a = 0 = 0 \cdot m$$

Congruence is symmetric.

If $a \equiv b, \bmod m,$ then $a - b = m \cdot k$ ($k$ an integer)
But if $a - b = m \cdot k$ then $b - a = m \cdot (-k)$ ($-k$ an integer)

and this is the condition that

$$b \equiv a, \bmod m$$

Congruence is transitive.
If $a \equiv b, \bmod m$ and $b \equiv c, \bmod m$
then $a - b = k_1 m$ ($k_1$ an integer)
And $b - c = k_2 m$ ($k_2$ an integer)
Hence $(a - b) + (b - c) = a - c = (k_1 + k_2)m$
and since $k_1 + k_2$ is an integer

$$a \equiv c, \bmod m$$

We may conclude that set $A$ is an equivalence class; it is the set of all integers congruent to 1 (or any other element of the set), modulo 4. As representative element of this equivalence class, we choose the smallest non-negative element. We shall circle the element to indicate that it represents the equivalence class, set $A$ = ①. At this point it would be well to review the definition of a rational number as an equivalence class of ratios of two integers. Thus the equivalence class

$$\{1:2, 2:4, 3:6, \ldots, n:2n, \ldots\}$$

is, by definition, a rational number. We chose as representative element the ratio 1:2, and agreed to write it as $\frac{1}{2}$.

Every integer is a member of exactly one of the following equivalence classes, modulo 4:

$$\{1, 5, 9, \ldots, 4n + 1, \ldots\}$$
$$\{2, 6, 10, \ldots, 4n + 2, \ldots\}$$
$$\{3, 7, 11, \ldots, 4n + 3, \ldots\}$$
$$\{0, 4, 8, 12, \ldots, 4n, \ldots\}$$

whose representative elements are

①, ②, ③, ⓪

These representative elements are the possible remainders when an integer is divided by 4. Any other element of a given equivalence class can also be used to indicate the class. Thus, ① and ⑤ are merely two ways to designate the same class of integers modulo 4. This is precisely the same situation as using $\frac{1}{2}$ or $\frac{2}{4}$ or $\frac{7}{14}$ or any other element of the equivalence class of ratios as different names for the same rational number.

### EXERCISES

1. If each element of the set of integers is assigned to some equivalence class modulo 7 how many equivalence classes are needed?
2. Indicate the equivalence classes needed in Exercise 1, supplying the five smallest non-negative elements in each set. What is the representative element of each set?
3. In Exercise 2 add any two elements in the equivalence class ③. In what equivalence class is the sum?
4. In Exercise 2 add any element in ④ to any element in ⑤. In what class is the sum?
5. In Exercise 2 multiply any element in ③ by any element in ⑤. In what class is the product?
6. In Exercise 2 multiply any element in ② by any element in ④. In what class is the product?
7. In Exercise 2 multiply any two elements in ①. In what class is the product?
8. In Exercise 2 multiply any two elements in ⑥. In what class is the product?
9. Multiply any two elements of equivalence class ②, modulo 4. In what equivalence class, modulo 4, is the product?
10. Are there two equivalence classes, modulo 7, other than ⓪ whose product is class ⓪? If so, what are they?

## 12.2 Addition and Multiplication of Equivalence Classes of Integers

We have seen that congruence is an equivalence relation. Equality has, in addition to the reflexive, symmetric, and transitive properties of equivalence, the addition property and the multiplication property. That is, if

$$a = b$$

then

$$a + c = b + c$$

and

$$ac = bc$$

Are these also properties of congruence? An extension of these properties is, if

$$a = b \qquad \text{and} \qquad c = d$$

then
$$a + c = b + d$$

and
$$ac = bd$$

The corresponding properties of congruence are, if

$$a \equiv b \qquad \text{and} \qquad c \equiv d \qquad (\text{mod } m)$$

then
$$a + c \equiv b + d \qquad (\text{mod } m)$$

and
$$ac \equiv bd \qquad (\text{mod } m)$$

If $a \equiv b$ then ⓐ and ⓑ represent the same equivalence class, similarly for $c \equiv d$. Then the assertion that $a + c \equiv b + d$ amounts to the contention that any element of class ⓐ plus any element of class ⓒ will yield an element of the class $\textcircled{a + c}$. We illustrate with the set of equivalence classes, modulo 5.

$$\text{①} = \{1, 6, 11, 16, \ldots, 5n + 1, \ldots\}$$
$$\text{②} = \{2, 7, 12, 17, \ldots, 5n + 2, \ldots\}$$
$$\text{③} = \{3, 8, 13, 18, \ldots, 5n + 3, \ldots\}$$
$$\text{④} = \{4, 9, 14, 19, \ldots, 5n + 4, \ldots\}$$
$$\text{⓪} = \{0, 5, 10, 15, 20, \ldots, 5n, \ldots\}$$

If we select any element from ③ and any element from ④ their sum will be one of the elements of $\textcircled{3 + 4}$. We find $3 + 4 = 7$ in class ②. Hence $\textcircled{3 + 4}$ = ② and the sum will be an element of class ②. For example, 13 is an element of ③ and 19 is an element of ④. But $13 + 19 = 32$ which is of the form $5n + 2$, $(5 \cdot 6 + 2)$ is an element of class ②. Another example, 8 is an element of ③ and 9 is an element of ④. And we find $8 + 9 = 17$ as an element of ②. Select an element of ⓪, say 30, and an element of ①, say 11. The sum $30 + 11 = 41$ is an element of ①. To try another pair of elements from ⓪ and ①, 25 is an element of ⓪ and 6 is an element of ①, but $25 + 6 = 31$ is again an element of ①.

$$\text{If} \quad a \equiv b, \text{ mod } m$$

then $a$ and $b$ are elements of the same equivalence class modulo $m$, or

$$a - b = k_1 m, \quad k_1 \text{ an integer}$$

If
$$c \equiv d, \text{ mod } m$$

then $c$ and $d$ are elements of the same equivalence class modulo $m$, or

$$c - d = k_2 m, \quad k_2 \text{ an integer}$$

Then

$$(a - b) + (c - d) = k_1 m + k_2 m$$

or

$$(a + c) - (b + d) = (k_1 + k_2)m, (k_1 + k_2, \quad \text{an integer})$$

But this is precisely the condition under which

$$a + c \equiv b + d, \bmod m$$

and we conclude $a + c$ and $b + d$ are members of the same equivalence class modulo $m$.

We can now define what we mean by the addition of two equivalence classes of integers, modulo $m$. Let $\textcircled{a}$ and $\textcircled{b}$ be two equivalence classes modulo $m$. Find the Cartesian product $\textcircled{a} \times \textcircled{b}$. This is a set of ordered pairs; each element of $\textcircled{a}$ is matched as first component with each element of $\textcircled{b}$ as second component. Now add the components of each ordered pair to obtain an element of a new set. This new set we define as $\textcircled{a} + \textcircled{b}$. We have already shown that each element of this new set is an element of $\textcircled{a+b}$. Furthermore, since each element of $\textcircled{a+b}$ can be expressed as an element of $\textcircled{a}$ plus an element of $\textcircled{b}$ in an infinite number of ways, we can now say

$$\textcircled{a} + \textcircled{b} = \textcircled{a+b}$$

> The sum of two equivalence classes, $\textcircled{a}$ and $\textcircled{b}$, of integers, modulo $m$, is the equivalence class $\textcircled{a+b}$ of integers, modulo $m$.

The above argument can be duplicated verbatim, with addition replaced by multiplication, as soon as we show that if

$$a \equiv b \bmod m \qquad \text{and} \qquad c \equiv d \bmod m$$

then

$$ac \equiv bd \bmod m$$

Since $a \equiv b \bmod m$ implies $a - b = k_1 m$, $k_1$ an integer, we have

$$a = k_1 m + b$$

and

$$c = k_2 m + d$$

Then by multiplication

$$ac = k_1k_2m^2 + (k_1d + k_2b)m + bd$$

or

$$ac - bd = m[k_1k_2m + k_1d + k_2b]$$

and, since $k_1$, $k_2$, $m$, $d$, and $b$ each are integers, we have the difference $ac - bd$ as an integral multiple of $m$. Consequently,

$$ac \equiv bd, \text{ mod } m$$

In terms of equivalence classes, this result means if $a$ and $b$ are any two elements of the same equivalence class and $c$ and $d$ are any two elements of the same equivalence class, the products $ac$ and $bd$ are two elements of the same equivalence class.

For example, $7 \equiv 12$, mod 5, hence 7 and 12 are two elements of the same equivalence class, specifically $\textcircled{2}$ mod 5. Also $19 \equiv 4$, mod 5, hence 19 and 4 are two elements of the same equivalence class, specifically $\textcircled{4}$ mod 5. Hence $7 \times 19$ and $12 \times 4$ must be elements of the same equivalence class modulo 5. That is, they must be congruent, modulo 5. To verify this we note that

$$7 \times 19 = 133$$
$$12 \times 4 = 48$$
$$133 - 48 = 85 = 17 \times 5$$

This shows that $133 \equiv 48$ mod 5, 133 and 48 are elements of the same equivalence class, modulo 5. We can find the representative element of this class by dividing either 133 or 48 by 5. The remainder is 3 in either case. Hence $\textcircled{133} = \textcircled{48} = \textcircled{3}$.

If, instead of 7 and 12, we had used any other two elements of equivalence class $\textcircled{2}$, and instead of 19 and 4 we had used any other two elements of equivalence class $\textcircled{4}$, the two products would still be members of equivalence class $\textcircled{3}$.

We can now define the product of two equivalence classes. Let $\textcircled{a}$ and $\textcircled{b}$ be two equivalence classes, modulo $m$. Find the Cartesian product of these two classes. Multiply the components of each ordered pair in the Cartesian product. Let these products be the elements of a new set, which we define as the product of the equivalence classes $\textcircled{a}$ and $\textcircled{b}$. Thus, we have

$$\textcircled{a} \cdot \textcircled{b} = \textcircled{ab}$$

> The product of two equivalence classes, $\textcircled{a}$ and $\textcircled{b}$, of integers modulo $m$, is the equivalence class $\textcircled{ab}$ of integers modulo $m$.

### EXERCISES

1. Is the set of equivalence classes of integers, modulo $m$, a closed set relative to addition? Justify your answer. Do the same for multiplication.
2. Prove that addition of equivalence classes, modulo $m$, is commutative.
3. Prove that multiplication of equivalence classes, modulo $m$, is commutative.
4. Is multiplication of equivalence classes, modulo $m$, distributive over addition? Illustrate with an example from the set of classes, modulo 5.
5. Is addition of equivalence classes distributive over multiplication? Illustrate with an example from the set of classes, modulo 5.
6. Prove that the equivalence class $m$, modulo $m$, is the addition identity.
7. What is the multiplication identity of the set of equivalence classes, modulo 2?
8. Find the three smallest positive elements of ③ modulo 7 and the three smallest positive elements of ⑤ modulo 7.
9. Find the cross product of the sets in Exercise 8, then find a new set by adding the components of each ordered pair in the cross product.
10. Verify that all of the elements of the set obtained in Exercise 9 are elements of the same equivalence class, modulo 7.
11. Form a new set from the cross product found in Exercise 9 by multiplying the components of each ordered pair to obtain the elements of the new set.
12. Verify that all of the elements of the set found in Exercise 11 are members of the same equivalence class, modulo 7.

## 12.3 Equivalence Classes and Real Numbers Contrasted

The modulo tables that we have used were operational tables of residues with respect to the modulus. For example from the table of multiplication, modulo 7, we find $3 \times 5 = 1$. We interpret this to mean $3 \times 5 \equiv 1$, modulo 7. And because of the properties of congruence, it can be interpreted to mean the product of any number congruent to 3 times any number congruent to 5 is a number congruent to 1.

We can now give it a somewhat different interpretation. Each element of the table may be considered an equivalence class of integers, modulo $m$. We shall call these equivalence classes *residue* classes. If the modulus is 7 the residue class 2 means the class of all integers congruent to 2, modulo 7. Under this interpretation $3 \times 5 = 1$ means the residue class 3 multiplied by the residue class 5 is equal to the residue class 1. In the modulo 7 system there are only 7 objects, the residue classes 0, 1, 2, 3, 4, 5, and 6. There is no object 9. Of course, 9 belongs to one of the residue classes, but 9 is not an element of the system.

In contrasting the set of real numbers with a set of residue classes the most obvious difference is in the number of elements. The set of real numbers is an infinite set, but any set of residue classes is a finite set.

In many respects residue classes do behave as real numbers. For example, addition and multiplication of residue classes are commutative and associative operations, and multiplication is distributive over addition. This follows from the definitions of addition and multiplication of residue classes. It is only necessary to show that integers under congruence satisfy these properties. We know $a$, $b$, $c$ integers,

$$\begin{aligned} a + b &= b + a \\ a + (b + c) &= (a + b) + c \\ ab &= ba \\ a(bc) &= (ab)c \\ a(b + c) &= ab + ac \end{aligned}$$

Any two numbers that are equal must also be congruent; equality implies congruence even though congruence does not imply equality. Then, since the statements of equality of integers are true, the corresponding statements of congruence must also be true.

$$\begin{aligned} a + b &\equiv b + a \\ a + (b + c) &\equiv (a + b) + c \\ ab &\equiv ba \\ a(bc) &\equiv (ab)c \\ a(b + c) &\equiv ab + bc \end{aligned}$$

Since these statements are true for congruence of integers they must be true statements of equality of residue classes.

Residue classes always have addition and multiplication identities. The addition identity is the residue class 0. Consider the set of residue classes, modulo $m$. The members of this set are designated by the integers $r$, $0 \leq r < m$. From the definition of addition of residue classes we know that the sum

$$0 + r$$

is the residue class in which the sum of any element of 0 plus any element of $r$ is found. Any element of class 0 is an integer of the form $k_1m$, $k_1$

an integer. Any element of the class $r$ is an integer of the form $k_2m + r$, $k_2$ an integer. The sum

$$k_1m + k_2m + r = (k_1 + k_2)m + r$$

and since $k_1 + k_2$ is an integer,

$$(k_1 + k_2)m + r$$

is an element of the residue class $r$. Then residue class 0 is the addition identity because for any residue class $r$

$$0 + r = r$$

*Example:* In modulo 7, we have $42 \equiv 0$ and $81 \equiv 4$. Hence the sum $42 + 81$ should be congruent to 4.

$$42 + 81 = 123$$

and since $123 = 17 \cdot 7 + 4$

$$123 \equiv 4$$

The multiplication identity is residue class 1. To prove this we must show that for any class $r$,

$$1 \cdot r = r$$

The product $1 \cdot r$ is the residue class in which any element of class 1 multiplied by any element of class $r$ belongs.

Any element of class 1 is an integer of the form $k_1m + 1$. Any element of the class $r$ is an integer of the form $k_2m + r$. The product

$$(k_1m + 1)(k_2m + r) = (k_1k_2m + k_2 + k_1r)m + r$$

Since $k_1k_2m + k_2 + k_1r$ is an integer, the product $(k_1k_2m + k_2 + k_1r)m + r$ is an element of residue class $r$. Hence residue class 1 is the multiplication identity.

*Example:* In modulo 9 we have $82 \equiv 1$ and $13 \equiv 4$. Hence the product $82 \times 13$ should be congruent to 4.

$$82 \times 13 = 1066 = 118 \cdot 9 + 4$$

Hence

$$1066 \equiv 4$$

## EQUIVALENCE CLASSES AND REAL NUMBERS CONTRASTED

Every real number has an additive inverse and every real number different from zero has a multiplicative inverse. Are these also properties of residue classes?

In any set of residue classes, modulo $m$, corresponding to each class $r$, $0 \leq r < m$, there is a class $m - r$. Classes $r$ and $m - r$ are additive inverses provided their sum is the addition identity.

$$r + (m - r) = 0$$

To show this, we must show that the sum of any element of $r$ plus any element of $(m - r)$ is an element of 0. Any element of $r$ is an integer of the form $k_1m + r$ and any element of $(m - r)$ is an integer of the form $k_2m + (m - r) = (k_2 + 1)m - r$. The sum

$$k_1m + r + k_2m + m - r = (k_1 + k_2 + 1)m + 0$$

and is therefore an element of residue class 0. Hence any element $r$ of a set of residue classes modulo $m$ has an additive inverse $m - r$.

*Example:* In modulo 11 we have $157 \equiv 3$ and $415 \equiv 8 = 11 - 3$. Hence the sum $157 + 415$ should be congruent to zero.

$$157 + 415 = 572$$

$$572 = 52 \cdot 11 + 0$$

Hence

$$157 + 415 \equiv 0, \text{ mod } 11$$

If all nonzero elements of a residue class have multiplicative inverses this means that for any $r \neq 0$ there exists an element $r'$ such that $r \cdot r' = 1$. If this is true then any member of residue class $r$ times any member of residue class $r'$ is a member of residue class 1.

We know that this is not a property of the set of integers; the only integers that have integers as multiplicative inverses are $\pm 1$. On the other hand all nonzero rational numbers, as well as all nonzero real numbers, do have multiplicative inverses. In regard to multiplicative inverses residue classes do not behave like either the integers or the real numbers. Examination of the table of multiplication of residue classes, modulo 8, reveals that four elements, 1, 3, 5, and 7 have multiplicative inverses. It happens that each is its own inverse. However, 2, 4, and 6 fail to have multiplicative inverses. There is no element by which any of 2, 4, or 6 can be multiplied for product 1.

| | 0 | 1 | 2 | 3 | 4 | 5 | 6 | 7 |
|---|---|---|---|---|---|---|---|---|
| 0 | 0 | 0 | 0 | 0 | 0 | 0 | 0 | 0 |
| 1 | 0 | 1 | 2 | 3 | 4 | 5 | 6 | 7 |
| 2 | 0 | 2 | 4 | 6 | 0 | 2 | 4 | 6 |
| 3 | 0 | 3 | 6 | 1 | 4 | 7 | 2 | 5 |
| 4 | 0 | 4 | 0 | 4 | 0 | 4 | 0 | 4 |
| 5 | 0 | 5 | 2 | 7 | 4 | 1 | 6 | 3 |
| 6 | 0 | 6 | 4 | 2 | 0 | 6 | 4 | 2 |
| 7 | 0 | 7 | 6 | 5 | 4 | 3 | 2 | 1 |

In contrast, if we examine the table of multiplication of residue classes, modulo 7, we find that each nonzero element has a multiplicative inverse.

| | 0 | 1 | 2 | 3 | 4 | 5 | 6 |
|---|---|---|---|---|---|---|---|
| 0 | 0 | 0 | 0 | 0 | 0 | 0 | 0 |
| 1 | 0 | 1 | 2 | 3 | 4 | 5 | 6 |
| 2 | 0 | 2 | 4 | 6 | 1 | 3 | 5 |
| 3 | 0 | 3 | 6 | 2 | 5 | 1 | 4 |
| 4 | 0 | 4 | 1 | 5 | 2 | 6 | 3 |
| 5 | 0 | 5 | 3 | 1 | 6 | 4 | 2 |
| 6 | 0 | 6 | 5 | 4 | 3 | 2 | 1 |

The multiplication identity, 1, and its additive inverse, 6, are their own inverses; 2 and 4 are inverses; and 3 and 5 are inverses.

We can now conclude that the set of residue classes, modulo 7, satisfies all the properties of a field. See page 222.

**EQUIVALENCE CLASSES AND REAL NUMBERS CONTRASTED**

### EXERCISES

1. We have seen that each of residue classes 1, 3, 5, and 7, modulo 8 is its own multiplicative inverse. Construct the multiplication table for these four residues.
2. Prove that the residues 1, 3, 5, and 7, modulo 8 under multiplication is a group.
3. Prove that the residues 0, 1, 3, 5, and 7, modulo 8 under addition and multiplication is not a field.
4. Construct the multiplication table for residues 1, 5, 7, and 11, modulo 12. Compare this table with the one in Exercise 1.
5. The numbers 1, 3, 5, and 7 bear a relationship to 8 that 1, 5, 7, and 11 bear to 12. What is this relationship?
6. Prove that in the set of residues modulo $m$, residue class $(m - 1)$ is its own multiplicative inverse.
7. Prove: If $a$ and $b$ are integers and $a - b = b - a$ then $a = b$.
8. Prove: If $a$ and $b$ are residue classes, modulo 8 and $a - b = b - a$ then $a$ is not necessarily equal to $b$.
9. Illustrate with 65 and 107 that residue class 1, modulo 8, is the multiplication identity.
10. Illustrate with 38, 45, and 19 that the set of residue classes, modulo 11, satisfies the distributive principle.
11. Which elements of the set of residue classes, modulo 10, have multiplicative inverses? What is the inverse of each?
12. Show that each nonzero element of the set of residue classes, modulo 13, has a multiplicative inverse.
13. Under what circumstances will a set of residue classes, modulo $m$, have an element that is its own addition inverse?
14. Find two nonzero elements of the set of residue classes, modulo 15, whose product is zero.

## 12.4 Residue Classes, Prime Modulus

We saw in Section 12.3 that the set of residue classes, modulo 7, satisfies the multiplicative inverse property of a field but the set of residue classes, modulo 8, does not. Experimentation with other moduli indicates that if this property is satisfied the modulus of the set of residue classes must be a prime number.

If this conjecture is true then for any $r \neq 0$ there exists an $r'$ such that $r \cdot r' = 1$, $r$ and $r'$ residue classes modulo $m$, a prime. As a preliminary to proving this we need to establish another proposition.

If $r_1$, $x$ are elements of a residue class and $r_1 \cdot x = r_1$ then $x$ is the multiplication identity 1. Any element of the class $r_1$ is an integer of the form $k_1m + r_1$. Any integer of the class $x$ is an integer of the form $k_2m + x$. The product $r_1 \cdot x$ is the class of which the integer $(k_1m + r_1)(k_2m + x)$ belongs. But the product

$$(k_1m + r_1)(k_2m + x) = (k_1k_2m + r_1k_2 + xk_1)m + r_1x$$

If this is a member of class $r_1$ then the integral equation

$$r_1x = r_1$$

is satisfied. If $r_1$ and $x$ are integers and $r_1x = r_1$ then $x = 1$ and equivalence class $x$ is the multiplication identity.

To return to the original question, we wish to show every $r \neq 0$ of a set of residue classes modulo $m$ has a multiplicative inverse provided $m$ is prime.

Consider any two residues $r_1$ and $r_2$ different from 0 or 1. If $r_1 \cdot r_2 = 0$ then the integers $r_1$ and $r_2$ are such that $r_1 \cdot r_2 = km$. But since $m$ is prime and $r_1$, $r_2 < m$, the fundamental theorem of arithmetic requires that $r_1$ and $r_2$ are factors of $k$. Then dividing by $r_1 \cdot r_2$ we find $m \leq 1$ which is impossible. Then $r_1 \cdot r_2 = r_3$, a nonzero residue. If $r_3 = 1$ then $r_1$ and $r_2$ are inverses, which is to be proved. If $r_3 = r_1$ then $r_2 = 1$ contrary to the original assumption that $r_1$, $r_2$ are different from 0 or 1. Similarly, if $r_3 = r_2$ this implies $r_1 = 1$. Hence, either $r_3 = 1$ or it is a nonzero residue different from $r_1$ or $r_2$. Next consider $r_1 \cdot r_3$. If $r_1 \cdot r_3 = 1$ then $r_1$ and $r_3$ are inverses. If $r_1 \cdot r_3 = r_2$ we have, replacing $r_3$ with its equal $r_1 \cdot r_2$,

$$r_1 \cdot r_1 \cdot r_2 = r_2$$

and it follows that $r_1 \cdot r_1 = 1$, or $r_1$ is its own inverse. We conclude that $r_1$ has an inverse or $r_1 \cdot r_3 = r_4$ where $r_4$ does not equal 0, 1, $r_1$, $r_2$ or $r_3$. If $r_1 \cdot r_4 \neq 1$ we can repeat the argument showing that $r_1 \cdot r_4 = r_5$, a new nonzero residue. But there are only a finite number of residue classes. Hence, we must ultimately find some element $r$ that is the multiplicative inverse of $r_1$.

We can illustrate the essence of the above argument with residue classes, modulo 7. The essence of the argument is the following: Begin with a residue different from zero or one. Find the product of two such residues. If the product is 1 we have found two multiplicative inverse elements.

For example, $3 \times 5 = 1$; hence 3 and 5 are multiplicative inverses. If the product is not 1, multiply the first factor by the product. For example $5 \times 6 = 2$ then $5 \times 2 = 3$ and finally $5 \times 3 = 1$. Here again, we have 3 and 5 as inverses. If this process is continued we ultimately find two factors whose product is 1, or we complete a "circuit." That is, we come back to the original product. This must be true because there are only a finite number of residues. If a circuit is completed a pair of inverses is implied. For example, $6 \times 5 = 2$ and $6 \times 2 = 5$ is a circuit. If we substitute the value of 2 from the first equation in the second we have

$$6 \times 6 \times 5 = 5$$
$$6 \times 6 = 1$$

and 6 is its own inverse. An example of a longer circuit is

$$2 \times 3 = 6$$
$$2 \times 6 = 5$$
$$2 \times 5 = 3$$

If we substitute the value of 6 from the first equation in the second we have

$$2 \times 2 \times 3 = 5$$

Then substituting the value of 3 from the third equation we have

$$2 \times 2 \times 2 \times 5 = 5$$
$$2 \times 2 \times 2 = 1$$

Now we have that 2 and $2 \times 2 = 4$ are multiplicative inverses. Another example yields the same pair.

$$4 \times 3 = 5$$
$$4 \times 5 = 6$$
$$4 \times 6 = 3$$

Hence, $$4 \times 4 \times 3 = 6$$

and $$4 \times 4 \times 4 \times 6 = 6$$
$$4 \times 4 \times 4 = 1$$

and 4 is the multiplicative inverse of $4 \times 4 = 2$.

The techniques employed in the solution of systems of linear equations utilize only the operations involved in a field. That is, we arrive at a solution by manipulation of the coefficients by addition, subtraction, multiplication, and division. This can be reduced to addition and multiplication since subtraction can be accomplished by addition of the additive inverse, and division can be done by multiplication by the multiplicative inverse.

Since a set of residue classes with prime modulus satisfy all field properties under addition and multiplication we can solve systems of linear equations with coefficients elements of such a field.

*Example:* If the coefficients are elements of the set of residue classes, modulo 5, solve the following equation for $x$:

$$3x - 4 = x + 2$$

*Solution:* $3x - 4 = x + 2$ is equivalent to $3x + 1 = x + 2$ because 1 is the additive inverse of 4. If we add $4x$ to each side we have

$$4x + 3x + 1 = 4x + x + 2$$

Now apply the distributive property, and we have

$$(4 + 3)x + 1 = (4 + 1)x + 2, \quad \text{or}$$
$$2x + 1 = 0 \cdot x + 2$$

Adding 4, the inverse of 1, to both sides, we have

$$2x + 1 + 4 = 2 + 4$$
$$2x + 0 = 1$$
$$2x = 1$$

Multiply both sides by 3, the multiplicative inverse of 2, and we have

$$3 \cdot 2x = 3 \cdot 1$$
$$x = 3$$

Similarly, we can solve a system of two linear equations in 2 variables.

*Example:* Solve the system:

$$2x - y = 3$$
$$x + 2y = 1$$

the coefficients being elements of the set of residue classes, modulo 7.

*Solution:* First replace $-y$ with $+6y$ since 1 and 6 are additive inverses.

$$2x + 6y = 3$$
$$x + 2y = 1$$

Since 2 and 5 are additive inverses, multiplication by 5 in the second equation will enable us to eliminate $x$ by addition.

$$\begin{aligned} 2x + 6y &= 3 \\ 5x + 3y &= 5 \\ \hline 2x + 5x + 6y + 3y &= 1 \\ (2 + 5)x + (6 + 3)y &= 1 \\ 0 \cdot x + 2y &= 1 \\ 2y &= 1 \end{aligned}$$

Since 2 and 4 are multiplicative inverses we multiply by 4:

$$y = 4$$

Substituting this value of $y$ in the first equation, we have

$$\begin{aligned} 2x + 6 \cdot 4 &= 3 \\ 2x + 3 &= 3 \\ 2x + 3 + 4 &= 3 + 4 \\ 2x + 0 &= 0 \\ 2x &= 0 \\ 4 \cdot 2x &= 4 \cdot 0 \\ x &= 0 \end{aligned}$$

The solution of the system is the pair (0, 4).

## EXERCISES

**1.** Consider the set of residues, modulo 11. In this system we find the following circuit: $3 \times 2 = 6$, $3 \times 6 = 7$, $3 \times 7 = 10$, $3 \times 10 = 8$, $3 \times 8 = 2$. Use these facts to prove 3 has a multiplicative inverse. Find its inverse.

**2.** Prove that no circuit can be found similar to the one in Exercise 1 if we start with 2 instead of 3?

**3.** In the context of Exercise 2 how do we arrive at the fact that 2 has a multiplicative inverse?

**4.** Find a circuit similar to the one in Exercise 1 beginning with 9 rather than 3.

*Solve the following equations, coefficients elements of the field of residue classes, modulo 7:*

**5.** $6x - 5 = x + 2$

**6.** $2x - 3 = 4x + 5$

**7.** $(x - 5)(x + 3) = 0$

*Solve the following systems of equations, coefficients elements of the field of residue classes, modulo 5:*

**8.** $x + 2y = 3$
$2x + y = 1$

**9.** $2x - y = 4$
$3x + y = 1$

**10.** $x + 3y = 2$
$4x + 2y = 1$

**11.** The equation in Exercise 7 is a quadratic equation. Try to solve the following quadratic equation by using the quadratic formula. The coefficients are residue classes, modulo 7.

$$x^2 + 3x + 6 = 0$$

Discuss the possibility of solving quadratic equations whose coefficients are elements of a set of residue classes, with prime modulus.

## 12.5 Residue Classes, Composite Modulus

Since a residue class with a prime modulus is a field, all of the theorems of Section 8.3 are valid in such a modulo system. Some, but not all, of them are also valid in a modulo system with composite modulus. If the theorem requires the multiplicative inverse property it is not valid when the modulus is composite.

Theorem 1 is valid in any modulo system. The theorem asserts that if $a$ is any element of a set of residue classes $a \times 0 = 0$. This follows immediately from the fact that the product of integers $(k_1m + a)$ and $k_2m$, or $(k_1k_2m + k_2a)m$ is an integral multiple of $m$.

Theorem 2, the converse of Theorem 1, does not hold for a composite modulus. The theorem requires that if the product of two residues is zero at least one of the residues is zero. A counter example is sufficient to show that this does not hold. In modulo 8 we have $4 \times 6 = 0$.

If it is possible for the product of two nonzero elements to be zero the factors are *divisors of zero*. From the equation $4 \times 6 = 0$ we have that 4 and 6 are divisors of zero modulo 8.

With a composite modulus we know there must be residues different from 0 or 1 whose product is zero. For example, if the modulus is 12 we have residue $4 \times 3 = 0$ because integers $4 \times 3 = 12$. However, it is not essential that a divisor of zero be a factor of the modulus. For example, in modulo 12 we have residues $8 \times 9 = 0$ because integers $8 \times 9 = 72 = 6 \cdot 12$. Any residue that has a factor other than 1 in common with the modulus is a divisor of zero. This is consistent with what we have found for a prime modulus. No residue can have a factor in common with a prime modulus. There are no divisors of zero. It is impossible for two nonzero factors to have a product zero.

Theorem 3, the cancellation property for addition, holds in any modulo system. This follows from the fact that we always have additive inverses.

*Example:* For a prime modulus consider modulo 7. If $a + 5 = b + 5$ then $a = b$. From the addition table we have $3 + 5 = 1$.

| | 0 | 1 | 2 | 3 | 4 | 5 | 6 |
|---|---|---|---|---|---|---|---|
| 0 | 0 | 1 | 2 | 3 | 4 | 5 | 6 |
| 1 | 1 | 2 | 3 | 4 | 5 | 6 | 0 |
| 2 | 2 | 3 | 4 | 5 | 6 | 0 | 1 |
| 3 | 3 | 4 | 5 | 6 | 0 | 1 | 2 |
| 4 | 4 | 5 | 6 | 0 | 1 | 2 | 3 |
| 5 | 5 | 6 | 0 | 1 | 2 | 3 | 4 |
| 6 | 6 | 0 | 1 | 2 | 3 | 4 | 5 |

The theorem requires that no other number plus 5 can equal 1. This is evident when we observe that 1 appears in each column exactly one time. Similarly, each other residue appears exactly one time in each column and each row.

*Example:* For a composite modulus consider modulo 6. From the table we see $3 + 5 = 2$. Since 2 appears opposite 3 exactly one time there is no other element which we may add to 3 for sum 2. Here again, each residue appears exactly one time in each column and row.

| | 0 | 1 | 2 | 3 | 4 | 5 |
|---|---|---|---|---|---|---|
| 0 | 0 | 1 | 2 | 3 | 4 | 5 |
| 1 | 1 | 2 | 3 | 4 | 5 | 0 |
| 2 | 2 | 3 | 4 | 5 | 0 | 1 |
| 3 | 3 | 4 | 5 | 0 | 1 | 2 |
| 4 | 4 | 5 | 0 | 1 | 2 | 3 |
| 5 | 5 | 0 | 1 | 2 | 3 | 4 |

In contrast to Theorem 3, Theorem 4 is valid for a prime modulus but not a composite modulus. This is the cancellation law for multiplication. Comparison of the multiplication tables modulo 7 and modulo 6 illustrates the difference.

| | 0 | 1 | 2 | 3 | 4 | 5 | 6 |
|---|---|---|---|---|---|---|---|
| 0 | 0 | 0 | 0 | 0 | 0 | 0 | 0 |
| 1 | 0 | 1 | 2 | 3 | 4 | 5 | 6 |
| 2 | 0 | 2 | 4 | 6 | 1 | 3 | 5 |
| 3 | 0 | 3 | 6 | 2 | 5 | 1 | 4 |
| 4 | 0 | 4 | 1 | 5 | 2 | 6 | 3 |
| 5 | 0 | 5 | 3 | 1 | 6 | 4 | 2 |
| 6 | 0 | 6 | 5 | 4 | 3 | 2 | 1 |

MULTIPLICATION, MOD 7

| | 0 | 1 | 2 | 3 | 4 | 5 |
|---|---|---|---|---|---|---|
| 0 | 0 | 0 | 0 | 0 | 0 | 0 |
| 1 | 0 | 1 | 2 | 3 | 4 | 5 |
| 2 | 0 | 2 | 4 | 0 | 2 | 4 |
| 3 | 0 | 3 | 0 | 3 | 0 | 3 |
| 4 | 0 | 4 | 2 | 0 | 4 | 2 |
| 5 | 0 | 5 | 4 | 3 | 2 | 1 |

MULTIPLICATION, MOD 6

In the case of modulo 7, each residue appears in each column and row exactly one time. But in modulo 6 this is not true. In modulo 6 we have

$$2 \times 2 = 4 \qquad \text{and} \qquad 2 \times 5 = 4$$

**RESIDUE CLASSES, COMPOSITE MODULUS**

Hence

$$2 \times 2 = 2 \times 5$$

But contrary to Theorem 4

$$2 \neq 5$$

Theorems 5 through 8 are concerned with both addition and multiplication. Since none of them involve multiplicative inverses they are valid in any modulo system.

To illustrate Theorem 5 in modulo 6 consider

$$a \times (-b) \text{ if } a = 4 \text{ and } b = 5$$

The additive inverse of 5 is 1. Hence, by the theorem, $4 \times 1$ must equal the inverse of $4 \times 5$. The product $4 \times 5 = 2$. But the additive inverse of 2 is 4 and this is the product $4 \times 1$.

To illustrate the same theorem in modulo 7 consider $a = 2$ and $b = 4$. The additive inverse of 4 is 3. Hence $2 \times 3$ must equal the additive inverse of $2 \times 4$. But $2 \times 3 = 6$ and $2 \times 4 = 1$, the additive inverse of 6.

Theorem 6 requires that the product of the additive inverses of two residues is equal to the product of the residues.

*Example:* In modulo 7, the additive inverse of 2 is 5; the additive inverse of 4 is 3. Hence $5 \times 3$ must equal $2 \times 4$. Each product is equal to 1.

In modulo 6, the additive inverse of 2 is 4, the additive inverse of 3 is 3. Hence $4 \times 3 = 2 \times 3$ and $4 \times 3 = 0 = 2 \times 3$.

By Theorem 7, the sum of two additive inverses is equal to the inverse of the sum of the residues.

*Example:* In modulo 7, the additive inverse of 5 is 2, the additive inverse of 3 is 4. Hence $2 + 4$ equals the additive inverse of $5 + 3$. But $5 + 3 = 1$ the additive inverse of 6, and $2 + 4 = 6$.

By Theorem 8,

$$a + (-b) = -[b + (-a)]$$

To illustrate this in modulo 7 let $a = 3$ and $b = 5$. Then $-a = 4$ and $-b = 2$. The theorem requires

$$3 + 2 = \text{the additive inverse of } 5 + 3$$

But $3 + 2 = 5$ and $5 + 3 = 2$ whose additive inverse is also 5.

## EXERCISES

*In Exercises* 1–6 *consider all numbers as residue classes, modulo* 6

1. Verify that $-(a + b) = -a + -b$ when $a = 4$ and $b = 5$. Do the same with $a = 3$ and $b = 1$.

2. Verify that $a(-b) = -ab$ when $a = 3$ and $b = 5$. Do the same $a = 2$ and $b = 4$.

3. Verify that $(-a)(-b) = ab$ when $a = 5$ and $b = 3$. Do the same with $a = 4$ and $b = 2$.

4. Verify that $a + (-b) = -[b + (-a)]$ when $a = 4$ and $b = 3$. Do the same with $a = 5$ and $b = 2$.

5. Find two elements $a$ and $b$, $a \neq b$, such that $a - b = b - a$.

6. We define subtraction of residue classes in the usual way: $a - b = x$ if and only if $b + x = a$. Demonstrate that $a - b = a + (-b)$ by letting $a = 3$ and $b = 5$ and evaluating each side.

7. We define division of residue classes in the usual way: $a \div b = x$ if and only if $b \times x = a$. Demonstrate that $a \div b = a \times$ the multiplicative inverse of $b$ by letting $a = 5$ and $b = 3$, elements of the set of residue classes, modulo 7.

8. In view of Exercise 7, if the modulus is composite and $b$ does not have a multiplicative inverse, then $a \div b$ should not exist. Demonstrate this in modulo 6 if $a = 5$ and $b = 3$. Does the problem lie in the fact that there is no $x$ such that $3x = 5$ or does it lie in the fact that there is more than one such $x$?

9. Find in modulo 5 elements $a \neq 1$ and $b$ such that $b \times a = b \div a$. Explain how this is possible.

# 13 Complex Numbers

WE SAW IN CHAPTER 10 THAT MANY QUADRATIC EQUATIONS HAVE NO REAL roots. As simple an equation as $x^2 + 1 = 0$ has no real roots. When we attempt to find a solution we get

$$x^2 = -1$$

and $x$ must be a number whose square is a negative number. If $x$ is a real number, either positive or negative, $x^2$ must be positive. In this chapter we wish to extend the system of real numbers in order to remove this difficulty.

## 13.1 The Imaginary Unit

The equation $x^2 + 1 = 0$ cannot have a solution unless there is a number whose square is equal to $-1$. To this end, we create such a number, we use the symbol $i$.

> Definition: The number $i$ is a number such that
>
> $$i^2 = -1$$

The number $i$ cannot be a real number. We give it the name *imaginary*: The single number $i$ is sufficient to supply the equation $x^2 + 1 = 0$ with one solution. In Chapter 10 we found that a quadratic equation usually has either two or no real roots. The exceptional case being when the graph of $y = ax^2 + bx + c$ is tangent to the $x$-axis the equation $ax^2 + bx + c = 0$ has a single real solution. A positive real number has two real square roots that are additive inverses. Thus, the square roots of 4 are 2 and $-2$. If this relationship is to be preserved we wish to say that $-i$ is also a square root of $-1$. Hence we have

$$i^2 = -1 \qquad \text{and} \qquad (-i)^2 = -1$$

Note that the latter is consistent with the idea that

$$-a = -1 \cdot a$$

For then we have

$$(-i)^2 = (-1)i(-1)i = (-1)^2 i^2 = 1 \cdot (-1) = -1$$

Are $i$ and $-i$ the only two imaginary numbers? What shall we say are the solutions to the equation?

$$x^2 + 4 = 0$$

Here we need a number whose square is $-4$. If we express $-4$ as $-1 \cdot 4$ and find the square roots of each factor we have four possibilities

$$i \cdot 2$$
$$-i \cdot 2$$
$$i \cdot -2$$
$$-i \cdot -2$$

But if the laws of multiplication of real numbers are to apply this reduces to $2i$ and $-2i$.

We can express the square root of any negative number as $\pm i$ times the square root of a positive number in the same way we have expressed the square root of $-4$. Furthermore, if the principal square root is to be positive we have $\sqrt{-1} = i$ and $-\sqrt{-1} = -i$. Then for any negative real number $-a$ we have

$$\sqrt{-a} = \sqrt{-1}\sqrt{a} = i\sqrt{a}$$

### EXERCISES

*Assume the rules of signs for real numbers hold for imaginary numbers in the following:*

**1.** Simplify each of the following
(a) $\sqrt{-25}$ (b) $\sqrt{-4} - \sqrt{-1}$ (c) $-\sqrt{121}$ (d) $-\sqrt{-121}$ (e) $2\sqrt{-9}$
(f) $2 + \sqrt{-9}$

**2.** Show that $i^3 = -i$

**3.** Show that $i^4 = 1$

**4.** Show that $-i = \dfrac{1}{i}$

**5.** Express each of the following as 1, $-1$, $i$, or $-i$:
(a) $i^{13}$ (b) $i^{-2}$ (c) $i^7$ (d) $i^0$ (e) $i^{-5}$ (f) $i^{15}$

**6.** If we consider $\sqrt{1}$ as $\sqrt{(-1)(-1)}$ do we find the principal square root of 1? Do we find any square root of 1?

## 13.2 The Roots of Any Quadratic Equation

The imaginary unit $i$ makes it possible to express the square root of a negative number as $i$ times a real number. Is this sufficient to solve any quadratic equation? That is, is the root of any quadratic equation either a real number or $i$ times a real number?

Consider the equation

$$2x^2 - x + 5 = 0$$

If we use the method of completing the square we have

$$x^2 - x/2 = -(\tfrac{5}{2})$$

$$x^2 - x/2 + \tfrac{1}{16} = -(\tfrac{5}{2}) + \tfrac{1}{16}$$

$$(x - \tfrac{1}{4})^2 = -\tfrac{39}{16}$$

$$x - \tfrac{1}{4} = \sqrt{-\tfrac{39}{16}} \qquad \text{or} \qquad x - \tfrac{1}{4} = -\sqrt{-\tfrac{39}{16}}$$

$$x - \tfrac{1}{4} = \frac{i\sqrt{39}}{4} \qquad\qquad x - \tfrac{1}{4} = -\frac{i\sqrt{39}}{4}$$

$$x = \tfrac{1}{4} + \frac{i\sqrt{39}}{4} \qquad\qquad x = \tfrac{1}{4} - \frac{i\sqrt{39}}{4}$$

Now what kind of number is $x$? Is it real or imaginary? It is neither one, yet appears to be a little of both.

If we solve the general quadratic by completing the square we have

$$ax^2 + bx + c = 0$$

$$x^2 + b/a \cdot x = -c/a$$

$$x^2 + \frac{b}{a}x + b^2/4a^2 = b^2/4a^2 - c/a$$

$$(x + b/2a)^2 = \frac{b^2 - 4ac}{4a^2}$$

$$x + b/2a = \pm\sqrt{\frac{b^2 - 4ac}{4a^2}}$$

$$x = -\frac{b}{2a} \pm \frac{\sqrt{b^2 - 4ac}}{2a}$$

$$x = \frac{-b \pm \sqrt{b^2 - 4ac}}{2a}$$

This is known as the quadratic formula. The solution is a real number provided $b^2 - 4ac \geq 0$. The expression $b^2 - 4ac$ is known as the *discriminant* of the equation. Its value tells us the nature of the roots of the equation.

To return to the question: Is $\frac{1}{4} + \frac{i}{4}\sqrt{39}$ a real number or an imaginary number? It is certainly the sum of a real number $\frac{1}{4}$ and an imaginary number $\frac{i}{4}\sqrt{39}$. Since it cannot be expressed as either a real number or $i$ times a real number we have the motivation for still another kind of number. We call $\frac{1}{4} + \frac{i}{4}\sqrt{39}$ a *complex number*.

> Definition: If $a$ and $b$ are real numbers,
>
> $$a + bi$$
>
> is a complex number.

This definition does not preclude the possibility that $a = 0$ or $b = 0$ or for that matter both $a$ and $b$ being 0. Under this interpretation we may consider any real number $a$ as a complex number $a + bi$ with $b = 0$. If $b \neq 0$ we call the complex number an *imaginary number*.

Returning to the quadratic formula, it is now evident that the roots of any quadratic equation with real coefficients are complex numbers. They are real numbers if the discriminant $b^2 - 4ac \geq 0$. They are imaginary numbers if the discriminant $b^2 - 4ac < 0$. When $b^2 - 4ac = 0$ the equation has a single real root. This is called a repeated root. If it is agreed that a repeated root is considered the same root twice, every quadratic equation in $x$ has exactly 2 roots.

It may seem odd to call the single root a repeated root. This is not done merely in order to say the quadratic always has two roots. An equation of the form

$$(x - a)^2 = 0$$

can be solved by setting each linear factor equal to zero.

$$(x - a)(x - a) = 0$$

$$(x - a) = 0 \quad \text{or} \quad (x - a) = 0$$

$$x = a \qquad\qquad x = a$$

Furthermore, when we consider the graphic solutions, this is consistent with the fact that a tangent is the limiting position of a secant, which cuts the curve in two places.

## EXERCISES

*Determine the discriminant of each of the following equations and from this determine the nature of the roots:*

**1.** $3x^2 - 2x + 5 = 0$

**2.** $x^2 + 3x + 4 = 0$

**3.** $2x^2 - 4x - 3 = 0$

**4.** $6x^2 + 5x - 4 = 0$

**5.** In the equation $x^2 + bx + c = 0$ if $b$ and $c$ are real numbers and $c < 0$ what kind of roots does the equation have?

**6.** If the discriminant of a quadratic equation is zero can we conclude that the roots are equal regardless of the coefficient field?

**7.** If the discriminant of a quadratic equation is positive are the roots real regardless of the coefficient field?

*Solve the following equations:*

**8.** $x^2 - 5ix + 1 = 0$

**9.** $2x^2 + 3x - 7 = 0$

**10.** $x^2 - ix + 3i = 0$

**11.** $2x^2 + 5x + 3 = 0$

**12.** $x^2 - 2x + 5 = 0$

## COMPLEX NUMBERS

## 13.3 Addition and Multiplication of Complex Numbers

The complex numbers defined in the last section are sufficient for expressing the roots of any quadratic equation. But if the system is to have any utility, practically or theoretically, we must determine how to operate with complex numbers.

We wish to define addition and multiplication of complex numbers in such a way that the properties of a field are preserved. Furthermore, the definitions must be consistent with the idea that the complex number $a + bi$ and the real number $a$ are the same if $b = 0$.

Definition 1
Two complex numbers $a + bi$ and $c + di$ are equal

$$a + bi = c + di$$

if and only if $a = c$ and $b = d$.

The *real component* of $a + bi$ is $a$ and the *imaginary component* is $b$. The definition requires that if two complex numbers are equal their real components must be equal and the imaginary components must be equal.

Definition 2
The sum of two complex numbers $a + bi$ and $c + di$ is

$$a + bi + c + di = (a + c) + (b + d)i$$

In addition of complex numbers, the real component of the sum is the sum of the real components of the addends, and the imaginary components of the sum is the sum of the imaginary components of the addends. The definition guarantees closure of complex numbers under addition.

*Example:* $(3 + 4i) + (2 - i) = 5 + 3i$

$$(2 + 3i) + (2 - 3i) = 4 + 0 \cdot i = 4$$

$$(-5 + 2i) + (5 + 4i) = 0 + 6 \cdot i = 6 \cdot i$$

Definition 3

The product of two complex numbers $a + bi$ and $c + di$ is

$$(a + bi)(c + di) = (ac - bd) + (ad + bc)i$$

If two complex numbers are treated as ordinary binomials, we have

$$(a + bi)(c + di) = ac + bci + adi + bdi^2$$

But since $i^2 = -1$ this reduces to

$$(ac - bd) + (bc + ad)i$$

if we apply the distribution property to the terms containing $i$.

*Example:*
$$\begin{aligned}(3 - 2i)(4 + i) &= 12 - 8i + 3i - 2i^2 \\ &= 14 - 5i \\ (5 + 3i)(5 - 3i) &= 25 + 9 + 0 \cdot i \\ &= 34 \\ (2 + i)(-2 - i) &= -4 + 1 - 4i \\ &= -3 - 4i\end{aligned}$$

Since in the product $(ac - bd)$ is a real number and $(ad + bc)$ is a real number, the product is of the form $a + bi$. The complex numbers are closed under multiplication.

## EXERCISES

1. Compare the sums $(-5 + 3i) + (4 - 2i)$ and $(4 - 2i) + (-5 + 3i)$.
2. Evaluate $(a + bi) + (c + di)$ and $(c + di) + (a + bi)$. Compare the results.
3. Compare the products
$$(3 - i)(-5 + 3i) \text{ and } (-5 + 3i)(3 - i).$$
4. Evaluate $(a + bi)(c + di)$ and $(c + di)(a + bi)$. Compare the results.
5. Find $(3 + 4i)[(2 - 3i) + (-4 - 2i)]$.
6. Find $(3 + 4i)(2 - 3i) + (3 + 4i)(-4 - 2i)$ and compare the result with that of Exercise 5.

**7.** Show that

$(a + bi)[(c + di) + (e + fi)]$ and $(a + bi)(c + di) + (a + bi)(e + fi)$

are equal.

**8.** Find the product $(3 - 7i)(1 + 0 \cdot i)$.

**9.** Find the sum $(8 - 5i) + (-8 + 5i)$.

**10.** Find the sum $(3 - 7i) + (0 + 0 \cdot i)$.

**11.** Find the product $(3 + 2i)(3/13 - 2/13i)$.

## 13.4 The Field of Complex Numbers

That the set of complex numbers conform to the associative, commutative, and distributive principles follows from the exercises of the last section. If the complex numbers are a field, what additional properties must be satisfied? There must be addition and multiplication identities and inverses.

If the desired equivalence between the complex numbers $a + 0 \cdot i$ and the real numbers $a$ is to be established then the addition identity must be $0 + 0 \cdot i$.

$$\begin{aligned}(a + bi) + (0 + 0 \cdot i) &= (a + 0) + (b + 0)i \\ &= a + bi\end{aligned}$$

Hence $0 + 0 \cdot i$ is the addition identity.

The same equivalence would indicate $1 + 0 \cdot i$ as the multiplication identity.

$$\begin{aligned}(a + bi)(1 + 0 \cdot i) &= (a \cdot 1 - b \cdot 0) + (a \cdot 0 + b \cdot 1)i \\ &= a + bi\end{aligned}$$

Hence $1 + 0 \cdot i$ is the multiplication identity.

The definition of addition indicates what the additive inverse of $a + bi$ is. Since we add real components we need the additive inverse of the real component as the real component of the inverse. Similarly, we need the additive inverse of the imaginary component. Thus, the additive inverse of any complex number $a + bi$ is $-a - bi$

$$(a + bi) + (-a + -b)i = (a + -a) + (b + -b)i = 0 + 0 \cdot i$$

It is not as simple to find the multiplicative inverse of a nonzero complex number. However, we would expect the inverse of $a + bi$ to be $1/(a + bi)$. Can this be expressed in the form $a + bi$?

Two complex numbers are conjugates if they have the same real components and additive inverse imaginary components. Thus, $a + bi$ and $a - bi$ are conjugates. The product of any two conjugate complex numbers is a real number.

$$\begin{aligned}(a + bi)(a - bi) &= (a^2 + b^2) + (ab - ab)i \\ &= a^2 + b^2\end{aligned}$$

We can *rationalize* a fraction in the form $1/(a + bi)$ that is, make the denominator real. This is done by multiplying numerator and denominator by the conjugate of the denominator.

$$\frac{1}{a + bi} = \frac{1}{a + bi} \cdot \frac{a - bi}{a - bi} = \frac{a - bi}{a^2 + b^2}$$

and this is the complex number

$$\frac{a}{a^2 + b^2} - \frac{b}{a^2 + b^2}\, i$$

This result should be the multiplicative inverse of $a + bi$.

$$\begin{aligned}(a + bi)&\left(\frac{a}{a^2 + b^2} - \frac{b}{a^2 + b^2}\, i\right) \\ &= \left(\frac{a^2}{a^2 + b^2} + \frac{b^2}{a^2 + b^2}\right) + \left(\frac{ab}{a^2 + b^2} - \frac{ab}{a^2 + b^2}\right) i \\ &= \frac{a^2 + b^2}{a^2 + b^2} + \frac{ab - ab}{a^2 + b^2}\, i = 1 + 0 \cdot i\end{aligned}$$

This completes the demonstration that the complex numbers under addition and multiplication are a field. In addition to the properties of a field, the real numbers satisfy the order relations of trichotomy and closure for positive elements. See page 233. Do the complex numbers also satisfy these properties?

The law of trichotomy requires that each number be one and only one of the following: it is zero (the complex number $0 + 0 \cdot i$), it is positive, or its additive inverse is positive. What shall we consider a positive complex number? If for $a + bi$ to be positive, both $a$ and $b$ must be positive, is the law of trichotomy satisfied? Under this agreement $3 + 5i$ is positive, the additive inverse of $-4 - 3i$ is positive, but what about $2 - 4i$? It is not positive, nor is its additive inverse $-2 + 4i$ positive, and it certainly is not zero.

We might let $a + bi$ be positive if $a$ is positive. Here $2 + 5i$ is positive. The additive inverse of $-2 + 4i$ is positive. In fact, this would satisfy trichotomy except for complex numbers of the form $0 + bi$, $b \neq 0$. But neither $0 + 5i$ nor its additive inverse $0 - 5i$ would be positive.

Suppose we define positive complex numbers thus: $a + bi$ is positive if $a$ is positive or if $a = 0$ and $b$ is positive. This definition would satisfy the law of trichotomy. Here every complex number $a + bi$ is either $0 + 0 \cdot i$, has $a$ positive or the additive inverse $-a + -(bi)$ has $-a$ positive, has $a = 0$ and $b$ positive or has an additive inverse with $a = 0$ and $b$ positive. But with this definition of positive elements let us examine the law of closure for positive elements. Under this rule $3i$ and $5i$ are positive numbers, but the product $3i \cdot 5i = -15$ is a negative number. The law of closure is violated.

Any definition of positive complex numbers will violate either the law of trichotomy or the law of closure, or both. We must conclude that, although a field, the set of complex number under addition and multiplication is not an ordered field.

### EXERCISES

**1.** Find the sum $(3 + 0 \cdot i) + (-4 + 0 \cdot i)$.

**2.** If we associate the complex number $a + 0 \cdot i$ with the real number $a$ is the association preserved under addition?

**3.** Find the sum $(0 + 5i) + (0 + -3i)$.

**4.** If we associate the complex number $0 + bi$ with the real number $b$ is the association preserved under addition?

**5.** Find $(4 + 0 \cdot i)(7 + 0 \cdot i)$.

**6.** If we associate the complex number $a + 0 \cdot i$ with the real number $a$ is the association preserved under multiplication?

**7.** Find $(0 + 3i)(0 + -8i)$.

**8.** If we associate the complex number $0 + bi$ with the real number $b$ is the association preserved under multiplication?

**9.** Find the quotient $(2 - 3i) \div (1 + 5i)$.

**10.** Show that division by the complex number $(0 + 0 \cdot i)$ cannot be performed.

## 13.5 Algebraic Structure

Two algebraic structures have played a dominant role in the mathematics which we have developed to this point. They are the *group* and the *field*.

Recall that a group must satisfy four properties: *closure*, *associativity*, *identity*, and *inverse*. The groups that we have studied also are commutative. A field can be defined in terms of a group thus: a field is a system that is a *commutative addition group*, its nonzero elements are a *commutative multiplication group*, and the *distributive property* is satisfied.

Any residue class is a commutative addition group. If the modulus is a prime number the residue class is a field. But it is not an ordered field. Consider the set of residue classes, modulo 7. If this is an ordered field we must be able to designate a set of residues as positive so that the trichotomy and closure properties of order are satisfied. We have the usual addition identity 0. The remaining elements must be designated so that only one of each pair of additive inverses is a positive element. We have 1 and 6, 2, and 5, and 3 and 4 as additive inverses. Suppose 1, 2, and 3 are positive. We then do not have closure under addition for positive elements because $2 + 3 = 5$, a negative element. If 1, 2, and 4 are taken as positive, we have $2 + 4 = 6$, a negative element. We next try 1, 5, and 3 as positive. Now we have $1 + 5 = 6$, a negative element. Nor will 1, 5, and 4 serve, since $5 + 4 = 2$, a negative element. We must conclude that 1 cannot be positive, for this exhausts all possibilities involving 1 as a positive element. But neither can 6 be positive, because $6 \times 6 = 1$, a negative element. Since neither 1 nor 6 can be positive we cannot satisfy trichotomy, we must conclude that the set of residues modulo 7 cannot be an ordered field.

The set of rational numbers, a subset of the reals, is an ordered field. This is not the only subset of the real numbers that is a field. Consider the set of numbers $a + b\sqrt{3}$, $a$ and $b$ rational numbers. This set under addition and multiplication is a field. Since this is a subset of the real numbers, and the real numbers obey the associative, commutative, and distributive properties, this set must obey these properties.

Is the set $a + b\sqrt{3}$ a closed set under addition and multiplication? The sum

$$(a + b\sqrt{3}) + (c + d\sqrt{3}) = (a + c) + (b + d)\sqrt{3}$$

as a consequence of the associative and commutative properties of addition, and the distributive property. But $(a + c) + (b + d)\sqrt{3}$ is a number of the set since $a + c$ is a rational number and $b + d$ is a rational number.

$$(a + b\sqrt{3})(c + d\sqrt{3}) = (ac + 3bd) + (bc + ad)\sqrt{3}$$

We can verify this by straight multiplication of the binomials.

$$\begin{array}{l} \quad a + b\sqrt{3} \\ \quad c + d\sqrt{3} \\ \hline ac + cb\sqrt{3} \\ \qquad + ad\sqrt{3} + bd\sqrt{3}\sqrt{3} \\ \hline ac + (cb + ad)\sqrt{3} + 3bd \end{array}$$

It remains to show that the identity and inverse properties are satisfied. If $a = b = 0$, then $a + b\sqrt{3} = 0$, the addition identity.

If $a = 1$ and $b = 0$, then $a + b\sqrt{3} = 1$, the multiplication identity.

The additive inverse of $a + b\sqrt{3}$ is obviously $-a - b\sqrt{3}$ because

$$(a + b\sqrt{3}) + (-a - b\sqrt{3}) = 0$$

The multiplicative inverse $a + b\sqrt{3}$ should be $\dfrac{1}{a + b\sqrt{3}}$. Can this be expressed in the form $a + b\sqrt{3}$? We rationalize the fraction

$$\frac{1}{a + b\sqrt{3}} \cdot \frac{a - b\sqrt{3}}{a - b\sqrt{3}} = \frac{a - b\sqrt{3}}{a^2 - 3b^2}$$

$$= \frac{a}{a^2 - 3b^2} - \frac{b}{a^2 - 3b^2}\sqrt{3}$$

We conclude that the set of numbers $a + b\sqrt{3}$ under addition and multiplication is a field. It is an ordered field because each element is a real number.

## EXERCISES

1. Demonstrate with $(5 + 6\sqrt{3})$ and $(2 - \sqrt{3})$ that numbers of the form $(a + b\sqrt{3})$ are commutative under addition.

2. Demonstrate with $(3 - \sqrt{3})$, $(1 + 2\sqrt{3})$, and $(2 + \sqrt{3})$ that numbers of the form $(a + b\sqrt{3})$ are associative under addition.

3. Demonstrate with $(5 + 6\sqrt{3})$ and $(2 - \sqrt{3})$ that numbers of the form $(a + b\sqrt{3})$ are commutative under multiplication.

4. Demonstrate with $(3 - \sqrt{3})$, $(1 + 2\sqrt{3})$, and $(2 + \sqrt{3})$ that numbers of the form $(a + b\sqrt{3})$ are associative under multiplication.

5. Demonstrate with $(2 + \sqrt{3})$, $(3 - 3\sqrt{3})$, and $(5 + \sqrt{3})$ that numbers of the form $(a + b\sqrt{3})$ obey the distributive property.

6. Find the quotient $(3 - 2\sqrt{3}) \div (2 + 3\sqrt{3})$.

7. Find the additive inverse of $(-5 + 3\sqrt{3})$.

8. Find the multiplicative inverse of $(-5 + 3\sqrt{3})$.

COMPLEX NUMBERS

# 14 Functions

OF THE MANY RELATIONS STUDIED IN MATHEMATICS ONE OF THE MOST BASIC is that of a *function*. In this chapter we wish to explore the nature of the *function* relation with particular attention to a special kind of function called a *polynomial*.

## 14.1 Relations

In Chapter 1 we studied mathematical relations with an emphasis on the characteristics of a relation. In particular, an equivalence relation was defined as one that is reflexive, symmetric, and transitive. Not all relations have all three of these properties. For example, the "greater than" relation is transitive but it is not reflexive or symmetric.

But here we wish to raise another kind of question. Just what *is* a relation? Bob loves Mary. "Loves" is the relation. It is a connection that operates from Bob to Mary. It may or may not work the other way around. If it works both ways the relation is symmetric. In order to have a relation there must be two sets of objects, called the *domain* and the *range*. The relation is the rule that assigns to each element of the domain one or more elements of the range. If Bob loves Mary, Bob is an element of the domain and Mary is an element of the range. If Mary also loves Bob then Mary is also an element of the domain and Bob is also an element of the range. If Bob happens to be a Casanova the relation may assign many more elements to him.

The title of Chapter 9 is "Linear Relations in Two Variables." One such relation is the "greater than" relation. Consider the statement

$$x + y > 4$$

The replacement set for $x$ is the set of real numbers. We call this replacement set the domain. The replacement set for $y$ is, in the above statement, also the set of real numbers. This is the range. The sentence $x + y > 4$ is an $(x, y)$ relation. It is the rule that assigns one or more values of $y$ to each value of $x$. For example, $x = 4$ is assigned to $y = 6$ because it is true that $4 + 6 > 4$. But many other values of $y$ are also assigned to $x = 4$; for example, $y = 1$, or 9,106. Not all values of $y$ are assigned to $x = 4$; for example, $y = 0$, or $-5$, or $-10$ are not, because when $y$ is assigned any of these values with $x = 4$ the statement is not true.

$$4 + 0 > 4 \text{ is false}$$

Notice that some of the values of $y$ which are assigned to $x = 4$ may also be assigned to other values of $x$. A few of the $(x, y)$ pairs that satisfy the relation are

| $x$ | $y$ |
|---|---|
| 1 | 5 |
| 1 | 7 |
| 2 | 5 |
| 2 | 7 |

We have more than one $x$ paired with a given $y$ and more than one $y$ paired with a given $x$.

We can define a relation in terms of the $(x, y)$ pairs that satisfy it. Recall that the cross product $A \times B$ of two sets $A$ and $B$ is the set of all ordered pairs one can obtain by pairing each element of $A$ with each element of $B$.

> A relation is a rule that selects a subset of the cross product $D \times R$, where $D$ is the domain of the relation and $R$ is its range.

In the definition of a relation, the domain is the set of first elements, and the range is the set of second elements. It follows that the subset of the cross product which the rule selects must have each element of $D$ as first component of at least one element, and each element of $R$ as second component of at least one element.

Suppose, for example, we have $D = \{1, 2, 3, 4\}$ and $R = \{5, 6, 7\}$ then

$$D \times R = \{(1, 5), (1, 6), (1, 7), (2, 5), (2, 6), (2, 7), (3, 5), (3, 6), (3, 7), (4, 5), (4, 6), (4, 7)\}$$

A subset of $D \times R$ is $\{(1, 5), (2, 6), (3, 6), (3, 7)\}$. A rule might well select this set of ordered pairs. But if it does the domain of the relation is $\{1, 2, 3\}$, not $\{1, 2, 3, 4\}$.

### EXERCISES

**1.** If $X = \{1, 3, 5, 7, 11\}$ and $Y = \{1, 2, 3, 4\}$, find $X \times Y$.

**2.** State whether each of the following is the set selected by a relation in which $X$ is the domain and $Y$ is the range:
(a) $\{(1, 2), (2, 1), (3, 3), (7, 4)\}$
(b) $\{(1, 1), (3, 3), (5, 1), (3, 5), (7, 4), (11, 1)\}$
(c) $\{(1, 1), (3, 3), (4, 5), (7, 11)\}$
(d) $\{(1, 4), (3, 3), (5, 2), (7, 1), (11, 3)\}$

**3.** State why each of the sets in Exercise 2 that is not selected by an $X$, $Y$ relation fails to be one.

**4.** If $X = \{0, \pm 3, \pm 4, \pm 5\}$ and $Y = \{0, \pm 3, \pm 4, \pm 5\}$ the relation $x^2 + y^2 = 25$ selects what subset of $X \times Y$?

**5.** Using the same $X$ and $Y$ as in Exercise 4, what subset of $X \times Y$ does the relation $3x = 4y$ select?

**6.** Find the intersection of the sets found in Exercises 4 and 5.

**7.** Would it be possible for the domain and range of the relation $x^2 + y^2 = 25$ to be the set of real numbers? If not, what is the maximum domain and range?

**8.** If the domain and range are the set of real numbers supply the missing components in each of the following pairs such that the relation $x^3 - y^3 + 5 = 0$ is satisfied:

$$(1, \_), (\_, 1), (3, \_), (\_, 2), (0, \_)$$

## 14.2 A Special Type of Relation

A function is a special kind of relation.

> A function is a relation that assigns only one element of the range to each element of the domain.

Thus, we see that a function requires a set of elements, the domain, usually designated by the variable $x$; and a set of elements, the range, usually designated by $y$. The rule that associates one $y$ to each $x$ is the function.

The statement $x + y > 4$ is a relation but not a function, but $x + y = 4$ is a function. If the equation is expressed as

$$y = 4 - x$$

we emphasize the fact that "$y$ is a function of $x$," $y$ is the function $4 - x$. This is the rule, we assign to each value of $x$ the value $4 - x$. Three of the pairs are (1, 3), (4, 0), (5, −1). We frequently see the notation

$$f(x) = 4 - x$$

The symbol $f(x)$ is read "$f$ function of $x$," it does not mean $f$ multiplied by $x$.

Every linear equation in $x$ and $y$ expresses implicitly $y$ as a function of $x$. If we solve the general linear equation

$$ax + by = c$$

then for $y$ we have

$$y = -\left(\frac{a}{b}\right)x + \frac{c}{a}$$

a linear function of $x$.

We have also had occasion to study the quadratic function. When the quadratic equation

$$ax^2 + bx + c = 0$$

was solved graphically we found the graph of the function

$$y = ax^2 + bx + c$$

The solution was obtained by finding the $x$-intercepts of the graph. At those points we have $y = 0$. Those values of $x$ for which the function $ax^2 + bx + c$ is zero are precisely the values of $x$ that satisfy the equation

$$ax^2 + bx + c = 0$$

Corresponding to each value of the range of a linear function there is only one value of the domain. In the equation $3x + 4y = 7$, $x = 1$, and $y = 1$ make the statement true. Any other value of $x$ paired with $y = 1$ will make the statement false. In this respect the quadratic function differs from the linear function. Consider the function $y = x^2 + 3x - 7$. If $x = 0$, $y = -7$. But this is not the only value of $x$ that can be paired with $y = -7$. If $x = -3$, we also have $y = -7$.

In fact, there is only one element of the range, that is, value, of $y$, that is not paired with two values of $x$. That one value is the *vertex* of the graph. The pair $[-(\frac{3}{2}), -(\frac{37}{4})]$ is the vertex of the graph. The minimum value of the function is $-(\frac{37}{4})$. The graph is symmetric to the line $x = -(\frac{3}{2})$. This line is the *axis* of the curve. The domain of the function is the set

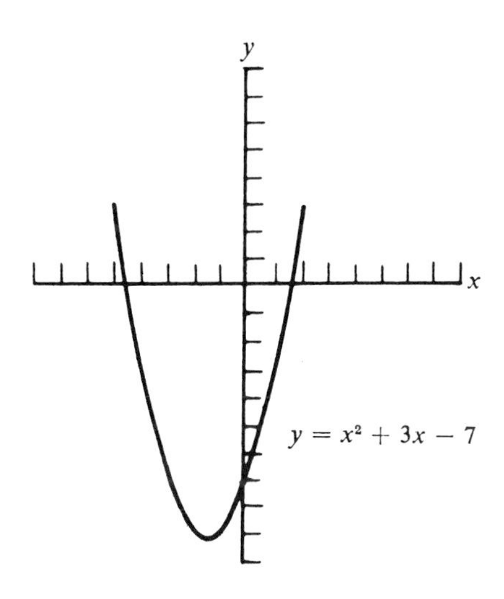


of real numbers, but the range is the set of real numbers greater than or equal to $-(\frac{37}{4})$. Corresponding to any value of the range, other than $y = -(\frac{37}{4})$, there are two values of $x$, equidistant from $x = -(\frac{3}{2})$.

## EXERCISES

**1.** If each of the following sets defines a relation, which ones define a function?
   (a) $\{(1, 3), (2, 3), (5, 3), (7, 3)\}$
   (b) $\{(3, 5), (4, 6), (7, 9), (-3, 5), (-4, 6), (-7, 9)\}$
   (c) $\{(5, 0), (5, 1), (5, 3), (5, 5)\}$
   (d) $\{(1, 3), (2, 5), (3, 7), (1, -3), (2, -5), (3, -7)\}$
   (e) $\{(3, 5), (7, 9), (8, -1)\}$

**2.** If the domain of the relation $y = 3x - 7$ is $0 \leq x \leq 10$ what is its range?

**3.** Determine which of the following rules is a function:
   (a) $x + y^2 = 7$
   (b) $x^3 - 2x^2 + x = y$
   (c) $x - 3y = 7$
   (d) $y = x^2 + 4x - 6$

## A SPECIAL TYPE OF RELATION

4. Is the relation $x = y^2 + 4$ a function? Complete the following ordered pairs so that they satisfy this relation:

$$(\_, 0), (\_, -1), (\_, 1), (\_, -2), (\_, 2), (\_, 3), (\_, -3)$$

5. In view of the definition of a function, what distinguishing characteristic will the graph of a function have as opposed to the graph of a relation in general?

6. Can the graph of a function be a closed curve? Why?

7. Can the graph of a relation be a closed curve? If so, what conclusion can be made relative to its domain and range?

8. Is it possible for the graph of a function to fail to cross the $x$-axis? The $y$-axis? Justify your answers.

## 14.3 The Function $\frac{c}{x}$

The function $y = \frac{c}{x}$ is the simplest example of an inverse relationship between the variables $x$ and $y$. We found in the linear function $y = mx + b$ that the change in one variable is a constant multiple of the change in the other. The change in $y$ is $m$ times as great as the corresponding change in $x$. If $m < 0$ one variable decreases as the other increases. But regardless of $m$, the rate of change is constant—in fact it is always $m$. Unless arbitrarily limited, the domain and range are the entire set of real numbers. If $m > 0$ the product $xy$ can be made larger than any specified number. If $m < 0$ the product $-xy$ can be made larger than any specified number.

In contrast to the linear function, in the quadratic function $y = ax^2 + bx + c$ one variable increases as the other decreases through part of the domain, and through the remainder of the domain they both decrease or both increase.

The inverse function $y = \frac{c}{x}$ behaves in still another way. If we multiply by $x$ we have $xy = c$. This form shows the distinguishing characteristic of the inverse function. The product of the variables must equal the constant $c$.

If $c > 0$ then $x$ and $y$ must agree in sign; both must be positive or both negative. If $c < 0$ then $x$ and $y$ must disagree in sign; one must be negative and the other positive. Consequently, we find the graph of the function in the first and third quadrants or in the second and fourth quadrants. If $c \neq 0$ the graph can touch neither axis. Hence the function has no zero.

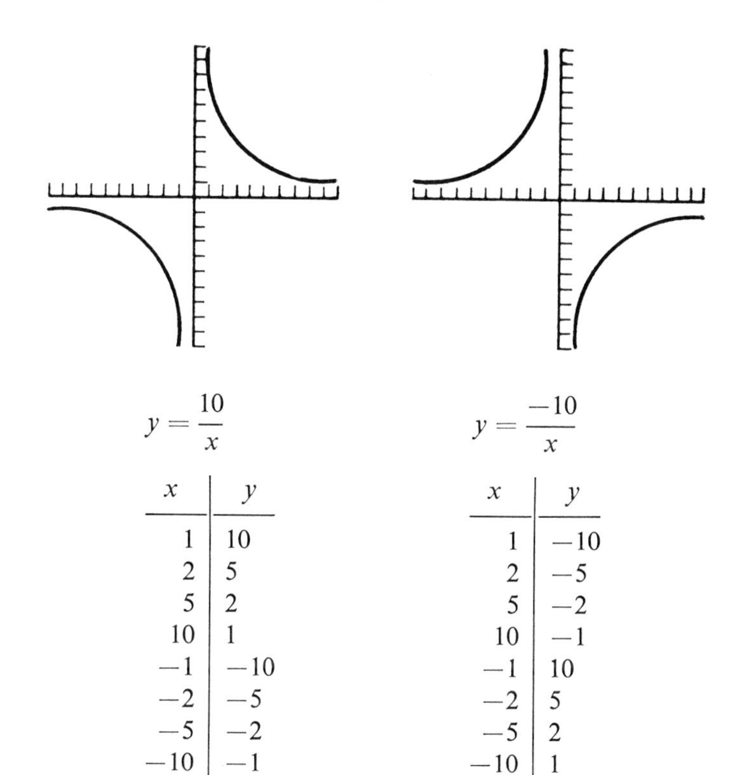

$y = \frac{10}{x}$

| $x$ | $y$ |
|---|---|
| 1 | 10 |
| 2 | 5 |
| 5 | 2 |
| 10 | 1 |
| −1 | −10 |
| −2 | −5 |
| −5 | −2 |
| −10 | −1 |

$y = \frac{-10}{x}$

| $x$ | $y$ |
|---|---|
| 1 | −10 |
| 2 | −5 |
| 5 | −2 |
| 10 | −1 |
| −1 | 10 |
| −2 | 5 |
| −5 | 2 |
| −10 | 1 |

## EXERCISES

**1.** Use the following table of values to graph the function $y = \frac{12}{x}$. Plot the points and connect them with a smooth curve. What happens to the curve at $x = 0$?

| $x$ | 1 | 2 | 3 | 4 | 6 | 12 | −1 | −2 | −3 | −4 | −6 | −12 |
|---|---|---|---|---|---|---|---|---|---|---|---|---|
| $y$ | 12 | 6 | 4 | 3 | 2 | 1 | −12 | −6 | −4 | −3 | −2 | −1 |

**2.** Follow a procedure similar to that in Exercise 1 and graph the function $y = \frac{-12}{x}$.

**3.** Using the same axis as in Exercise 1, construct the graph of $y = \frac{6}{x}$.

**4.** Using the same axis as in Example 2, construct the graph of $y = \frac{-6}{x}$.

### THE FUNCTION $c/x$

5. On the basis of the results of Exercises 1–4 it appears that the graph of the function $y = \frac{c}{x}$ does what as the value of $c$ approaches zero? Construct the graph of $y = \frac{0}{x}$.

6. The length and width of a rectangle are $x$ and $y$, respectively. Its area is 64 square feet. What is the maximum value of $x$? The minimum value? Why is the graph of this relation confined to the first quadrant? Construct the graph.

7. If the temperature is constant the volume occupied by a given quantity of gas is inversely related to the pressure exerted on it, that is, $V = \frac{c}{p}$. If a given quantity of gas filled 100 cubic centimeters of space when under 10 pounds pressure per square inch find the constant $c$.

8. In Exercise 7 what is the pressure if the volume is changed to 25 cubic centimeters?

9. In Exercise 7 what is the volume if the pressure is changed to 25 pounds per square inch.?

10. In Exercise 7 what assumption underlies the conclusion that the volume of the gas can be made as large as we please?

## 14.4 Polynomials

A *polynomial* is a function of the form

$$a_0x^n + a_1x^{n-1} + a_2x^{n-2} + \ldots + a_{n-1}x + a_n$$

The constant term is $a_n$ and the coefficients are $a_0$ through $a_{n-1}$. The highest degree term is $a_0x^n$; $n$ a positive integer. Since $n$ is a positive integer, the exponent in each term except the constant is also a positive integer. The *degree* of the polynomial is the degree of the highest degree term. The polynomial

$$4x^6 + 3x^4 - x + 7$$

is a polynomial of degree 6. Notice that some terms are missing. We can think of this as terms with zero coefficients.

$$4x^6 + 0x^5 + 3x^4 + 0x^3 + 0x^2 - x + 7$$

Although the exponents of the terms of a polynomial must be positive integers, this restriction is not placed on the coefficients.

The coefficients of the terms of a polynomial can be from the field of rational numbers, real numbers, or complex numbers. It is important to know the coefficient field of a polynomial.

*Example:* $\sqrt{3}x^4 + 5x^2 - 3$ is a fourth degree polynomial with real coefficients. $2x^7 + x^6 - 5x^3 + 3x - 1$ is a seventh degree polynomial with rational coefficients.
$ix^3 - 3x^2 + 15ix$ is a third degree polynomial with complex coefficients.

Of course, any polynomial with rational coefficients can be thought of as one with real coefficients or complex coefficients, but it does not work the other way. The last illustration in the example just given can only be considered a polynomial with complex coefficients.

The importance of the coefficient field is illustrated in the following example:

*Example:* Find the factors of the polynomial $x^4 - 2$. The solution depends entirely upon the desired coefficient field. With rational coefficients the polynomial cannot be factored. But if the coefficient field is the real number field, we have

$$x^4 - 2 = (x^2 + \sqrt{2})(x + \sqrt[4]{2})(x - \sqrt[4]{2})$$

In the field of complex numbers we get a different result

$$x^4 - 2 = (x + i\sqrt[4]{2})(x - i\sqrt[4]{2})(x + \sqrt[4]{2})(x - \sqrt[4]{2})$$

## EXERCISES

*Factor the following in the field of rational coefficients. If the polynomial cannot be factored it is a* prime polynomial *in this field.*

**1.** $x^2 + x - 1$

**2.** $12x^2 - 5x - 3$

**3.** $16x^4 - y^4$

**4.** $16x^4 + y^4$

**5.** Factor any of the results in Exercises 1–4 that can be further factored in the real coefficient field.

**6.** Factor any of the results in Exercise 1 through 4 that can be further factored in the complex coefficient field.

7. Factor the following in the real coefficient field:

$$x^2 + (2 - \sqrt{3})x - 2\sqrt{3}$$

8. Factor the following in the complex coefficient field:

$$x^2 - ix + 2$$

## 14.5 The Division Algorithm

If a polynomial is equated with zero the result is a *polynomial equation.*

$$a_0x^n + a_1x^{n-1} + \ldots a_{n-1}x + a_n = 0$$

> *The Fundamental Theorem of Algebra*
>
> Every polynomial equation with complex coefficients has a root.

The Fundamental Theorem, though easily stated, is by no means easily proved. We shall take it as an axiom. However, we should be sure we see the impact of the theorem. If the coefficients are integers, or rational numbers, or real numbers they are elements of the complex field. The theorem does not claim that every polynomial equation has a root in its coefficient field. The equation $x^2 + 2 = 0$ has coefficients in the rational field but it has no rational solution. The equation also has coefficients that are elements of the real field but it has no real solution. Its coefficients are also elements from the field of complex numbers, and the fundamental theorem requires that the equation has at least one complex number as solution. In this particular instance the equation has two roots, both of which are imaginary numbers.

On the other hand the equation

$$x^2 - ix - 1 + i = 0$$

does not have real coefficients but it does have the real number 1 as a solution. The fundamental theorem requires only that it has a complex root, and 1 is a complex number, $1 + 0 \cdot i$.

According to the *Division Algorithm* if $f(x)$ is a polynomial of degree $n$ and $g(x)$ is a polynomial of degree $< n$

$$f(x) = q(x)g(x) + r(x)$$

where the degree of $q(x)$ is $< n$ and the degree of $r(x)$ is less than that of $g(x)$.

*Example:* If $f(x) = x^5 + x^4 + 2x^3 - 2x^2 - 8x + 5$ and

$$g(x) = x^3 + 3x - 5$$

$$x^5 + x^4 + 2x^3 - 2x^2 - 8x + 5 = (x^2 + x - 1)(x^3 + 3x - 5) + (x^2 - 2)$$

where

$$q(x) = x^2 + x - 1 \qquad \text{and} \qquad r(x) = (x^2 - 2)$$

The Division Algorithm merely asserts that we can always divide a polynomial of degree $n$ by another polynomial of degree less than $n$, obtaining for quotient a polynomial of degree less than $n$ and for remainder a polynomial of degree less than that of the divisor. This same theorem may be applied to positive integers. If $m$ and $n$ are positive integers with $m > n$ we know there exist numbers $q$ and $r$ such that

$$m = n \cdot q + r$$

where $0 < q < m$ and $0 \leq r < n$. The last qualifying phrase merely states that $q$, the quotient, must be positive and less than the dividend, $m$, and the remainder, $r$, may be zero but must be less than the divisor, $n$.

The division of polynomials is accomplished in a manner similar to division of integers.

*Example:* Find $(3x^4 - 3x^2 + x - 6) \div (x^2 - x + 1)$

*Solution:*

$$\begin{array}{r|l} & 3x^2 \\ \hline x^2 - x + 1 & 3x^4 \qquad\qquad - 3x^2 + x - 6 \\ & 3x^4 - 3x^3 + 3x^2 \\ \hline & \qquad 3x^3 - 6x^2 + x - 6 \end{array}$$

The first step consists of dividing the highest term of the dividend, $3x^4$, by the highest term of the divisor, $x^2$. This quotient is $3x^2$. The next step consists of multiplying the obtained quotient term, $3x^2$, by the divisor. This yields $3x^4 - 3x^3 + 3x^2$. Next we subtract this product from the quotient. The remainder is $3x^3 - 6x^2 + x - 6$. The entire process is now repeated with the remainder $3x^3 - 6x^2 + x - 6$ as a new dividend.

$$
\begin{array}{r|l}
 & 3x^2 + 3x \\
\cline{2-2}
x^2 - x + 1 & 3x^4 \qquad\quad - 3x^2 + x - 6 \\
 & 3x^4 - 3x^3 + 3x^2 \\
\cline{2-2}
 & \qquad\quad 3x^3 - 6x^2 + x - 6 \\
 & \qquad\quad 3x^3 - 3x^2 + 3x \\
\cline{2-2}
 & \qquad\qquad\quad - 3x^2 - 2x - 6
\end{array}
$$

If we continue in this way we ultimately obtain as remainder a polynomial of lower degree than that of the divisor. This polynomial is the remainder $r(x)$ of the Division Algorithm theorem.

$$
\begin{array}{r|l}
 & 3x^2 + 3x - 3 \\
\cline{2-2}
x^2 - x + 1 & 3x^4 - 3x^2 + x - 6 \\
 & 3x^4 - 3x^3 + 3x^2 \\
\cline{2-2}
 & \qquad\quad 3x^3 - 6x^2 + x - 6 \\
 & \qquad\quad 3x^3 - 3x^2 + 3x \\
\cline{2-2}
 & \qquad\qquad\quad -3x^2 - 2x - 6 \\
 & \qquad\qquad\quad -3x^2 + 3x - 3 \\
\cline{2-2}
 & \qquad\qquad\qquad\quad -5x - 3
\end{array}
$$

In this division $f(x) = 3x^4 - 3x^2 + x - 6$, $g(x) = x^2 - x + 1$, $q(x) = 3x^2 + 3x - 3$, and $r(x) = -5x - 3$. You should verify by multiplication the correctness of the Division Algorithm equation:

$$
\begin{aligned}
&3x^4 - 3x^2 + x - 6 \\
&\qquad = (x^2 - x + 1)(3x^2 + 3x - 3) + (-5x - 3)
\end{aligned}
$$

The close relationship between division of polynomials and division of integers is even more apparent when we realize that an integer, expressed in the usual way, defines a polynomial. If we express 3076 in terms of powers of 10 we have

$$3076 = 3 \times 10^3 + 0 \times 10^2 + 7 \times 10 + 6$$

This is the polynomial

$$3x^3 + 7x + 6$$

evaluated at $x = 10$. The digits of an integer are the coefficients of a polynomial in $x$ evaluated at $x = 10$. Incidentally, when an integer is expressed in a base other than 10 the digits are merely coefficients of a polynomial evaluated at $x$ equal the base of notation. For example, $4306_{(\text{seven})}$ indicates the polynomial $4x^3 + 3x^2 + 6$ evaluated at $x = 7$.

### EXERCISES

**1.** Perform the division

$$(x^5 - 5x^3 + x^2 - 6) \div (x^3 - x + 3)$$

and check the result by multiplication.

**2.** Divide

$$(x^4 - 3x^3 + x^2 - x + 3) \div (x - 2)$$

**3.** Evaluate $x^4 - 3x^3 + x^2 - x + 3$ when $x = 2$.

**4.** Divide

$$(x^5 + x^4 - 3x^3 + x - 5) \div (x + 1)$$

**5.** Evaluate $x^5 + x^4 - 3x^3 + x - 5$ when $x = -1$.

**6.** Divide

$$(x^4 + 3x^3 - 5x^2 + 8x - 4) \div (x + 2)$$

**7.** Evaluate $x^4 + 3x^3 - 5x^2 + 8x - 4$ when $x = -2$.

**8.** Divide

$$2x^3 + x^2 - 20x - 3 \div (x - 3)$$

**9.** Evaluate $2x^3 + x^2 - 20x - 3$ when $x = 3$.

**10.** Express 531, base eight, as a polynomial with $x$ replaced by 8. Evaluate the result.

## 14.6 The Remainder Theorem

The relationship exhibited by the Division Algorithm is an identity. That is, it is true for all permissible replacements of the variable. If we choose as divisor the polynomial $(x - a)$ the Division Algorithm equation becomes

$$f(x) = (x - a)g(x) + r(x) \qquad \text{(I)}$$

The symbol $f(a)$ is used to indicate the value of the function $f$ evaluated at $x = a$. For example, if $f(x) = 2x^3 - x + 6$ then

$$f(a) = 2a^3 - a + 6, \quad f(4) = 2 \cdot 4^3 - 4 + 6 = 130$$

$f(1) = 2 \cdot 1^3 - 1 + 6 = 7$, and in particular

$$f(0) = 2 \cdot 0 - 0 + 6 = 6$$

Since Equation I is true for all permissible replacements for $x$, we replace $x$ with $a$ to obtain

$$f(a) = (a - a)g(a) + r(a)$$

$$f(a) = r(a) \qquad \text{(II)}$$

Equation II is known as the Remainder Theorem.

| If $f(x)$ is divided by $(x - a)$ the remainder is $f(a)$. |
|---|

*Example:* Find the remainder when $(x^4 - 3x^2 + x - 5)$ is divided by $(x - 5)$

*Solution:* $f(x) = x^4 - 3x^2 + x - 5$

$$f(5) = 5^4 - 3 \cdot 5^2 + 5 - 5 = 550$$

We may check this by division.

$$\begin{array}{r|l} & x^3 + 5x^2 + 22x + 111 \\ \hline x - 5 & x^4 - 3x^2 + x - 5 \\ & x^4 - 5x^3 \\ \hline & 5x^3 - 3x^2 + x - 5 \\ & 5x^3 - 25x^2 \\ \hline & 22x^2 + x - 5 \\ & 22x^2 - 110x \\ \hline & 111x - 5 \\ & 111x - 555 \\ \hline & 550 \end{array}$$

If $(x - a)$ is a factor of $f(x)$ this means the remainder is zero. Hence, the Factor Theorem.

| If $f(a) = 0$, then $(x - a)$ is a factor of $f(x)$. |
|---|

*Example:* Use the Factor Theorem to determine whether $(x - 2)$ is a factor of

$$x^4 - 3x^3 + x^2 + x + 2$$

*Solution:* $f(x) = x^4 - 3x^3 + x^2 + x + 2$
$f(2) = 16 - 24 + 4 + 2 + 2 = 0$
Hence $(x - 2)$ is a factor of

$$x^4 - 3x^3 + x^2 + x + 2$$

*Check:*

$$\begin{array}{r|l} & x^3 - x^2 - x - 1 \\ \hline x - 2 & x^4 - 3x^3 + x^2 + x + 2 \\ & x^4 - 2x^3 \\ \hline & -x^3 + x^2 + x + 2 \\ & -x^3 + 2x^2 \\ \hline & -x^2 + x + 2 \\ & -x^2 + 2x \\ \hline & -x + 2 \\ & x - 2 \\ \hline \end{array}$$

*Example:* Use the factor theorem to determine whether $x + 3$ is a factor of

$$x^4 + 3x^3 + x^2 + x - 3$$

*Solution:* $f(-3) = (-3)^4 + 3(-3)^3 + (-3)^2 + (-3) - 3$
$= 81 - 81 + 9 - 3 - 3 = 3$

## THE REMAINDER THEOREM

Hence $(x + 3)$ is not a factor. In fact if $x^4 + 3x^3 + x^2 + x - 3$ is divided by $x + 3$ the remainder is 3.

$$
\begin{array}{r|l}
 & x^3 + x - 2 \\
x + 3 & x^4 + 3x^3 + x^2 + x - 3 \\
 & x^4 + 3x^3 \\
\hline
 & \qquad\qquad x^2 + x - 3 \\
 & \qquad\qquad x^2 + 3x \\
\hline
 & \qquad\qquad\quad -2x - 3 \\
 & \qquad\qquad\quad -2x - 6 \\
\hline
 & \qquad\qquad\qquad\quad 3
\end{array}
$$

## EXERCISES

1. Divide $x^5 - 3x^3 + 4x^2 + 2x + 5$ by $x - 1$.
   If $f(x) = x^5 - 3x^3 + 4x^2 + 2x + 5$ find $f(1)$.
2. Determine the remainder when $2x^5 + x^4 - 5x^3 - x^2 + 2x - 1$ is divided by
   (a) $(x - 1)$
   (b) $(x + 1)$
   (c) $x$
   (d) $(x + 2)$
3. Use the factor theorem to determine whether each of the following polynomials is a factor of $2x^3 + 3x^2 + 11x + 6$:
   (a) $(x + 1)$
   (b) $(x + 2)$
   (c) $(x + \frac{1}{2})$
   (d) $(x - \frac{1}{6})$
   (e) $(x + 3)$

*Use the factor theorem to factor each of the following polynomials:*

4. $6x^3 - 25x^2 + 32x - 12$
5. $x^3 - 3x^2 - 4x + 12$
6. $x^4 - 13x^2 + 36$
7. $x^3 + x^2 - 10x + 8$
8. $x^3 - 3x^2 + 3x - 1$
9. $x^5 - 9x^3$
10. $x^4 + 4x^3 + 3x^2 - 4x - 4$

## 14.7 Solution of Polynomial Equations

Although the Fundamental Theorem of Algebra guarantees at least one root for any polynomial equation with complex coefficients, this does not mean the root can be found readily. However, if the equation has a rational root, $r$, we can divide by $(x - r)$ and then have an equation of degree one less than that of the original equation, and the fundamental theorem applies to the new equation.

The Factor Theorem can be quite helpful in discovering rational roots.

*Example:* Find the rational roots of the equation

$$2x^3 - x^2 - 13x - 6 = 0$$

*Solution:* An equivalent equation is obtained if we divide by the coefficient of the highest degree term. Dividing by 2, we have

$$x^3 - \frac{x^2}{2} - \frac{13}{2}x - \frac{6}{2} = 0$$

If the polynomial has a factor in the form $(x - a)$, $a$ must be a factor of $-(\frac{6}{2})$. This is of help in applying the factor theorem. The possible values of $a$ are $\pm 1$, $\pm 2$, $\pm 3$, $\pm 6$, $\pm(\frac{1}{2})$, $\pm(\frac{3}{2})$

$$f(1) = 1 - \tfrac{1}{2} - \tfrac{13}{2} - \tfrac{6}{2} = -9$$

Hence $(x - 1)$ is not a factor.

$$f(-1) = -1 - \tfrac{1}{2} + \tfrac{13}{2} - \tfrac{6}{2} = 2$$

Hence $(x + 1)$ is not a factor.

$$f(2) = 8 - \tfrac{4}{2} - \tfrac{26}{2} - \tfrac{6}{2} = -10$$

Hence $(x - 2)$ is not a factor

$$f(-2) = -8 - \tfrac{4}{2} + \tfrac{26}{2} - \tfrac{6}{2} = 0$$

Hence, $(x + 2)$ is a factor.
We can divide the original polynomial by $(x + 2)$ and factor the resulting quadratic polynomial. However, this is not essential. We can continue with the origin polynomial.

$$f(3) = 27 - \tfrac{9}{2} - \tfrac{39}{2} - \tfrac{6}{2} = 0$$

Hence $(x - 3)$ is a factor.

Since $-2$ and 3 are two of the factors of $-(\frac{6}{2})$ the remaining factor must be $-\frac{1}{2}$. We can verify this, using the factor theorem

$$f(-\tfrac{1}{2}) = -\tfrac{1}{8} - \tfrac{1}{8} + \tfrac{13}{4} - \tfrac{6}{2} = 0$$

Hence $(x + \frac{1}{2})$ is a factor.
We now have the equation

$$(x + \tfrac{1}{2})(x - 3)(x + 2) = 0$$

The solution set is found by equating each linear factor to zero.

$$x + \tfrac{1}{2} = 0;\ x = -\tfrac{1}{2}$$
$$x - 3 = 0;\ x = 3$$
$$x + 2 = 0;\ x = -2$$

The solution set is $\{-\frac{1}{2}, 3, -2\}$.

A polynomial equation of degree $n$ may have as many as $n$ rational roots. If the polynomial has rational coefficients and has $n$ rational roots it can be factored into $n$ linear factors. However, the equation may well have no rational roots. Its roots may be irrational or imaginary. Since any linear polynomial equation or any quadratic polynomial equation can be solved, we can find all roots of a polynomial equation if the polynomial can be factored into linear and quadratic factors.

*Example:* Solve $x^5 - 4x^3 - x^2 + 4$ for rational roots.

*Solution:* The only possible rational roots are $\pm 1, \pm 2, \pm 4$.

$$f(1) = 1 - 4 - 1 + 4 = 0$$

Hence $(x - 1)$ is a factor.

$$f(-1) = -1 + 4 - 1 + 4 = 6$$

Hence $(x + 1)$ is not a factor.

$$f(2) = 32 - 32 - 4 + 4 = 0$$

Hence $(x - 2)$ is a factor.

$$f(-2) = -32 + 32 - 4 + 4 = 0$$

Hence $(x + 2)$ is a factor.

$$f(4) = 924 - 256 - 16 + 4 = 656$$

Hence $(x - 4)$ is not a factor.

$$f(-4) = -924 + 256 - 16 + 4 = -680$$

Hence $(x + 4)$ is not a factor.
We have the equation

$$(x + 2)(x - 2)(x - 1)(x^2 + x + 1) = 0$$

Setting each factor equal to zero we have

$$(x + 2) = 0; \quad x = -2$$
$$(x - 2) = 0; \quad x = 2$$
$$(x - 1) = 0; \quad x = 1$$
$$(x^2 + x + 1) = 0; \qquad x = \frac{-1 + \sqrt{1 - 4}}{2}$$

The solution set of the original equation is

$$\left\{-2, 2, 1, \frac{-1 + i\sqrt{3}}{2}, \frac{-1 - i\sqrt{3}}{2}\right\}$$

If the polynomial of a polynomial equation cannot be factored into linear and quadratic factors there are many ways to find approximations to its real roots. The simplest of these depends upon the fact that if $f(a) > 0$ and $f(b) < 0$ there is an odd number of zeros of the function

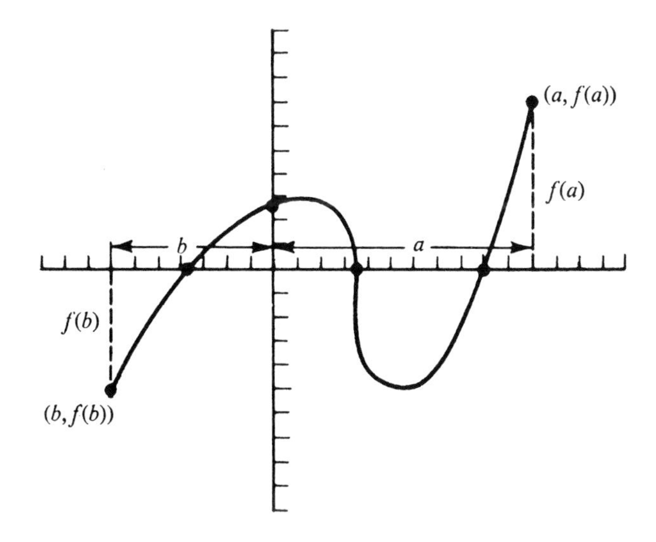


SOLUTION OF POLYNOMIAL EQUATIONS

between $a$ and $b$. This can be seen to be true intuitively by examination of the graph of the function. If $f(a) > 0$ and $f(b) < 0$ the graph is on opposite sides of the $x$-axis at $x = a$ and $x = b$. It is intuitively evident that we must cross the $x$-axis an odd number of times if we start on one side of the axis and end on the other.

*Example:* Locate between consecutive integers the real roots of

$$x^4 - 7x^2 + 10 = 0$$

*Solution:*

$f(0) = 10$

$f(1) = 4$

a root between $x = 1$ and $x = 2$

$f(2) = -2$

a root between $x = 2$ and $x = 3$

$f(3) = 28$

$f(0) = 10$

$f(-1) = 4$

a root between $x = -1$ and $x = -2$

$f(-2) = -2$

a root between $x = -2$ and $x = -3$

$f(-3) = 28$

## EXERCISES

*Completely solve the following equations:*

**1.** $x^4 + x^3 + 2x - 4 = 0$

**2.** $x^3 - x - 6 = 0$

**3.** $x^3 + 5x^2 + 3x - 4 = 0$

**4.** $x^4 - 2x^3 - 3x^2 + 8x - 4 = 0$

**5.** Find the rational roots of the following equations. Evaluate the other real roots between consecutive integers.

(a) $x^3 - 2x^2 - 6x + 4 = 0$
(b) $x^4 + x^3 - 11x^2 + 3x + 14 = 0$

## FUNCTIONS

# Answers to Exercises

**Section 1.1, page 4**

1. (a) {Alaska, Hawaii, Oregon, Washington, California}
   (b) {1, 3, 5, 7, 9, 11}
   (c) {12, 14, 16, 18}
   (d) $\{\frac{1}{1}, \frac{1}{3}, \frac{1}{5}, \frac{1}{7}, \frac{1}{9}\}$

3. The set of all men 100 feet tall is well defined; it is the null set.
   (a) There are many shades of red.
   (b) Who decides what is good?
   (c) How smart is smart?

5. If they are equal they are equivalent; each element can be put in correspondence with itself. If they are equivalent they are not necessarily equal. In fact they may have no elements in common.

**Section 1.2, page 9**

1. (a) {1, 2, 3, 4, 5, 6, 7, 8, 9, 10, 12, 14}
   (b) {2, 4, 6, 8, 10}
   (c) {1, 2, 3, 4, 5, 6, 7, 8, 9, 10, 12, 14}
   (d) {2, 4, 6, 8, 10}

3. { }, {cat}, {dog}, {bird}, {rabbit}, {cat, dog}, {cat, bird}, {cat, rabbit}, {dog, bird}, {dog, rabbit}, {bird, rabbit}, {cat, dog, bird}, {cat, dog, rabbit}, {cat, bird, rabbit}, {dog, bird, rabbit}, {cat, dog, bird, rabbit} 16

5. 32

7. (a) $U$, (b) $\varnothing$, (c) $\varnothing$, (d) $U$, (e) $A$, (f) $\varnothing$, (g) $U$, (h) $A$

**Section 1.3, page 17**

1. {1, 3, 4, 5, 6, 7, 8, 10}

5. (a) $U$ is the set of all positive integers
   (b) $A \cap A' = \varnothing$
   (c) $A \cup (A' \cap A) = A$

9. $A \cap B = \varnothing$, $A' \cap B = B$, $A \cap B' = A$, $\varnothing \cup B \cup A = B \cup A = A \cup B$

**Section 1.4, page 21**

1. (a) None (b) transitive (if elements are distinct) (c) symmetric, transitive (if elements are distinct) (d) symmetric (e) none (f) reflexive (g) transitive (h) none (i) none (j) symmetric (k) reflexive, symmetric, transitive (l) transitive (m) transitive (n) symmetric.

3. Pays the debts of (for most people it is reflexive).

5. Less than, applied to numbers.

**Section 2.1, page 27**

1. Tie ten knots in the rope

3. a, e

5. Children (only child), parents

**Section 2.3, page 32**

1. $$\begin{array}{cccccc} 1, & 3, & 5, & \ldots & (2n-1) & \ldots \\ \updownarrow & \updownarrow & \updownarrow & & \updownarrow & \\ 1, & 2, & 3, & \ldots & n & \ldots \end{array}$$

3. $$\begin{array}{ccccc} 5, & 10, & \ldots, & 5n, & \ldots \\ \updownarrow & \updownarrow & & \updownarrow & \\ \frac{1}{1}, & \frac{1}{2}, & \ldots, & \frac{1}{n}, & \ldots \end{array}$$

5. By showing they cannot be placed in one-to-one correspondence.

7. $\aleph_0$

9. $$\begin{array}{ccccc} 1, & \frac{1}{2}, & \frac{1}{3}, & \frac{1}{n}, & \ldots \\ \updownarrow & \updownarrow & \updownarrow & \updownarrow & \\ 10, & 20, & 30, & 10n, & \ldots \end{array}$$
   The set of unit fractions and the set of multiples of ten.

**Section 2.4, page 35**

1. $A \cap B = \{2, 4, 6, 8, 10\}$ $A \cup B = \{1, 2, 3, 4, 5, 6, 7, 8, 9, 10, 12, 14\}$

3. It is not a proper subset of itself, but is a proper subset of all other sets.

5. No. $\{1\}$ is an element, but 1 is not. There is a difference in kind between a set and its elements.

7. $C$ is a set of 4 elements. $D$ is a set of 2 elements, each an ordered pair.

9. $n(A) = 5$, $n(B) = 4$, $n(A \cap B) = 4$, $n(A \cup B) = 5$

11. $n(A \cup B) = 7$, $n(B \cap A) = 0$

**Section 2.5, page 38**

1. (a) No, $12 \div 5$ is not a counting number.
   (b) No, $7 - 5$ is not an odd counting number.
   (c) No, $5 - 8$ is not a counting number.
   (d) No, $7 + 8$ is not a one digit number.
   (e) No, teh, eth, eht, het, hte, are not words.

3. b, c

5. Yes, 1.

**Section 2.7, page 46**

1. (a) $(-9) + 13 = 13 - 9 = 4$
   (b) $(-16) + (-29) = -(16 + 29) = -45$
   (c) $(-27) + 19 = -(27 - 19) = -8$
   (d) $(-15) + 37 = 37 - 15 = 22$
   (e) $(-8) + (-26) = -(8 + 26) = -34$
   (f) $17 + (-63) = -(63 - 17) = -46$
   (g) $63 + (-17) = 63 - 17 = 46$
   (h) $(-23) + (-42) = -(23 + 42) = -65$

3. (a) 21
   (b) 21
   (c) 21
   (d) $-14$
   (e) $-14$
   (f) 11
   (g) 11

**Section 2.8, page 50**

1. (a) 2, (b) 3, (c) $-38$, (d) 37

3. (a) $-38$, (b) 33, (c) 6

5. (a) 3 order of subtrahends does not affect remainder.
   (b) 46 successive subtraction may be performed by subtracting the sum of the subtrahends.
   (c) 33 adding the same amount to minuend and subtrahend does not affect the remainder.

**Section 2.9, page 53**

1. (a) a loss
   (b) a distant south
   (c) population decrease
   (d) a distant north
   (e) a deceleration
   (f) feet below sea level
   (g) a date B.C.
3. Subtract the absolute values (numbers without regard to sign) and attach the sign of the addend with the greater absolute value.
5. Add the absolute values (numbers without regard to sign) and attach the common sign.

**Section 2.10, page 58**

1. (a) 4 (b) 4 (c) 4 (d) 3;0 (e) +1 (f) 5;2 (g) 6
3. 0–0, 3–3, 1–5, 2–4
5. Yes. No. Yes. b is its own inverse.

**Section 3.1, page 63**

1. (a) $\{(a, 1), (a, 2), (b, 1), (b, 2), (c, 1), (c, 2)\}$
   (b) $\{(1, a), (a, a), (x, a)\}$
   (c) $\{(1, 2), (1, b), (1, z), (a, 2), (a, b), (a, z), (x, 2), (x, b), (x, z)\}$
   (d) $\{(1, a), (1, b), (1, c), (2, a), (2, b), (2, c)\}$
3. 8, 9
5. The empty set

**Section 3.2, page 70**

1. $\{(1, 0), (1, y), (a, 0), (a, y), (x, 0), (x, y)\}$
3. $\{(1, x), (1, y), (a, x), (a, y), (x, x), (x, y)\}$
5. Because $B$ and $C$ are not disjoint
7. (a) Distributive property
   (b) Multiplication is commutative
   (c) $a \cdot 0 = 0$
   (d) addition is associative
   (e) addition is associative and commutative

**Section 3.4, page 73**

1. There are no replacements $a$.
3. Because 5 is a prime number.

5. $A = \{x, y\}$

7. $p \cdot m = r$; $r \div m = p$

**Section 3.6, page 76**

1. (a) 2, (b) 2, (c) 270, (d) 270, (e) 144, (f) 144

3. (a) 15, (b) 21, (c) 51, (d) $-8$

5. (a) $+$, (b) $-$, (c) $-$, (d) $+$

7. (a) $-2 \times -4$ (b) $1 \times -2$ (c) 2

11. (a) $-5$ (b) 10 (c) $-4$

**Section 3.7, page 82**

3. Any odd number is congruent to 1 or 3, modulo 4. Furthermore $1^2 \equiv 1$, mod 4 and $3^2 \equiv 1$ mod 4.

5. $3 \times 8 \equiv 0$, $4 \times 6 \equiv 0$, No.

7. Correct, $5 \equiv 5$

**Section 3.8, page 86**

1. (1–1), (2–4), (3–5), (6–6) are inverse pairs

3. 3

5. Division and multiplication are inverse operations and 6 is its own multiplicative inverse. Hence division by 6 and multiplication by 6 are equivalent.

7. (a) $4 \times 1 \equiv 6 + 5$; $4 \equiv 4$
   (b) $2 \times 3 \equiv 5 + 8$; $6 \equiv 6$

9. (a)

```
   543      - 3
   657      - 0
  ----        -
  3801        0
 2715         ↑
3258          |
------        ↓
356751 - 27 - 0
```

(b)

```
  321   - 6
   47   - 2
 ----     -
 2247   12 - 3
1284         ↕
-----
15087 - 21 - 3
```

11. $0^3 \equiv 0$, $1^3 \equiv 1$, $2^3 \equiv 8 \equiv -1$, $3^3 \equiv 0$, $4^3 \equiv 1$, $5^3 \equiv 8 \equiv -1$, $6^3 \equiv 0$, $7^3 \equiv 1$, $8^3 \equiv -1$

15. 19, 31, 43 are the three smallest positive numbers $> 7$. 5, 19, 26

17. $5 \equiv 5$ mod 7 (Reflexive)
    If $5 \equiv 12$ mod 7 then $12 \equiv 5$ mod 7 (Symmetric)
    If $5 \equiv 12$ mod 7 and $12 \equiv 19$ mod 7 then
    $5 \equiv 19$ mod 7 (Transitive)

19. (a) any factor of 578
    (b) any factor of 24
    (c) any factor of 120

**Section 3.9, page 93**

1. (a) by 2 rem. 1; by 3 rem. 2; by 5 rem. 1; by 9 rem. 2; by 11 rem. 6
   (b) by 2; by 3; by 5; by 9; by 11 rem. 1
   (c) by 2; by 3 rem. 2; by 5 rem. 2; by 9 rem. 8; by 11
   (d) by 2; by 3; by 5; by 9; by 11

3. 2 and 3 are relatively prime, but 2 and 4 are not. Divisibility by 4 implies divisibility by 2 but divisibility by 3 does not imply divisibility by 2.

5. Apply the tests for 4 and for 3.
   $2 \times 3 + 2 = 8$ hence divisible by 4
   $1 + 0 + 0 + 3 + 2 = 6$ hence divisible by 3 and by 12

7. Combine the tests for 2 and for 11.

9. (a) By 2 any digit
       By 3 $436\underline{1}82$ (or 4 or 7)
       By 4 not possible
       By 5 not possible
       By 6 $436\underline{1}82$ (or 4 or 7)
       By 9 $436\underline{4}82$
       By 11 $436\underline{2}82$
   (b) 2 — any digit in hundreds place, 0, 2, 4, 6 or 8 in ones place.
       By 3 — any two digits whose sum is congruent to 1, modulo 3.
       By 4 — any digit in hundreds, 0, 4, 8 in ones place.
       By 5 — any digit in hundreds, 0 or 5 in ones place.
       By 6 — an even digit in ones place, the sum of the digits congruent to 1, modulo 3.
       By 9 — a digit sum congruent to 4 modulo 9.
       By 11 — a digit sum congruent to 6 modulo 11.
   (c) By 2 impossible
       By 3 a digit sum congruent to 2 modulo 3.
       By 4 impossible
       By 5 impossible
       By 6 impossible
       By 9 a digit sum congruent to 8 modulo 9.
       By 11 the digit in ten thousands place 3 greater than in tens place, or 8 less than in tens place.

**Section 3.10, page 99**

1. True—Order of divisors can be changed.

3. False

5. True—Special case
7. False
9. True— division obeys right distributive law.
11. True—Successive division may be performed by dividing by the product of the divisors.
13. True—Multiplication is distributive with respect to subtraction.
15. False
17. True—Dividing dividend and divisor by the same non zero number does not change the quotient.
19. True—Subtracting the same number from subtrahend and minuend does not affect the remainder.
21. False
23. True—Division obeys the right distributive law.
25. False
27. True—Successive division can be performed by dividing by the product of the divisors.
29. True—Division obeys the right distributive law.
31. (c), (d)

**Section 4.4, page 108**

5. (a) MCMLIX (b) MMI (c) MDCCLXXVI (d) CCCXLVII
7. Egyptian is simplest
   Chinese is usually most compact
15. No, not to represent a positive whole number. The system does not require a symbol to indicate the absence of a power of 10. If there were no hundreds, no C's appeared in the numeral.
17. Yes. No.

**Section 4.5, page 111**

1. (a) 1000 (b) 1 (c) 36 (d) 512 (e) 7 (f) 1 (g) $\frac{1}{216}$ (h) 4 (i) 1 (j) 83 (k) $\frac{1}{9}$
3. (a) $4 \times 10^2 + 6 \times 10 + 8 \times 10^0 + 2 \times 10^{-1} + 3 \times 10^{-2}$
   (b) $1 \times 10^3 + 3 \times 10^0 + 4 \times 10^{-2}$
   (c) $7 \times 10^2 + 7 \times 10^0 + 7 \times 10^{-2}$
5. (a) 6583 (b) 405 (c) 7206.8 (d) 309.07

**Section 4.7, page 115**

3. $8 \times 10^2 + 7 \times 10 + 6 \times 10^0$
5. Symbol for 5,50 etc. Employs place value.
9. It is not a positional system.

**Section 4.8, page 121**

1. 1651 (eight)
3. 474 (ten)
5. 10101101 (two)
7. 252 (ten)
9. 3011 (four)
11. Twelve. In addition to the symbols 0–9, we need a digit symbol for ten and for eleven.

**Section 4.9, page 127**

5. 30032 (five)
7. 10001111 (two)
9. 20604 (eight)
11. Six
13. Missing number 302, base four.
15. Six
17. 113 (five)
19. 1575 (eight)
21. No. Any power of 1 is 1.
23. $\begin{array}{r} 1032 \\ 313 \\ \hline 113 \end{array}$
25. (a) twelve (b) eight (c) five (d) two
27. No. The base must be an even base less than 10 and greater than 3.
    321 (four) = 57 (ten)
    321 (six) = 121 (ten)

**Section 4.10, page 132**

1. (a) $\frac{4}{12} = \frac{1}{3}$ (b) $\frac{3}{6} = \frac{1}{2}$ (c) $\frac{14}{25}$ (d) $\frac{15}{49}$

3. (a) .132 (b) .321 (c) .44

5. .44 (eight); 100100 (two)

7. Write each base nine digit in base three.

**Section 4.12, page 138**

1. Seven

3. (a) $11\frac{3}{4}$ (b) $51\frac{13}{64}$ (c) $\frac{61}{64}$ (d) $\frac{15}{16}$

5. Yes. Yes. Two is a prime factor of both eight and ten.

7. Disadvantage

9. The system is unchanged except for the end play. Never allow the opponent to play to $1 - 1$.

11. Yes. It works with any base but one must be careful to recognize odd numbers if an odd base is used.

13. 25641 (seven)

15. $10 - 8 - 2$

**Section 4.13, page 140**

1. $237 + 194 + 36 = (7 + 4 + 6) + (30 + 90 + 30) + 200 + 100 = 7 + (10 + 30 + 90 + 30) + (200 + 100) = 7 + 60 + (100 + 200 + 100) = 7 + 60 + 400 = 400 + 60 + 7 = 467$

3. $47 \times 23 = (40 + 7)23 = 40 \times 23 + 7 \times 23 = 40(20 + 3) + 7(20 + 3) = 40 \times 20 + 40 \times 3 + 7 \times 20 + 7 \times 3 = 7 \times 3 + 7 \times 20 + 40 \times 3 + 40 \times 20 = 21 + 140 + 120 + 800 = (1 + 20) + (140 + 120) + 800 = 1 + (20 + 140 + 120) + 800 = 1 + 280 + 800 = 1 + 80 + 200 + 800 = 1 + 80 + 1000 = 1000 + 80 + 1 = 1081$

**Section 5.1, page 144**

1. Yes. Even, because adding an even number does not change the parity of the number: even plus even is even, odd plus even is odd.

3. Additive inverse of even is even. Additive inverse of odd is odd.

5. Tells nothing about the number of even addends. There must be an even number of odd addends.

7. There must be at least one even factor. Tells nothing about odd factors.

9. It must be odd because 2b is even.

11. It must be odd.

**Section 5.2, page 151**

1. If $n = 1$; $\dfrac{1(1+1)}{2} = 1$.

   Assume the statement true for $n = k$.

$$1 + 2 + 3 + \ldots + k = \frac{k(k+1)}{2}$$

   Add $k + 1$ to each side

$$\begin{aligned} 1 + 2 + 3 + \ldots + k + 1 &= \frac{k(k+1)}{2} + k + 1 \\ &= \frac{k(k+1) + 2(k+1)}{2} \\ &= \frac{(k+1)(k+2)}{2} \end{aligned}$$

   Thus the statement is true for $n = k + 1$ whenever it is true for $n = k$. It is true for $n = 1$. Then by the principle of finite induction, it is true for all $n$.

3. 15150

7. By definition, we add $d$ to any term to determine the next. Hence we must add $d$ for each term except the first, $(n - 1)d$ must be added to the first term.

9. If $n = 1$, the statement is true, $1 = 1$. Assume it is true for $n = k$

$$1 + 3 + 5 + \ldots + (2k - 1) = k^2$$

   Add the next odd integer $2k + 1$

$$\begin{aligned} 1 + 3 + 5 + \ldots + (2k + 1) &= k^2 + 2k + 1 \\ &= (k + 1)^2 \end{aligned}$$

   Hence the statement is true for $n = k + 1$ whenever it is true for $n = k$. And because it is true for $n = 1$, it is true for all natural numbers $n$.

**Section 5.3, page 154**

1. 2, 3, 5, 7, 11, 13, 17, 19, 23, 29, 31, 37, 41, 43, 47, 53, 59, 61, 67, 71, 73, 79, 83, 89, 97

3. In decades, first to tenth, there are 4, 4, 2, 2, 3, 2, 2, 3, 2, and 1.
   They seem to be decreasing.

5. If $n = 1$; $2^{2^n} + 1 = 5$
   If $n = 2$; $2^{2^n} + 1 = 17$
   If $n = 3$; $2^{2^n} + 1 = 257$
   Yes, they are prime

7. It is the multiplication identity. We can think of a number as having 1 as factor as many times as we wish. If 1 were a prime any positive integer could be classified as prime or composite.

**Section 5.4, page 159**

1. 36

3. $M = -1, N = 1, GCD = 78 = -1 \cdot 468 + 1 \cdot 546$

5. 432

7. No. $8 = 2 \cdot 2 \cdot 2$ and $15 = 3 \cdot 5$ have no prime factors in common.

9. One.

**Section 5.5, page 160**

1. $2 \times 3 \times 5 \times 7 \times 11 \times 13 + 1 = 59 \times 509$

3. $34 = 17 + 17 = 3 + 31 = 5 + 29 = 11 + 23$
   $50 = 3 + 47 = 7 + 43 = 13 + 37 = 19 + 31$
   $76 = 3 + 73 = 5 + 71 = 17 + 59 = 23 + 53 = 29 + 47$
   $88 = 5 + 83 = 17 + 71 = 29 + 59 = 41 + 47$
   $100 = 3 + 97 = 11 + 89 = 17 + 83 = 29 + 71 = 41 + 59 = 47 + 53$

**Section 6.1, page 164**

1. (a) 5, 9
   (b) 6, 9 : 21, 8 : 28
   (c) 5 : 15, 4 : 20, 12 : 20

3. (a) 3, (b) 3 (c) 9 (d) $\frac{5}{2}$

5. \$30, \$45, \$75

7. 300 lbs. fuel A, 500 lbs. fuel B, 700 lbs. fuel C

**Section 6.2, page 167**

1. $k \cdot 0 : k \cdot 0 = 0 : 0$ for any $k$.

3. 2

5. $\dfrac{1}{\sqrt{2}}$

7. Yes $\sqrt{3} : \sqrt{5}$

9. Yes, in the sense that it may be considered 12 : 5, the representative element of an equivalence class of ratios.

11. $3 \div 4$, $3 : 4$. It is the representative element of an equivalence class of ratios $3k : 4k$.

**Section 6.4, page 171**

1. Given $a$, $b$, $c$, $d$ integers $bd \neq 0$.

$$\frac{a}{b} \times \frac{c}{d} = \frac{a \times c}{b \times d}$$

But $a \times c$ and $b \times d$ are integers. Hence $\frac{a \times c}{b \times d}$ is a rational number.

3. (a) $\frac{10}{18} \times \frac{a}{2b} = \frac{2}{3} \times \frac{5a}{12b}$

$$\frac{10a}{36b} = \frac{10a}{36b}$$

(b) $-3 \times \frac{-2}{35} = \frac{6}{5} \times \frac{1}{7}$

$$\tfrac{6}{35} = \tfrac{6}{35}$$

(c) $\frac{4a}{7b} \cdot \frac{b}{a} = \frac{a}{b} \cdot \frac{4b}{7a}$

$$\tfrac{4}{7} = \tfrac{4}{7}$$

(d) $\tfrac{12}{15} \times \tfrac{5}{6} = \tfrac{6}{5} \times \tfrac{10}{18}$

$$\tfrac{2}{3} = \tfrac{2}{3}$$

5. $\frac{0}{b} = \frac{0}{c}$ if and only if

$0 \cdot c = b \cdot 0$
$0 \cdot c = 0 = b \cdot 0$

7. $\frac{a}{b} \cdot \frac{0}{c} = \frac{a \cdot 0}{b \cdot c} = \frac{0}{bc} = 0$

**Section 6.5, page 174**

1. By definition, $a$, $b$, $c$, $d$ integers, $bd \neq 0$.

$$\frac{a}{b} + \frac{c}{d} = \frac{ad + bc}{bd}$$

Since the integers are closed under addition and multiplication $ad + bc$ is an integer and $bd$ is an integer. Hence $\frac{ad + bc}{bd}$ is a rational number.

3. (a) $\frac{3}{4} + \frac{-56}{20} = \frac{19}{20} + \frac{-60}{20}$

$$\frac{-41}{20} = \frac{-41}{20}$$

(b) $\frac{-a}{b} + \frac{b + 2a}{2b} = \frac{-2a + b}{2b} + \frac{a}{b}$

$$\tfrac{1}{2} = \tfrac{1}{2}$$

(c) $\frac{-17}{3} + \frac{2}{3} = \frac{-15}{3} + \frac{0}{3}$

$$\frac{-15}{3} = \frac{-15}{3}$$

(d) $\frac{a}{2b} + \frac{2 + 2a}{b} = \frac{a + 4}{2b} + \frac{2a}{b}$

$$\frac{5a + 4}{2b} = \frac{5a + 4}{2b}$$

5. $\frac{a}{b} + \frac{c}{d} = \frac{a + c}{b + d} = \frac{c + a}{d + b} = \frac{c}{d} + \frac{a}{b}$

$$\frac{a}{b} + \left(\frac{c}{d} + \frac{e}{f}\right) = \frac{a}{b} + \frac{c + e}{d + f} = \frac{a + c + e}{b + d + f}$$

$$\left(\frac{a}{b} + \frac{c}{d}\right) + \frac{e}{f} = \frac{a + c}{b + d} + \frac{e}{f} = \frac{a + c + e}{b + d + f}$$

7. The additive identity would have to be $\frac{0}{0}$ which cannot be a rational number if it is to mean an implied division.

**Section 6.6, page 177**

1. $\frac{a}{b} - \frac{c}{d} = \frac{ad - bc}{bd}$

   Since the integers are closed to subtraction and multiplication $ad - bc$ and $bd$ are each integers, and hence $\frac{ad - bc}{bd}$ is a rational number.

3. (a) $\frac{1}{10} \neq \frac{-1}{10}$

   (b) $\frac{1}{12} \neq \frac{-1}{12}$

   (c) $\frac{ac - b}{bc} \neq \frac{b - ac}{cb}$

5. (a) $\frac{14}{15} \neq \frac{15}{14}$

   (b) $\dfrac{b}{a} \neq \dfrac{a}{b}$

   (c) $\frac{10}{4} \neq \frac{15}{24}$

7. (a) $\dfrac{34}{55}$ (b) $\dfrac{5}{140}$ (c) $\dfrac{22}{3}$ (d) $\dfrac{-1}{11}$

9. No. $(a + b)^2 = ab$ is satisfied by $a = b = 0$. But $a = 0$, $b = 0$ are not permitted if $\dfrac{1}{a}, \dfrac{1}{b}$ are rational numbers.

11. No. If there were it would satisfy the equation $a^2 = -1$.

**Section 6.7, page 182**

1. (a), (d) simple; (b), (c) complex; (b), (d) proper; (a), (c) improper

5. $\dfrac{a}{b} > \dfrac{a}{d}$ if and only if $abd^2 > b^2ad$
   If $a$, $b$, $d$, are positive
$$abd^2 > b^2ad \leftrightarrow d > b$$

7. $\frac{29}{70}$ (There are infinitely many correct answers.)

9. $a > 0$ implies $a - 0 =$ a positive number. But if $a$ is positive, $a - 0$ does equal the positive number $a$, $a - 0 = a$.

**Section 7.1, page 187**

1. (b), (d), (e), (g), (h)

3. $31500 \times 10^{-4} + 51 \times 10^{-4} + 320700 \times 10^{-4} + 18340 \times 10^{-4} =$
   $(31500 + 51 + 320700 + 18340)10^{-4} = 370591 \times 10^{-4} = 37.0591$

5. $.035 \times 41.3 \times 3.6 = 35 \times 10^{-3} \times 413 \times 10^{-1} \times 36 \times 10^{-1} =$
   $(35 \times 413 \times 36) \times 10^{-5}$

7. (a) $.00221 \div 1.7 = (221 \times 10^5) \div (17 \times 10) = 221 \times 10^5 \times \frac{1}{17} \times 10^{-1} =$
   $221 \times \frac{1}{17} \times 10^5 \times 10^{-1} = (221 \div 17) \times (10^5 \div 10)$
   (b) $2.21 \div .0013 = (221 \times 10^{-2}) \div (13 \times 10^{-4}) = 221 \times 10^{-2} \times \frac{1}{13} \times$
   $10^4 = 221 \times \frac{1}{13} \times 10^{-2} \times 10^4 = (221 \div 13) \times (10^{-2} \div 10^{-4})$
   (c) $.0221 \div .017 = (221 \times 10^{-4}) \div (17 \times 10^{-3}) = 221 \times 10^{-4} \times \frac{1}{17} \times$
   $10^3 = 221 \times \frac{1}{17} \times 10^{-4} \times 10^3 = (221 \div 17) \times (10^{-4} \div 10^{-3})$
   (d) $22.1 \div 1.3 = (221 \times 10^{-1}) \div (13 \times 10^{-1}) = 221 \times 10^{-1} \times \frac{1}{13} \times 10 =$
   $221 \times \frac{1}{13} \times 10^{-1} \times 10 = (221 \div 13) \times (10^{-1} \div 10^{-1})$

**Section 7.2, page 197**

1. Let $N = .24\bar{9}$
   Then $100N = 24.\bar{9}$
   and $1000N = 249.\bar{9}$
   Subtracting $900N = 225$
   $$N = \frac{225}{900} = \frac{1}{4} = .25$$

3. Both are equal to $\frac{41}{333}$

5. $.\overline{428571}$; the same.

7. $.\overline{999999} = 1$; $\frac{1}{7} \times 7 = 1$

9. $\frac{1}{16}$, $\frac{9}{40}$, $\frac{10}{128}$

11. .312 (eight)

13. When the fraction is expressed as an integer divided by an integral power of ten, the exponent of ten is the number of decimals in the decimal fraction.

15. $\frac{4}{7}$ and $\frac{5}{6}$ repeat. $\frac{2}{5}$ terminates.

17. $\frac{1}{7} = .\overline{142857}$
    $\frac{1}{13} = .\overline{076923}$
    $\frac{1}{11} = .\overline{09}$
    $\frac{1}{17} = .\overline{0588235294117647}$

19. $\frac{2}{3} = .6$ (nine)
    $\frac{1}{6} = .\bar{1}$ (seven)
    $\frac{1}{6} = .1\bar{4}$ (nine)
    $\frac{3}{5} = .\overline{4125}$ (seven)
    $\frac{3}{5} = .\overline{53}$ (nine)
    $\frac{2}{3} = .\bar{4}$ (seven)

21. Let $N = .44\bar{9}$
    Then $100N = 44.\bar{9}$
    and $1000N = 449.\bar{9}$
    $900N = 405$
    $N = \frac{405}{900} = \frac{45}{100} = .45$

**Section 7.3, page 204**

1. .122333 . . . ($n$ repeated $n$ times).

3. If $\frac{a}{b} = \sqrt{3}$ then $a^2 = 3b^2$; $b$ and hence $b^2$ has the factor 3 an even number of times. Also $a^2$ has the factor 3 an even number of times. But $a^2 = 3b^2$

has 3 as a factor an odd number of times. Therefore, there are no integers $a$, $b$ such that $\frac{a}{b} = \sqrt{3}$.

5. The assumption that $\frac{a}{b} = \sqrt[3]{2}$ leads to the equation $a^3 = 2b^3$. Hence $a^3$ has the factor 2 both a multiple of 3 times and one more than a multiple of 3 times.

7. Find the diagonal of a rectangle with sides 1 and $\sqrt{2}$.

9. .67

11. Continue the number as found in Exercise 10 with a non repeating endless decimal.

13. Use the argument as in Exercise 12 but continue with a non repeating endless decimal.

15. 
$$\begin{array}{r} .35426170 \\ .08372542 \\ \hline .\not{3}3798\not{6}12 \\ .43798712 \end{array}$$

19. $.\bar{9}$

21. Yes. If $a, b, c \ldots$ represent digits the inverse of $.abcd\ldots$ is $-.abcd\ldots$

23. No. $2 = 1.\bar{9}$, $1 = .\bar{9}$, $0 = -1 + .\bar{9}$ but this can be expressed as an endless decimal only as $.\bar{0}$

**Section 7.4, page 209**

1. (a) A measure between 12.45 ft and 12.55 ft.
   (b) A quantity between $\frac{3}{6}$ and $\frac{5}{6}$
   (c) A quantity between .665 and .675
   (d) A measure between 12.495 feet and 12.505 feet
   (e) A measure between $3\frac{15}{16}$ inches and $4\frac{1}{16}$ inches.

3. Yes, see 2(c). Yes .156 inches is more precise and more accurate than 200 inches. Yes, see 2(b). Yes, 156 inches and 4 inches have the same precision but different accuracy. Yes, 15 pounds and 15 ounces have the same accuracy but different precision.

5. (a) .5 miles, $\frac{5}{1260}$, $\frac{50}{126}\%$
   (b) .0005 centimeters, $\frac{5}{250}$, $2\%$
   (c) $\frac{1}{8}$ centimeter, $\frac{1}{2}$, $50\%$
   (d) 500 miles, $\frac{5}{250}$, $2\%$

**Section 7.5, page 216**

1. (a) 5 (b) 4 (c) 6 (d) 5 (e) 3 (f) 4

3. By first rule 854. By other two rules 855.

5. 4110

7. Absolute error $\frac{1}{300}$, relative error $\frac{1}{201}$.

**Section 7.6, page 218**

1. (a) $8.63 \times 10^4$ (b) $1.50 \times 10^8$ (c) $1.7 \times 10^{-5}$ (d) $8.30 \times 10^4$ (e) $7 \times 10^0$

3. (a) $7.69 \times 6.3 \times 10^2 = 48 \times 10^2 = 4800$
   (b) $58.7 \times 10^{11}$
   (c) $5 \times 10^3$

**Section 8.1, page 221**

1. No—not closure, no identity

3. No—no inverses

5. No—no inverses

7. Yes

9. No—no left hand inverse

**Section 8.2, page 225**

1. No multiplicative inverses

3. No inverses

7. The elements $b$, $c$, $d$ form a multiplication group. Hence we have a field if the distributive property holds. This can be established by verifying every case. (Quite a task!) An example:

$$\begin{aligned} b(c + d) &= b \cdot c + b \cdot d \\ b \cdot b &= b \cdot c + b \cdot d \\ b &= c + d \\ b &= b \end{aligned}$$

9. The proper factors of 12 are omitted from the modulo 12 multiplication table.

**Section 8.3, page 230**

1. If $a = 0$ or $b = 0$, then $ab = 0$. But $ab \neq 0$. Therefore neither $a$ nor $b$ is zero.

3. If $a = b$, then $a + c = b + c$ and
   if $c = d$, then $b + c = b + d$.
   Since equality is transitive, $a + c = b + d$.

5. (a) $-15$ (b) $-12$ (c) 21 (d) 10

7. (a) $-8$ (b) 7 (c) 4 (d) $-3$

**Section 8.4, page 232**

1. If $I$ is the identity

$$I \cdot X = X$$

   for any element $X$.
   Let $X = I$

$$I \cdot I = I$$

   Hence $I$ is its own inverse

3. No. Yes. The rational numbers are dense.
   The natural numbers are discrete.

5. No. $5 - 12 = -7$, not a natural number.
   Yes. In a field every element has an additive inverse.

7. Closure $+$, $x$; commutatively $+$, $x$; associativity $+$, $x$; distributivity $x$ over $+$; multiplicative identity.

9. $a \cdot c \div c = b \cdot c \div c$
   $a \cdot 1 = b \cdot 1$
   $a = b$
   If $c = 0$ we cannot divide by $c$. Furthermore, $ac = bc$ when $a \neq b$ if $c = 0$ because $0 \cdot x = 0$ for all $X$.

**Section 8.5, page 234**

1. Since $a - 0 = a$ if $a$ is positive $a - 0$ is positive. Hence $a > 0$.

3. $a > 0 \rightarrow a$ is positive
   $b < 0 \rightarrow b$ is negative and $-b$ positive
   $a - b = a + (-b)$ is then positive and $a > b$

5. $1 > -7$ because $1 - (-7) = 8$, a positive number; $-1 > 7$ is false because $-1 - 7 = -8$, a negative number.

**Section 8.6, page 236**

1. $x > -5$

3. $x > 21$

5. All real numbers

7. The null set

9. $3 < x < 4$

**Section 8.7, page 238**

1. $x = 24$

3. $x = 1$

5. $x = \sqrt{5}$

7. none

9. none

**Section 9.2, page 243**

1. (4, 1) (9, 4)

3. $2x + 3y = 12$ (Infinitely many answers)

5. Yes, as many as there are lines through a point.

7. No.

9. 2

**Section 9.3, page 245**

1. (a) IV (b) III (c) III and IV (d) I and IV (e) I (f) II (g) IV

**Section 9.4, page 250**

1. $\frac{2}{5}, -\frac{7}{5}$

3. $\frac{3}{4}, -3$

5. $-\frac{2}{3}, -\frac{5}{3}$

7. $y = 3x$

9. $2x - 3y = 6$

**Section 9.5, page 253**

1. $y = 2x - 4$

3. Both are satisfied by $x = 5$, $y = 6$. That is, their graphs both pass through (5, 6) but they have different slopes.

5. They have different constant terms, but coefficients of $x$ and $y$ are the same. The lines are parallel.

7. $c = 11$

9. $y = -3x$

11. Through the origin, not coincident with an axis, or not through the origin and parallel to an axis.

13. Positive

15. It has no slope.

**Section 9.6, page 257**

1. $y < \frac{2}{3}x - 2$

3. It includes the line $2x - 3y = 6$. It is a closed half plane.

5. (1, 1); (3, 3)

**Section 9.7, page 259**

1. $-454°$

3. On the order of 72,000,000°

5. 15

7. \$1.75

9. Domain, set of positive integers. Range 45¢ + $3n$ ¢ ($n$ a positive integer). (The equation defines the function only for $W \geq 10$. For $0 < W < 10$ we have the constant function $C = .45$)

**Section 10.1, page 264**

1. (a) $\{3, -5\}$
   (b) $\{-1, 1, 3\}$
   (c) $\{2\}$

**Section 10.2, page 270**

1. (a) $x = \frac{1}{4}, (\frac{1}{4}, \frac{47}{8})$
   (b) $x = \dfrac{-3}{2}, \left(\dfrac{-3}{2}, \dfrac{-29}{4}\right)$
   (c) $x = -\frac{3}{4}, (-\frac{3}{4}, \frac{23}{8})$

9. Shifts the graph $c$ units on the $y$ axis.

**Section 10.3, page 274**

1. (a) $x^2 - 4xy + 4y^2$
   (c) $x^2 - \frac{2}{3}x + \frac{1}{9}$
   (e) $\dfrac{x^2}{4} - \dfrac{1}{3}xy + \dfrac{x^2}{9}$

2. (b) 9
   (d) $\frac{9}{4}$

3. (a) $\{1, \ -3\}$
   (c) $(-6 + \sqrt{37}, \ -6 - \sqrt{37})$
   (e) $(-1 + 2\sqrt{2}, \ -1 - 2\sqrt{2})$

**Section 10.4, page 277**

5. The set of real numbers

**Section 10.5, page 279**

1. (a) $(2x - 3)(x + 5)$
   (c) $(3x + 1)(2x - 1)$
2. (a) $\{\frac{3}{2}, -2\}$
   (c) $\{5, 3\}$
   (e) $\{-5, 3\}$
   (g) $-3 < x < 2$
   (i) $-2 < x < 1$

**Section 10.6, page 281**

1. $2\frac{1}{2}$ seconds
3. 6 seconds
5. 100 by 130 feet

**Section 11.1, page 286**

3. $\{(2, -1)\}$
5. The null set
7. $\frac{10}{3}$
9. No. The graphs are parallel or the same line.

**Section 11.2, page 291**

1. (a) strict (b) mixed (c) mixed (d) strict
5. (3, 2), (5, 9), $< 7$
   (4, $-1$), ($-1$, $-3$), (6, $-5$), (6, 1) $> 7$

**Section 11.3, page 295**

1. $\{(10, 1)\}$
3. $\{(3, 1)\}$
5. Dependent equations
7. $\{(\frac{5}{2}, \frac{9}{2})\}$

9. $\{(5, 0)\}$

11. $(3, -2)$, $(1, -3)$, $(2, 0)$

**Section 11.4, page 302**

1. $-13, -10, -7, -4, -1, 2$

3. $(-2, -13)$, $(3, 2)$ At the extreme right and left of all other of the named points.

5. Vertices $(4, -1)$, $(4, \frac{11}{3})$, $(\frac{6}{5}, \frac{23}{5})$
Other points. $(2, 4)$, $(3, 4)$, $(3, 3)$, $(3, 2)$, $(\frac{5}{2}, 3)$, $(\frac{7}{2}, 2)$

7. $-1$, $\frac{11}{3}$, $\frac{51}{5}$, vertices
8, 6, 5, 4, 6, 3 interior points

9. At the vertices

**Section 12.1, page 307**

1. 7

3. $10 + 17 = 27$, an element of ⑥, similarly for any two elements of ③.

5. $3 \times 12 = 36$, an element ①, similarly for any element of ③ times any element of ⑤.

7. $8 \times 15 = 120$, an element of ① $(120 = 7 \times 17 + 1)$.

9. ⓪

**Section 12.2, page 311**

1. Yes. As defined, the sum of two equivalence classes of integers modulo m is an equivalence class modulo m. Similarly for multiplication.

3. $\text{ⓐ} \cdot \text{ⓑ} = \text{(ab)}$
$\text{ⓑ} \cdot \text{ⓐ} = \text{(ba)}$
But since $ab = ba$, it follows that (ab) = (ba)

5. No.

$$\text{③} + (\text{④} \cdot \text{②}) \neq (\text{③} + \text{④})(\text{③} + \text{②}) \text{ mod } 5$$
$$\text{③} + \text{③} \neq \text{②} \cdot \text{⓪}$$
$$\text{①} \neq \text{⓪}$$

For example,

$$8 + 9 \cdot 7 \neq (8 + 9)(8 + 7)$$
$$71 \neq 255 \text{ mod } 5$$
$$1 \neq 0 \text{ mod } 5$$

7. It is class ①

9. ③ × ⑤ = {(3, 5), (3, 12), (3, 19), (10, 5), (10, 12), (10, 19), (17, 5), (17, 12), (17, 19), . . .}

11. and 12. {15, 36, 57, 50, 120, 190, 85, 204, 323, . . .} = ③ · ⑤ = ① mod 7

**Section 12.3, page 316**

3. It is sufficient to show that the given set is not closed under addition: $3 + 7 = 2$, not an element of the set.

5. 1, 3, 5, 7 are relatively prime to 8
   1, 5, 7, 11 are relatively prime to 12

7. $a - b = b - a$
   $2a = 2b$
   $a = b$

9. 65 is an element of class 1
   107 is an element of class 3
   $65 \times 107 = 6955$ is an element of class 3.

11. 1 is its own inverse
    3 and 7 are inverses
    9 is its own inverse 2, 4, 5, 6, 8 have no inverses.

13. If and only if $m$ is an even number.

**Section 12.4, page 320**

1. $3 \times 2 = 3 \times 3 \times 8 = 3 \times 3 \times 3 \times 10 = 3 \times 3 \times 3 \times 3 \times 7 = 3 \times 3 \times 3 \times 3 \times 3 \times 6.$
   But $3 \times 2 = 6$. Hence $3 \times 3 \times 3 \times 3 \times 3 \times 6 = 6$ or $3 \times 3 \times 3 \times 3 \times 3 = 1$.
   Then the inverse of 3 is $3 \times 3 \times 3 \times 3 = 4$

3. Rather than completing a circuit we find a factor that is the multiplicative inverse of 2.

5. $x = 0$

7. $x = 5$; $x = 4$

9. Dependent

11. The formula yields

$$x = \frac{4 \pm \sqrt{6}}{2}$$

but there is no element whose square is 6. The radicand must be a perfect square if the formula is to work.

**Section 12.5, page 325**

1. If $a = 4$ and $b = 5$
   $-(a + b) = -(4 + 5) = -3 = 3$
   $-a + -b = -4 + -5 = 2 + 1 = 3$
   If $a = 3$ and $b = 1$
   $-(a + b) = -(3 + 1) = -4 = 2$
   $-a + -b = -3 + -1 = 3 + 5 = 2$

3. If $a = 5$ and $b = 3$
   $(-a)(-b) = 1 \cdot 3 = 3$
   $ab = 5 \cdot 3 = 3$
   If $a = 4$ and $b = 2$
   $(-a)(-b) = 2 \cdot 4 = 2$
   $ab = 4 \cdot 2 = 2$

5. Any pair whose difference is 3, for example
   $5 - 2 = 2 - 5$

7. $5 \div 3 = 4$ (because $3 \cdot 4 = 5$)
   The inverse of 3 is 5
   $5 \times 5 = 4$

9. If $a = 4$, for any $b$, $b \times a = b \div a$ because 4 is its own inverse

$$3 \times 4 = 3 \div 4$$
$$2 = 2 \ (3 \div 4 = 2 \text{ because } 2 \cdot 4 = 3)$$

**Section 13.1, page 328**

1. (a) $5i$ (b) $i$ (c) $-11$ (d) $-11i$ (e) $6i$ (f) $2 + 3i$

3. $i^4 = i^2 \cdot i^2 = (-1)(-1) = 1$

5. (a) $i$ (b) $-1$ (c) $-i$ (d) 1 (e) $-i$ (f) $-i$

**Section 13.2, page 330**

1. D $= -56$ imaginary

3. D $= 40$ real

5. real

7. No. We know this is true only if the coefficients are real.

9. $x = \dfrac{-3 \pm \sqrt{65}}{4}$

11. $x = -1$ or $\dfrac{-3}{2}$

**Section 13.3, page 332**

1. Both are $-1 + i$

3. Both are $-12 + 14i$

5. $(3 + 4i)(-2 - 5i) = 14 - 23i$

7. $(a + bi)[(c + di) + (e + fi)] = (a + bi)[(c + e) + (d + f)i]$
   $= [a(c + e) - b(d + f)] + [b(c + e) + a(d + f)]i$
   $= (ac + ae - bd - bf) + (bc + be + ad + af)i$
   $(a + bi)(c + di) + (a + bi)(e + fi) = (ac - bd) +$
   $(bc + ad)i + (ae - bf) + (be + af)i = (ac - bd + ae - bf) +$
   $(bc + ad + be + af)i$

9. $0 + 0 \cdot i$

11. $1 + 0 \cdot i$

**Section 13.4, page 335**

1. $-1 + 0 \cdot i$

3. $2i$

5. $28 + 0 \cdot i$

7. 24

9. $-\frac{1}{2} - \frac{i}{2}$

**Section 13.5, page 337**

1. $(5 + 6\sqrt{3}) + (2 - \sqrt{3}) = 7 + 5\sqrt{3} = (2 - \sqrt{3}) + (5 + 6\sqrt{3})$

3. $(5 + 6\sqrt{3})(2 - \sqrt{3}) = -8 + 7\sqrt{3}$
   $(2 - \sqrt{3})(5 + 6\sqrt{3}) = -8 + 7\sqrt{3}$

5. $(2 + \sqrt{3})[(3 - 3\sqrt{3}) + (5 + \sqrt{3})] = (2 + \sqrt{3})(8 - 2\sqrt{3}) = 10 + 4\sqrt{3}$
   $(2 + \sqrt{3})(3 - 3\sqrt{3}) + (2 + \sqrt{3})(5 + \sqrt{3}) =$
   $(-3 - 3\sqrt{3}) + (13 + 7\sqrt{3}) = 10 + 4\sqrt{3}$

7. $5 - 3\sqrt{3}$

**Section 14.1, page 341**

1. $\{(1, 1), (1, 2), (1, 3), (1, 4), (3, 1), (3, 2), (3, 3), (3, 4), (5, 1), (5, 2), (5, 3), (5, 4), (7, 1), (7, 2), (7, 3), (7, 4), (11, 1), (11, 2), (11, 3), (11, 4)\}$

3. (a) 5, 11 not first elements
   (b) 2 not a second element
   (c) 5, 11 not first elements, 4 is a first element, 2 not a second element, and 5 and 11 are.

5. $\{(4, 3), (-4, -3)\}$

7. No. Domain $-5 \leq x \leq 5$, range $-5 \leq y \leq 5$

**Section 14.2, page 343**

1. (a), (b) and (e) are functions

3. (b), (c), and (d)

5. The graph will cut no vertical line more than one time.

7. Yes. Neither domain nor range can be the complete set of real numbers.

**Section 14.3, page 345**

5. Appears to approach the axes.

   Graph of $y = \frac{0}{x}$ is the $x$ axis and $y$ axis.

7. 1000

9. 40

**Section 14.4, page 347**

1. prime

3. $(4x^2 + y^2)(2x + y)(2x - y)$

5. (1) $\left(x + \frac{1 - \sqrt{5}}{2}\right)\left(x + \frac{1 + \sqrt{5}}{2}\right)$

   (4) $(4x^2 + \sqrt{8}xy + y^2)(4x^2 - \sqrt{8}xy + y^2)$

7. $(x + 2)(x - \sqrt{3})$

**Section 14.5, page 351**

1. $x^2 - 4 + \frac{-2x^2 - 4x + 6}{x^3 - x + 3}$

3. $-3$

5. $-3$

7. $-48$

9. 0

**Section 14.6, page 354**

1. $x^4 + x^3 - 2x^2 + 2x + 4 + \dfrac{9}{x - 1}$

   $f(1) = 9$

3. None are factors

5. $(x - 2)(x - 3)(x + 2)$

7. $(x - 1)(x + 4)(x - 2)$

9. $x^3(x + 3)(x - 3)$

**Section 14.7, page 358**

1. $\{1, -2, i\sqrt{2}, -i\sqrt{2}\}$

3. $\left\{-4, \dfrac{1 + \sqrt{5}}{2}, \dfrac{1 - \sqrt{5}}{2}\right\}$

5. (a) One root between 0 and 1; one root between 3 and 4; one root $-2$.

# Index